MODERN SHIPS

MODERN SHIPS

by

R. Carpenter, D.S.C.

MODEL & ALLIED PUBLICATIONS LTD.
13-35 Bridge Street, Hemel Hempstead, Herts.
1970

Trade Distributors:

ARGUS PRESS LTD., 12-18 PAUL STREET,
LONDON, E.C.2.

Printed and Bound in Great Britain by
Staples Printers Limited, at their Rochester, Kent, establishment

Contents

Acknowledgments
PHOTOGRAPHS & ILLUSTRATIONS

Grateful thanks is expressed to the undernoted who have made photographs and drawings available.

CHAPTER 1

British Petrolcum Co. Ltd.
P.L.A.
Blandford Shipping Co. Ltd.
D. W. A. Mercer
"An Esso Photograph"
Gulf Oil Co. Ltd.

CHAPTER 2

Tate & Lyle
The Hunting Group of Companies
B.I.S.N. Co. Ltd.
Silver Line Ltd.

CHAPTER 3

Manchester Liners Ltd.
United States Lines
D. W. A. Mercer
P.L.A.

CHAPTER 4

D.F.D.S.
British Railways
Belfast Steamship Co. Ltd.
The Transport Ferry Service
Townsend Car Ferries Ltd. (Philip Holt)
Danish State Railways
D. W. A. Mercer

CHAPTER 5

Swedish American Line
Holland America Line Ltd.
French Line
Grace Line Inc.
Messageries Maritimes
D. W. A. Mercer
Canadian Pacific Steamships Ltd.
Collection of Eric Johnson, New Orleans

CHAPTER 6

Nigerian National Shipping Co. Ltd.
Glen Line Ltd.
Collection of Eric Johnson, New Orleans
Elders & Fyffes Ltd.
Johnson Line, Stockholm
Port Line Ltd.
Cayzer, Irvine Co. Ltd.
D. W. A. Mercer
Frank C. Strick & Co. Ltd.
New Zealand Shipping Co. Ltd.
Shipping World and Shipbuilder

CHAPTER 7

Sir R. Ropner & Co. Ltd.
Cable & Wireless Ltd.
Port Line Ltd.
Ben Line Steamers Ltd.

CHAPTER 8

Wm. France Fenwick Co. Ltd.
"An Esso Photograph"

CHAPTER 9

United Gowing Co. Ltd.
Gas Council
Collection of Eric Johnson, New Orleans
Evening Argus, Brighton
Moran International Towing Corporation
D. W. A. Mercer

CHAPTER 10

New Zealand Shipping Co. Ltd.
High Commissioner for New Zealand
Docks Board
British Petroleum Co. Ltd.
Shipping World and Shipbuilder
Central Electricity Generating Board
Ford Motor Co. Ltd.
Port of Rotterdam
P.L.A.
Cayzer, Irvine & Co. Ltd.
British Transport
Elders & Fyffes Ltd.
Shell Petroleum Co. Ltd.
Munck International A/S Bergen
Blohm & Voss
English China Clay Group
High Commissioner for Australia

CHAPTER 11

Bluc Star Line Ltd.
Port Line Ltd.
Ben Line Steamers Ltd.

CHAPTER 12

B.I.S.N. Co. Ltd.
British Antarctic Survey
Cable & Wireless Ltd.
Trinity House
Gas Council
Collection of Eric Johnson, New Orleans
Arthur Guinness Son & Co. (Dublin) Ltd.
P and O
Missions to Seamen

The P and O liner *Oronsay* is one of a large fleet of passenger ships built between 1948 and 1961. A single voyage may often take one of these ships right round the world, calling at such ports as Cape Town, Sydney, Auckland, Los Angeles and Port Everglades.

Photo courtesy: D. W. A. Mercer

Cover: The LASH ship *Acadia Forest* and the Italian liner *Galileo Galilei*.

Introduction

THIS book is concerned with the upheaval which has been taking place in the world's shipping industry during the last 15 years. It looks at the new generation of ships which has resulted and at the evolution of those ships which have remained unaltered in their basic design. It extends the story to cover the simultaneous development of docks and installations, many of which have had to be built in isolated and uninhabited territory as near as possible to the newly discovered sources of raw materials which the world is consuming with an ever-increasing appetite.

The transport of manufactured goods has been revolutionised by the acceptance of completely new concepts of cargo handling, such as containerisation, unit loads and vehicles on board ship.

This book describes, but in less detail, the shipbuilding facilities which in their turn have been developed or newly created to meet the demands of shipowners.

In reading this book it must be remembered that the ships described constitute but a very small fraction of the whole. In fact, one bulk carrier may represent over 100 similar vessels. There are on order at the moment over 200 tankers of similar size to the *Esso Northumbria.* Similarly, the ports and loading facilities included are representative, although the Port of Rotterdam stands out as unique in its past attainments and in its future potential. At the present time, capital investment in shipbuilding and dock development is probably greater than it has ever been before in peace time.

The final section of the book deals with organisations and bodies which are closely connected with ships, but which operate to some extent in the background and are often overlooked in books on shipping.

CHAPTER I

Oil Tankers

In writing about oil tankers it is pointless to record the name of the largest vessel in service. The largest ship often holds the title for no more than a few months, and it is surprising by how many tons the new record holder surpasses its predecessor.

Until 1939 tankers rarely exceeded 12,000 tons. They distributed products from the refineries, which were located as near as possible to the oil fields, and were able to meet the world demand for oil without difficulty. Standard tankers built during the war were slightly larger and faster, but it was not until the middle '50s that things really began to happen. Tonnages by this time had increased to the 20,000s; the next ten years or so saw unprecedented developments and ships of over 200,000 tons are now in service. Recently put into commission are vessels which carry 312,000 tons. It was predicted that these would be the largest vessels for sometime to come, but even during the compilation of this book considerably larger ships have been ordered.

Giant oil tankers have come into being for a variety of reasons. Demand for oil has developed steadily and it is highly probable that it would have proved to be impossible to man the tremendous number of 12,000 or even 20,000 ton ships which would have been required to cope with the demand.

The transport costs of oil are high (at one time they represented 30% of the price of the oil on discharge in Europe) and the oil companies sought ways of reducing costs in order to supply a more competitive product. It was found that the capital cost of a tanker decreases proportionately ton for ton as tonnage increases. Similarly the cost of fuel oil for ship purposes also decreases. The wages bill for the crew remains static since a 100,000 tonner needs no more men to operate it than a ship of 10,000 tons. Technical advances in hull design, together with the simultaneous development of the large-bore diesel engine and improved turbines have enabled the largest tankers to have service speeds of 17 knots and above, and this without significant effect on capital costs. 27,000 b.h.p. diesel engines are now installed as a matter of course and turbines geared to drive single screws develop horsepower in excess of 30,000. The use of computors to calculate stresses and strains and the production of improved shipbuilding materials have also played a part.

These large vessels are not, however, without disadvantages. There are very few ports in Northern Europe which can accept tankers over 100,000 tons, and the depth of water in the approaches to several ports which have developed extensive refinery installations makes it pretty certain that such ships will never enter. The latest tankers have drafts up to 91 ft. It is difficult to believe that in the open sea the keel of a ship can be less than 20 ft. from the bottom, but this is so, and there are parts of the North Sea, for instance, where this already happens with tankers of more modest dimensions.

Various steps have been, or are being, taken to overcome the problems.

The Port of Rotterdam has built a completely new harbour;

M.S. MYRINA (1967)
Owners: Deutsche Shell Tanker G.m.b.H.
Builders: Harland and Wolff Ltd.
Pametrada turbine, 27,000 b.h.p.
Single screw
Service speed 16 knots
Length overall 1,050 ft.
Beam 155 ft.
Draft 60 ft.
Deadweight tonnage 191,250

One of the largest tankers to have been launched in Europe, the *Myrina* is one of several vessels of generally similar tonnage on service or being built for Shell Oil. It is intended that the ship should operate via the Cape at all times and at a cheaper cost than that of the largest ship which could negotiate the Suez Canal. The *Myrina* is designed to carry crude oil, and makes an interesting comparison with the *Florida*, the *Myrina* has four centre tanks and wing tanks on each side, one group of these is almost the length of the *Florida*.

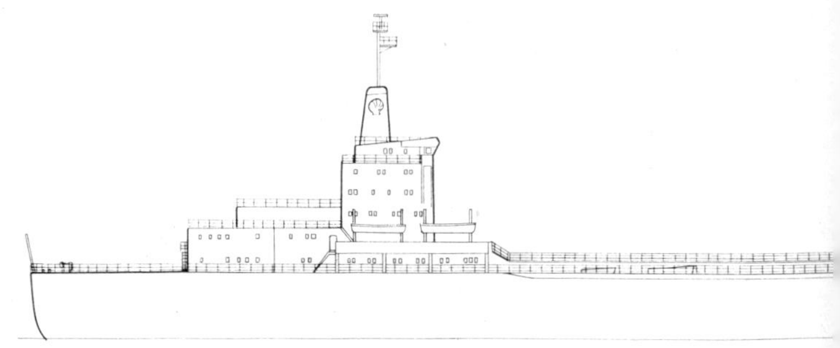

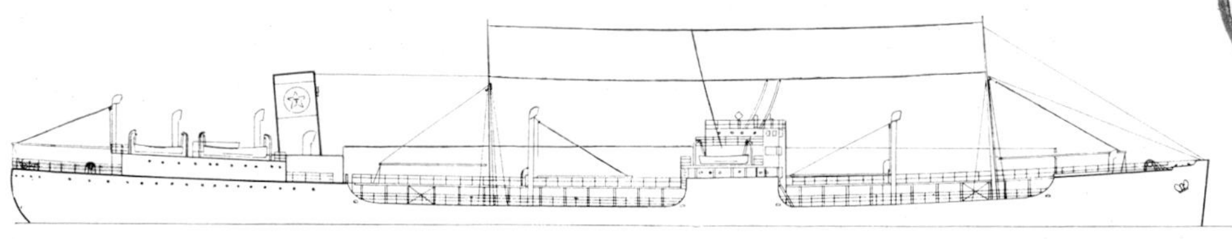

M.S. FLORIDA (1939)
Owners: Texas Company of Delaware
Builders: Sun Shipbuilding and Dry Dock Company
Doxford diesel, 4,850 s.h.p.
Single screw
Service speed 13 knots
Length overall 490·5 ft.
Beam 65 ft.
Deadweight tonnage 12,400

From 1914 until the late '40s, tankers of about 18,000 tons deadweight were the largest afloat and there were very few of them. In 1939 the majority of company-owned tankers were in the region of 12,000 tons and the *Florida* was a typical example. The bridge amidships was standard practice and most of them had a hold under the forecastle for the stowage of case oil or stores for refineries. Two pumprooms were also usual and the oil was contained in nine main centre tanks and numerous side tanks.

at the same time a deep channel has been driven for many miles out into the North Sea. This enables 200,000 tonners to enter and discharge direct to the refineries and port storage plants.

The Port of London has deepened one of the approach channels in the Thames Estuary. Awkward turns have been eliminated and cargoes of up to 130,000 tons are now regularly discharged in the port.

The British Petroleum Company has developed completely new terminals at Loch Long in Scotland and Milford Haven in Wales which were originally able to accept their new fleet of 100,000 tonners. Esso, BP and Gulf Oil have refineries at Milford Haven and tankers of up to 170,000 tons are regularly dealt with. Later improvements have enabled ships of 200,000 tons to enter and the channel is being still further widened for 250,000 ton ships.

The Port of Le Havre has in mind the construction of an artificial off-shore island where tankers of any size will be able to discharge in sheltered waters, either into smaller vessels for onward routing or into a pipeline to shore installations.

The Gulf Oil Company has completed an installation in Bantry Bay where the 300,000 ton tankers can discharge ashore or into smaller ships—a relative term since these smaller ships will eventually have tonnages in the region of 100,000.

Finally, Shell Oil are transferring oil from ship to ship in sheltered bays around the coast until permanent shore facilities become available.

There is little doubt that the really giant tanker is here to stay. For many years yet the smaller ships will continue to operate on long hauls, but the ultimate pattern would appear to be that vessels of 300,000 tons and upwards (some talk of ships with a capacity of ½ million tons) will carry the crude oil for the major part of its journey to the refineries; at some stage in the process smaller tankers will be required to complete the journey and it is well within the realms of possibility for ships within the 30,000–100,000 ton range to be relegated to coastal voyages only.

Small tankers up to 20,000 tons, which have a more complicated system of pumping and subdivision, are employed as product tankers, carrying the refined crude oil from refineries to small ports for storage and distribution.

Other vessels in the 500–1,000 tons range carry out a similar service to the smallest ports such as Shoreham in Sussex. Estuarial craft supply many depots on the Thames from down-river refineries.

In the middle '60s, the order books for tankers showed a preponderance of ships in the 50,000–75,000 ton range. As ships were delivered and others were ordered the position changed swiftly and at the end of 1969 it was as follows:

American yards had on order

a number of 100,000 tonners to meet the special requirements of the coastal trades. A few ships of up to 200,000 tons were due for delivery. Apart from product carriers and special vessels there were about 200 ships with tonnages over 200,000 tons.

Caltex Petroleum and Nippon Oil were seeking tenders for a ship of 475,000 tons deadweight. It was thought that the cost would be in the region of £15,000,000 and it was expected that the draught would be 98 ft. The proposed area of employment would be between the Persian Gulf and Japan, and it is not certain whether a ship of this size can negotiate the Straits of Malacca. Possibly the ship will have to be routed round the South of Indonesia.

The Tokyo Tanker Company had placed a firm order for a ship of 372,000 tons deadweight with a draught of 88 ft. The Gulf Oil Co. also had further 312,000 tonners on order. The following are examples of the "smaller" ships which will be coming into service between January, 1970 and the end of 1972:

BP Medway Tanker Co., Ltd., 215,000 tons deadweight, draught 63 ft.

United Overseas Corporation, 224,700 tons deadweight, draught 65 ft.

Lief Hoegh and Co., Ltd., 242,000 tons deadweight, draught 67 ft.

Chevron Transport Corporation, 261,000 tons deadweight, draught 86 ft.

M.S. BORGSTEN (1963)

Owners: Fred Olsen & Co.
Builders: Joseph L. Thompson
B. & W. diesel, 21,000 b.h.p.
Single screw
Service speed 17 knots
Length overall 870 ft. approx.
Beam 121·75 ft.
Draft 45 ft. 6 in.
Deadweight tonnage 86,800

The M.S. *Borgsten* was, at the time of her completion the largest tanker built in the U.K., and the advance in the size of tankers which have come from British yards since 1964 is indicated with the M.S. *Myrina*. The hull of the *Borgsten* is divided by two longitudinal bulkheads and 13 transverse bulkheads providing more than 30 compartments for oil and ballast.

The ship is unusual in appearance, the accommodation for officers and crew is contained in a single deck. The wheelhouse is set at the top of a tower structure 75 ft. above the load water line and a lift is provided. Two strengthening stays were added after the tanker had been in service for a short period.

Cargo can be discharged by four pumps at a rate of 8,000 tons per hour.

Olsens are well known for their practice of adorning each of their ships with a beautifully designed and cast figurehead. A break with tradition was made in the case of the *Borgsten* and the motif around the fore end of the forecastle is painted red and black.

The *Borgsten* is on a long-term charter with Shell Oil and this still has about 16 years to run.

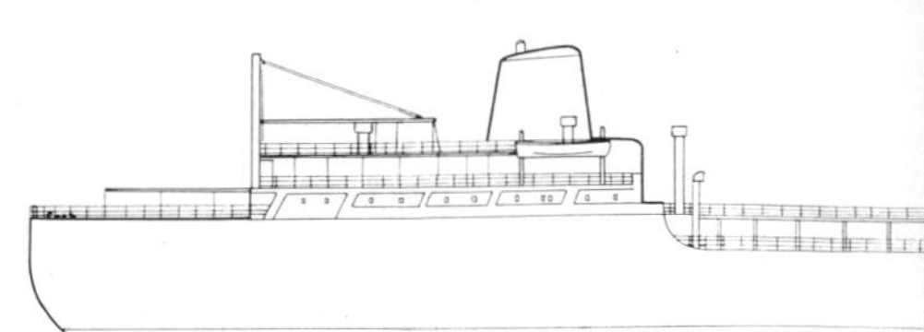

M.S. ORIENTAL DRAGON (1966)

Owners: Pacific Petroleum Carriers Inc., Hong Kong
(Managed by C. Y. Tung)
Builders: Mitsubishi Heavy Industries Ltd.
General Electric turbines, 28,400 s.h.p.
Single screw
Service speed 17·6 knots
Length overall 949 ft.
Beam 126 ft.
Draft 53 ft.
Deadweight tonnage 118,927

Largest tanker of a fleet which now totals more than 1,000,000 tons.

Also one of the largest tankers built in the last few years with bridge amidships and catwalks along the whole length of the upper deck. The officers' and crew's accommodation is of the highest standard.

Tonnage

In the chapters of this book devoted to cargo vessels and tankers, the tonnage has been given, wherever possible, in terms of deadweight. Deadweight tonnage is the actual amount of cargo, stores and fuel which a ship can carry and therefore allows reasonable comparison of sizes of various vessels.

Gross tonnage, which is given in the chapter on passenger ships, is a measure of cubic capacity (100 cu. ft. equalling 1 ton) and includes spaces devoted to both passengers and cargo. This is the normal method used to indicate the size of passenger ships.

Gross tonnage combined with deadweight tonnage in respect of passenger ships also gives, within broad limits, an indication of type, e.g. passenger only, passenger/cargo, cargo/passenger. The *Oriana* has a gross tonnage of 41,923 and a deadweight tonnage of 1,150, indicating high passenger accommodation (2,184) and

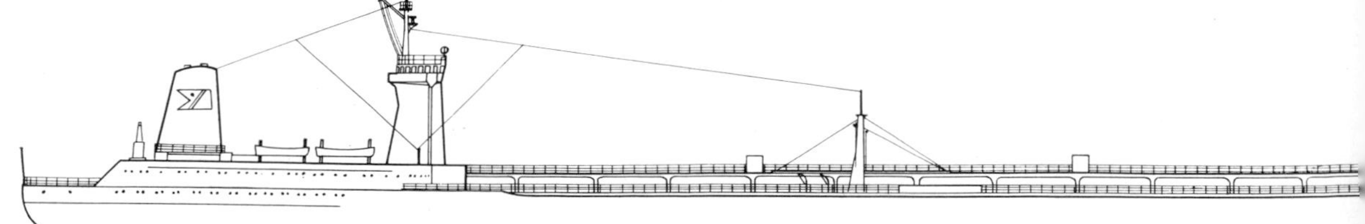

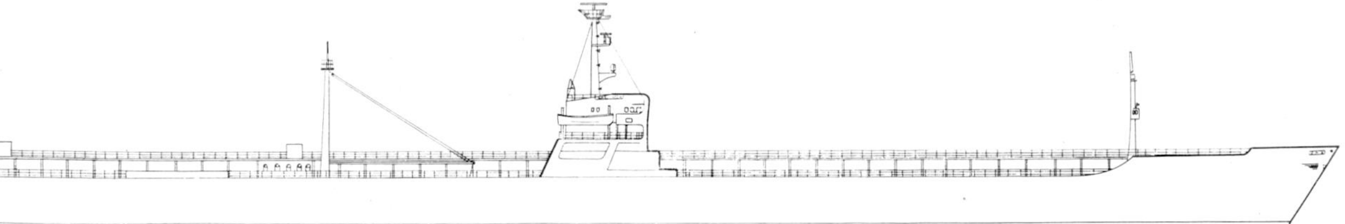

little or no cargo. The *Santa Magdalena* has a gross tonnage of 14,300 and a deadweight tonnage of 7,000. This suggests a medium-sized vessel which is very much concerned with the carriage of both passengers and cargo (the actual passenger capacity is 125). It should be pointed out, however, that these deductions are not always valid without further information because cross-channel steamers with gross tonnages in the region of 3,500 and deadweight tonnages of about 650 managed to carry 1,400 passengers.

Tank Cleaning

From time to time reports appear in newspapers of oil tankers which have gone on fire or which have had explosions on board. Fire and explosion can occur as the result of collision, but tankers are most vulnerable when the oil is being discharged and when they are empty—the latter applies particularly to product tankers, which carry highly volatile cargoes. Rigorous safety measures keep accidents to a minimum, and cleaning tanks is one of the most important of these.

As soon as possible after the tanks have been stripped they are cleaned. The system adopted varies from company to company, but the usual method used is the Butterworth system, in which cold sea water is pumped through nozzles at a pressure of about 180 lbs. per sq. in. The water pressure also rotates the nozzles in two planes and every part of the tank is subjected to the high-pressure water. In modern tankers the used water is pumped into a "Slop Tank" (actually a cargo compartment) where the water and oil separate, the water being pumped into the sea. At the end of the operation, the oil is retained in the tank and the next cargo is loaded on top. In crude oil tankers this process is often followed by circulating fan-inducted air through the tanks for several hours. In product tankers this is always done.

On entering harbours, either for repairs, or to dry dock, the process is taken further and tanks are cleaned with hot water. In addition, it is becoming the practice to add detergent. The oil remaining in the slop tank is discharged to shore installations, and the residue of oil, sand and scale, which cannot be pumped from the other tanks is removed manually. All parts of the tanks must be perfectly clean and no work can be carried out until they have been inspected and pronounced gas-free.

M.S. FERNCREST (1966)

Owners: FEARNLEY AND EGER, OSLO
Builders: ODENSE STAALSKIBS-VAERFT A/S.
Horten-Sulzer diesel, 20,700 b.h.p.
Single screw
Service speed 16 knots
Length overall 872 ft.
Beam 128 ft.
Deadweight tonnage 95,600

An example of a large tanker operated by a private company. Fearnley and Eger have a modern fleet of six large tankers and also own cargo liners and bulk carriers.

M.S. BERGE BERGESEN (1963)

Owners: SIG. BERGESON D.Y. & CO., STAVANGER
Builders: A/S ROSENBERG M/V, STAVANGER

M.S. *Ferncrest*
Photo courtesy: D. W. A. Mercer

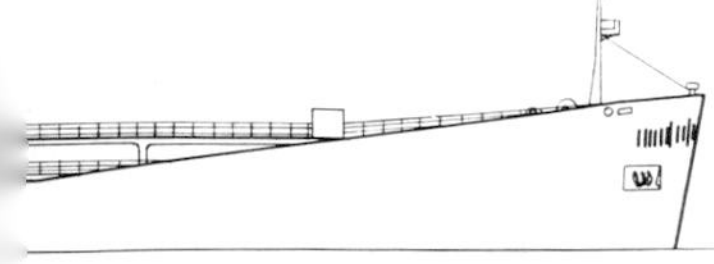

M.S. *Berge Bergesen*
Photo courtesy: D. W. A. Mercer

B. & W. diesel
Single screw
Service speed 17 knots
Length overall 869 ft.
Beam 122 ft.
Deadweight tonnage 91,375

The *Berge Bergesen* is a vessel belonging to one of the largest Norwegian tanker companies. All of the ships are diesel driven and have remarkably high service speeds; they are usually charted on long-term engagements by the major oil companies.

S.S. BULFORD (1968)

Owners: BLANDFORD SHIPPING CO. LTD.
Builders: SASEBO HEAVY INDUSTRIES CO. LTD.
IHI steam turbine, 26,000 s.h.p.

S.S. *Bulford*
Photo courtesy: Blandford Shipping Co. Ltd.

Single screw
Service speed 16 knots
Length overall 1,067 ft.
Beam 158 ft.
Draught 62 ft.
Deadweight tonnage 210,822

The *Bulford* is one of the largest tankers in the world, at one time the largest, and is on a 15-year charter to Shell. She regularly carries crude oil from the Persian Gulf and discharges a part of her cargo into smaller tankers at one of seven designated points around the coast. The first experimental transfer of cargo took place off Lyme Regis. Now, this operation is regularly carried out at points off the French coast near Le Havre, off Rotterdam and the Isle of Man, and off the east coast of England.

The *Bulford* has a highly automated engine room and this enormous ship is worked by 27 officers and men, the latter being employed as general purpose ratings.

S.S. ESSO NORTHUMBRIA (1969)

Owners: ESSO PETROLEUM CO. LTD.
Builders: SWAN HUNTER AND TYNE SHIPBUILDING LTD. (WALLSEND YARD)
Steam turbines, 32,000 s.h.p.
Single screw
Service speed about 16 knots
Length overall 1,143 ft.
Beam 170 ft.
Draught 65 ft. 6 in.
Deadweight tonnage 253,000

The *Esso Northumbria* is one of four sister ships jointly tendered for by the Swan Hunter Group and Harland and Wolff Ltd. at a total cost of about £26,000,000. The *Esso Northumbria* is the largest ship so far built on the Tyne, and the first Harland and Wolff ship will create a similar record for Northern Ireland.

This vessel is extensively eqipped with labour-saving devices, remote control equipment, automated boiler room, semi-automatic winches and hoists. An old-fashioned touch is added by the use of bicycles to cover the 300-yard-long deck.

The *Esso Northumbria* is manned by an integrated crew of 44 men, 31 of whom sail on each voyage whilst the others are on leave or attending courses. One engineer officer and one assistant man the engine room under normal conditions at sea. Navigating officers have already gained considerable experience of operating the largest tankers from the previous class of ships (190,000 tons deadweight) and they will already be familiar with the handling characteristics of the new vessels through attendance at training courses at Port Revel, near Grenoble. Here, on a man-made lake, they are required to manoeuvre with "sit in" scale models which simulate the movements and responses of the real thing. In addition, they have received training in the specialised control equipment with which these ships are fitted.

The *Esso Northumbria* was built diagonally across two building slipways, each capable of taking a ship of 100,000 tons deadweight. The bows overhung a service road, and a cofferdam was built around the stern so that work could go ahead at all states of the tide. The diagonal positioning of the ship allowed it to be launched into a bend of the river, which at this point is only 1,000 ft. wide, but even so it was necessary to excavate a large segment from the opposite bank.

Steel, mainly from mills at Scunthorpe and Middlesbrough, was prefabricated into 50-ton sections in a shed which is as large as an airship hangar. They were lifted into position by 150-ft. high travelling cranes. 3,000 men were directly employed in the construction of the *Esso Northumbria*, whilst hundreds of sub-contracting firms supplied equipment and materials.

This tanker entered service in October 1969, and carries crude oil from the Persian Gulf to Europe. She will also make occasional calls at the Esso Oil Terminal at Marsa el Brega, Libya, when the offshore loading berth is completed.

The following list gives an indication of the way in which the size of Esso tankers has grown in the last 15 years:

Year	*Name of Ship*	*Deadweight Tonnage*
1955	Esso Exeter	26,742
1959	Esso Portsmouth	38,200
1963	Esso Yorkshire	90,069
1966	Esso Mercia	166,820
1968	Esso Bernicia	190,000
1969	Esso Northumbria	253,000

The 253,000 deadweight tons *Esso Northumbria* on the slipway at the Wallsend yard of Swan Hunter & Tyne Shipbuilding Ltd.
Photo courtesy: Esso Photograph

S.S. BRITISH ADMIRAL (1965)

Owners: BP TANKER CO. LTD.
Builders: VICKERS LTD.
Steam turbines by Vickers-Armstrongs (Engineers) Ltd., to Pamatreda basis design.
25,000 s.h.p. Boiler pressure 600 lbs. p.s.i.
Single screw
Service speed about 15·5 knots
Length overall 917 ft. 6 in.
Beam 128 ft.
Deadweight tonnage 111,274

The *British Admiral* was built in 1965, the first of a series of similar ships. Two longitudinal bulkheads divide the cargo space into 21 compartments, 17 for oil and 4 for water ballast.

Four electrically-driven cargo pumps each have a capacity of 1,860 tons of crude oil per hour. Two ballast pumps have a combined capacity of 3,000 tons per hour.

The complete cargo and ballast system is remotely controlled from a control room at the fore end of the boat deck. Navigational equipment comprises: radar, radio equipment and direction finder, VHF radio telephone, gyro compass, automatic speed, distance and draft indicating gear and Decca Navigator.

Extremely comfortable accommodation, including a swimming pool, is provided for the crew.

The *British Admiral* is nor-

B.P. Tanker Company's 100,000-ton *British Admiral* arriving at B.P.'s Angle Bay Ocean Terminal, Pembs.
Photo courtesy: British Petroleum Co. Ltd

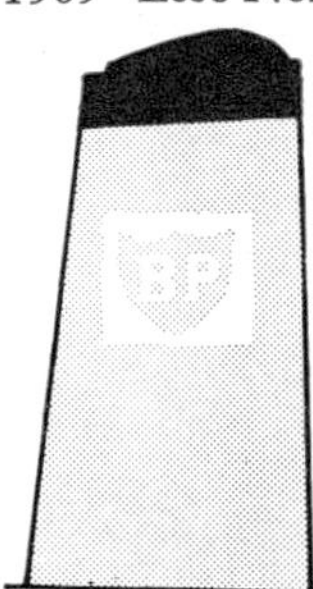

B.P. tankers now have their funnels painted in this design.

The after end of the S.S. *Universe Ireland*. This tanker is now in regular service between the Persian Gulf and Bantry Bay carrying full loads of 312,000 tons of crude oil.

The enormous size of the vessel is indicated by the standard lifeboats and the men on the bridge.

Photos courtesy: Gulf Oil Co. Ltd.

The S.S. *Enterprise Ireland* carrying out anchor trials. Whenever a ship weighs anchor, the cable is hosed down as it comes inboard to clean away the mud —often highly odoriferous—which adheres to it.

The pronounced ram—or bulbous —bows of modern ships make it necessary to place the hawse pipes so that the anchors do not foul the plating when raised or lowered. Normal practice is to place them aft of the ram bow and, as a result, it has also been necessary to install independent windlasses for each anchor.

The *Enterprise Ireland* was built in three sections, the bow, and two longitudinal hull sections, one much wider than the other. The three sections were married together in a floating dock.

mally employed between the Persian Gulf and Milford Haven. Prior to the closing of the Suez Canal, a part cargo was loaded for passage through the canal, topping-up being completed from a pipeline at Syracuse (Lebanon).

In the construction of the *British Admiral* the following are some of the components used:

Steelwork: 22,500 tons. Paint (hull and upperworks): 34 tons. Steel pipes: 12 miles. Copper and other pipes: 25 miles. Electric cable: 54 miles. Electric light fittings: 1,275. Chipboard and plywood (interior decorations): 11,800 sq. yards.

M.S. IMPERIAL OTTAWA (1967)

Owners: WESTERN OIL AND TRADING CO. LTD.
Builders: KAWASAKI DOCKYARD CO. LTD.
Kawasaki U-Type/1 turbines
Single screw
Service speed 17·5 knots
Length overall 907 ft. (approx.)
Beam 136 ft. (approx.)
Deadweight tonnage 110,187

The *Imperial Ottawa* is employed mainly in the import of crude oil from South America to Canada. Loading and discharge of oil is remotely controlled by a hydraulic system.

A high degree of automation is employed and the main engines, boilers and auxiliary machinery are controlled from a central console. Bridge control of the main turbines is also possible and electropneumatic systems allow an immediate change from programmed operation to bridge or engine room control. The data logger automatically monitors the pressure, temperature, etc., of the main and auxiliary machinery. Automatic or optional typewritten records are produced whilst there is automatic recording at the time of an alarm. Scanning is carried out under a memory system and

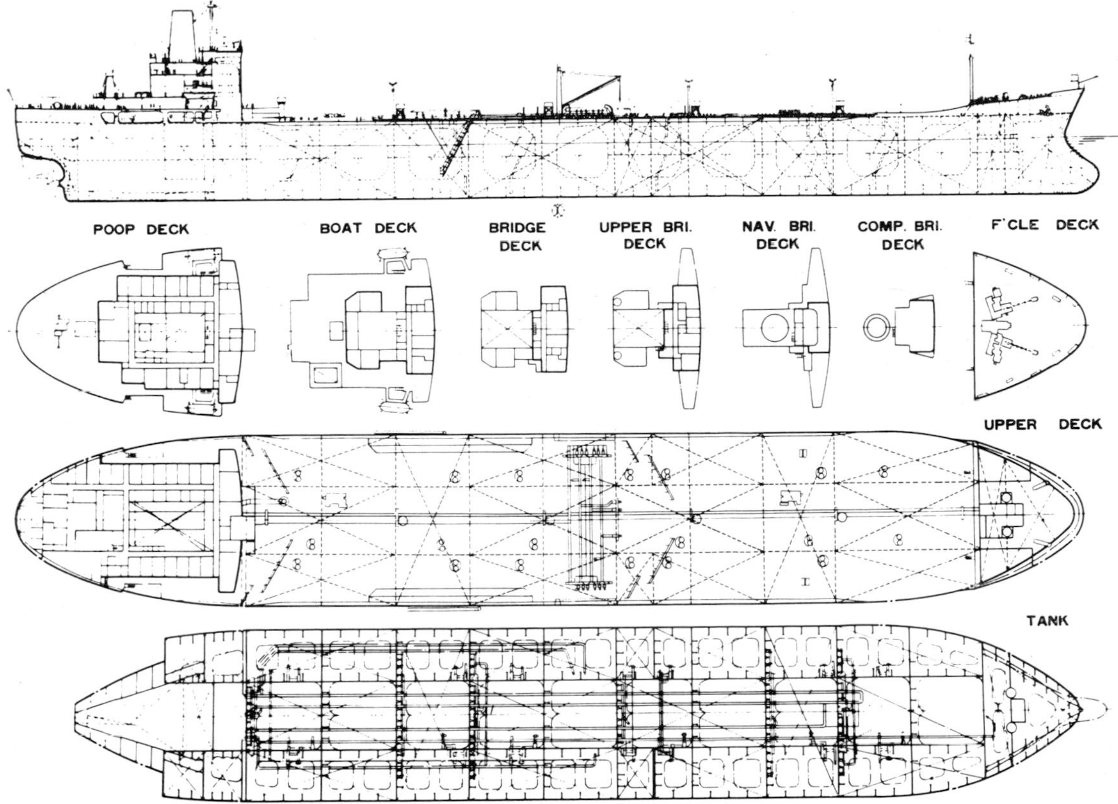

Drawing of *Imperial Ottawa*.
Photo courtesy: Shipbuilders' Association of Japan

if the alarm point is exceeded a lamp is lit and an alarm given. On return to normal the alarms automatically switch off. There are 119 service and 74 self-checking points including shaft torque and revolutions, shaft horsepower, fuel consumption, fuel consumption rate, fuel oil viscosity and feedwater rate. The boiler is automated and can be controlled from the console. The following operations are possible: burner ignition and extinction, combustion control, feedwater adjustment, opening and closing of damper and control and monitoring of gas air heater.

The total complement of this ship is 38 officers and men.

S.S. IDEMITSU MARU (1966)

Owners: IDEMITSU TANKER CO. LTD.
Builders: ISHIKAWAJIMA-HARIMA HEAVY INDUSTRIES CO. LTD.
Steam turbine, 33,000 h.p.
Single screw
Service speed 16·35 knots
Length overall 1,122 ft. (approx.)
Beam 163 ft. (approx.)
Draught 62 ft. (approx.)
Deadweight tonnage 200,302

At the time of her entry into service, the *Idemitsu Maru* was the largest tanker in the world. The previous largest tanker was the *Nissho Maru* and Ishikawajima-Harima had participated in that ship's design. They also had under construction in their own yard the 150,000 ton *Tokyo Maru* (in its turn the largest tanker in the world). Nevertheless the problems involved in building a ship with an additional capacity of over 50,000 tons were considerable and two years of careful study and investigation preceded the keel laying, which took place in February 1966. The *Idemitsu Maru* was launched in September 1966 and completed in December of the same year.

Extensive remote control is provided for oil handling operations and independent oil and ballast systems have been installed. A limited amount of remote control and data logging has been provided in the engine room.

The *Idemitsu Maru* carries oil from Ras Tanura or Mena Al Ahmadi in the Persian Gulf to the Tokuyama Oil Refinery of Idemitsu Kosan Co. Ltd. Cargoes will also be discharged at the Chiba Oil Refinery when the harbour facilities have been improved.

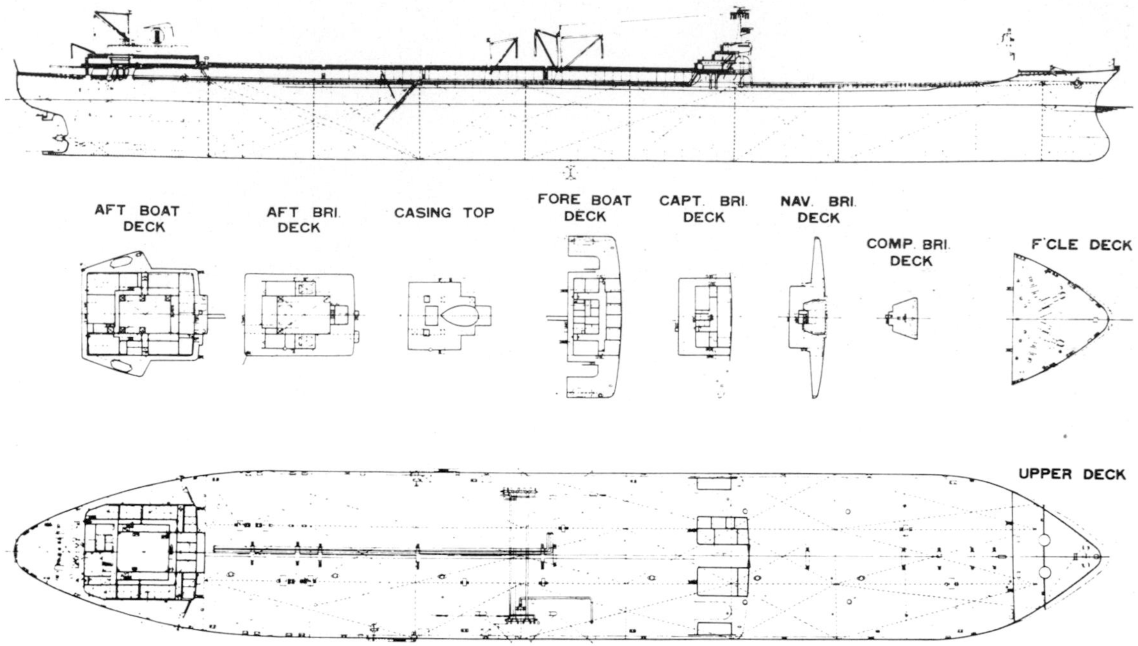

Drawing of *Idemitsu Maru.*
Photo courtesy: Shipbuilders' Association of Japan

The Ram Bow . . .

The bulbous ram bow of *Imperial Ottawa.*
Photo courtesy: Shipbuilders' Association of Japan

An illustration of the pronounced ram bow fitted to the S.S. *Imperial Ottawa.* In this ship the ram is faired into the hull lines. Another type of ram bow is like the fore-end of a torpedo and creates a noticeable angle at the point where it joins the hull.

Ram bows have the effect of reducing drag, especially when a ship is in light condition. Extra speed of up to half a knot can be obtained with ships designed in this way. At the same time the extra buoyancy created can often be utilised by a small increase in the amount of cargo carried.

The plate visible in the hull just above keel level covers the tunnel in which a side thruster is installed. The side thruster is another innovation, which, after a slow start, is now being widely adopted. The largest units now installed in ships have powers of 1,360 i.h.p. and are as efficient as small harbour tugs.

M.S. KAHO MARU (1966)

Owners: YAMASHITA SHINNIHON STEAMSHIP CO.
Builders: HITACHI SHIPBUILDING AND ENGINEERING CO. LTD.
B. & W. diesel, 27,600 b.h.p.
Single screw
Service speed 16 knots
Length overall 911 ft. (approx.)
Beam 144 ft. (approx.)
Deadweight tonnage 121,298

Loading and discharging of oil is remotely controlled from a central control room. In addition, an independent ballast pumping system permits simultaneous loading of oil and discharge of ballast—this is a practice which is being increasingly used in tankers of all sizes since the saving of time in port can be considerable.

There is limited remote control of the main engine from a central control room in the engine room.

The *Kaho Maru* was delivered to her owners in May 1966. Between that date and the end of 1967, nine round voyages had been completed between the Persian Gulf and Japan.

S.S. WORLD FRIENDSHIP (1965)

The *World Friendship*, belonging to the Niarchos Group, is typical of a large number of privately-owned tankers. She has a deadweight tonnage of 90,000, and on one voyage to Thames Haven achieved the distinction—although very short lived—of bringing the largest cargo of crude oil (87,000 tons) ever to enter the Thames. By 1968 the tonnage had risen to over 130,000 and as developments come to fruition, even that figure will be overtaken.

Of the world's tanker tonnage of over 108,000,000 tons, more than 70,000,000 tons is privately owned. It has always been the policy of the oil companies to maintain their own basic fleets and to meet the balance of their requirements by the charter of vessels. This may seem to be an unusual arrangement and one disadvantageous to the private shipowning company. The figures, however, indicate that this is not so and there has never been a shortage of shipowners willing to enter the business. In fact in recent years, many companies previously unconnected with this particular trade have built up their own fleets, usually for long-term charter to the oil companies.

Charters fall into two main groups, voyage charter and time charter.

A *Voyage Charter* can be for a single voyage or for a number of consecutive voyages. Under this type of charter the charterer pays an agreed rate of freight per ton of cargo loaded, and the owner pays for the ship's disbursements, bunkers and expenses. The freight may be payable on loading or on arrival at the port of discharge, but in practice it is more usually payable on discharge of cargo.

Freight rates are expressed as a percentage above or below "Intascale"*. "Intascale" was the rate of freight payable on a given date in 1962 for a certain voyage on the basis of certain charter conditions.

Examples of voyage charters are:

Persian Gulf to U.K. or Continent. *Vestfold*, 74,000 tons. Intascale minus 12½%.

Mediterranean to U.K. or Continent. *Gunny*, 16,000 tons. Intascale plus 15%.

Consecutive voyages. *Gervase Sleigh*, 16,000 tons. Intascale flat. Trading to August 1969 in direct continuation from November 1968.

---

* Now being superseded by a new scale known as 'World Scale'

The S.S. *World Friendship* in the Thames estuary en route to Thames Haven from Ras Tanura.
Photo courtesy: Port of London Authority

A *Time Charter* can be for any period of time. In practice, most time vessels are hired for periods between two and ten years. In a time charter it is usual to quote the hire in terms of shillings or dollars per summer deadweight ton per month. Out of the payment received the owner would have to pay his officers and crew, provide stores, provisions and repair and maintain the vessel and set aside the necessary sum for depreciation. The charterer, on the other hand, pays for bunkers and all port charges.

Examples of time charters are:

Pelikan, 19,916 tons. $3.50 per ton, two years trading (Esso).
Katina, 24,850 tons. $3.00 per ton, six months trading (Socal).

Bareboat Charter. In this type of charter, the charterer pays an an agreed amount and assumes responsibility for every aspect of the ship's operation including manning, stores, bunkers, etc. Bareboat charters are little used now.

The *Victor H. Kelly*, a "T 2" class standard American tanker. Deadweight tonnage about 16,000. Many of these ships were built during the war and their history has been similar to that of the "Liberty" ships. For many years they were employed by the major oil companies, but as new tonnage became available they were either scrapped or sold to tramping companies. Several are still in service. (1946)

The French tanker *Chambord*. With a deadweight tonnage of 32,572 the *Chambord* was an outstanding ship and pointed the way to future development. The majority of tankers were still built with forecastle, bridge and poop decks although one or two were already in service with a single unit superstructure aft. (1955)

Another French tanker, the *Montmartre* was also a notable ship of this period. With a deadweight tonnage of 30,230 the *Montmartre* ranked amongst the largest tankers. (1958)

Photos courtesy: D. W. A. Mercer

The Hunting tanker *Eskfield* approaching Rotterdam. The *Eskfield* has a deadweight tonnage of 33,769. This vessel was recently sold and is now trading under the name of *Torero*.

By 1960 there were 40 tankers in service with deadweight tonnages in excess of 50,000 tons, and it is interesting to note that in view of the enorm-powers now produced by diesel engines only one of these ships was propelled by this method. Included in the total were two ships of over 100,000 tons, the *Universe Daphne* and *Universe Apollo*. The ten largest tankers had been built in Japan. The following years saw a steady rise in tonnages, with the *Idemitsu Maru* (page 17) being the first to top the 200,000 mark. In the next few years there will be a steady stream of ships up to about 260,000 tons deadweight coming into service. Shipyards have full order books and if there is to be another leap forward in the size of tankers such ships will not be in service until 1973 or later. Since about 1955 tankers have been labelled as "Super", "Giant" and "Mammoth". What adjective will be used to describe 500,000 tonners? (1959)

Photo courtesy: D. W. A. Mercer

When the S.S. *Ardtaraig* arrived at the Loch Long (Finnart) BP Ocean Terminal she discharged the largest cargo of any kind so far received in Scotland. At a rate of 14,000 tons per hour the *Ardtaraig* pumped out 206,800 tons of crude oil. This vessel, with a total capacity of 214,000 tons on a draft of over 60 ft. is one of four sister ships in service or under construction. With the delivery of the fourth ship Trident Tankers Ltd. (a member of the P and O Group) will become the United Kingdom's largest independent tanker operators with ships totalling about 2,000,000 deadweight tons. (1969) *Photo courtesy: P and O Line*

Tugs berthing the *Esso Mercia* at the Esso Refinery, Milford Haven, in April, 1968, at the end of her maiden voyage. The cargo of 150,190 tons of crude oil was the largest delivered to the United Kingdom up to that time. The full capacity of the *Esso Mercia* is 170,800 on a draft of 59 ft. (1968)
Photo courtesy: An Esso photograph

M.S. *Flowergate* and cross-section.
Photo courtesy: The Turnbull Scott Shipping Co. Ltd.

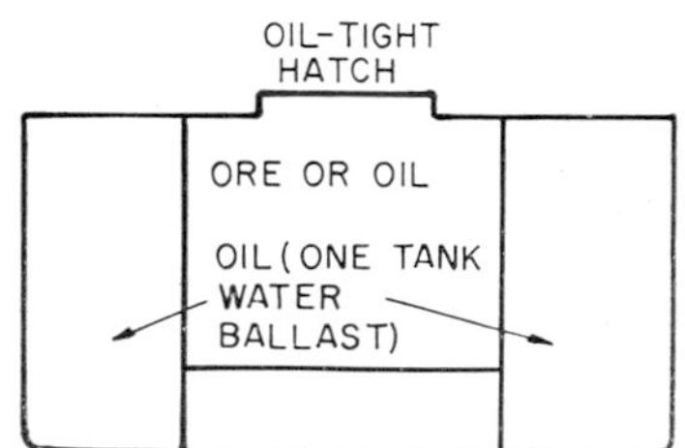

CHAPTER 2

Bulk Carriers

SINCE 1945, there have been periods when too many ships have been chasing too little cargo. At times charter rates have been so low that ships have been laid up or sold. When these periods of recessions coincided with similar conditions in the tramp oil trade matters were made worse by the transfer of tankers to the grain trade—with their hull subdivision which obviates the need for shifting boards they were ideal for this purpose. It is only fair to say that at other times such as the first closure of the Suez Canal and the Korean War, charter rates have been extremely high. It is an industry which has become used to years of lean and years of fat.

For obvious reasons, the owners who ran the most economic ships continued to make profits, or at least pay for the ships' depreciation costs, and a demand arose for larger and sometimes faster ships which would still further reduce the risk of unprofitable voyages or laying up. Shippers, too, demanded more efficient transport and gradually there came into being the bulk carrier which could carry a full deadweight of ores, grains, coal or other bulk products. From then on the story has been similar to that of tankers, although the overall conditions of the trade, such as loading and discharging facilities, have so far limited the largest ships to about 150,000 tons. These ships are limited in operation as are the giant tankers and the demand for smaller vessels remains high. For instance, the United Kingdom cannot accept ore carriers much above 20,000 tons and the position will not be remedied until the completion of the new harbour at Port Talbot; a similar installation may be established on the Clyde if a suitable site can be found for both harbour and steelworks.

Some of the smaller tramp ships in the 15,000-ton range are built with a view to securing charters on cargo liner berths. They are usually a little faster, have greater hull sub-division and more extensive cargo handling gear.

Several ships have also been built with the capacity to carry oil as well as the full range of other bulk products in an effort to reduce the number of voyages undertaken in ballast.

M.S. FLOWERGATE (1969)

Owners: THE TURNBULL SCOTT SHIPPING CO. LTD.
Builders: A/B GÖTAVERKEN
Götaverken diesel, 17,600 b.h.p.
Single Kamewa propeller
Service speed 15 knots
Length overall 830 ft.
Beam 131 ft.
Draught 48·5 ft.
Deadweight tonnage 106,600

The *Flowergate* is a combined oil–ore ship, the intention being that the dual function will reduce the number of voyages which the pure ore ship is required to make in ballast.

Ore is stowed in four centreline holds raised about 9 ft. above the double bottoms. There are ten wing tanks, eight of which are used for oil and two for water ballast. The ore holds are also capable of carrying oil and a complete pumping system is installed. The loading and discharge of oil is remotely controlled from a deckhouse between Nos. 2 and 3 holds; the pumping machinery, which has a total capacity of 7,500 tons per hour, is installed in a large pumproom immediately below.

In the wing tanks permanent cleaning units (high-pressure hot water and detergent) are installed. Portable units are carried for cleaning the main holds.

The following figures indicate the weight of an ore cargo as compared with oil, and the amount of water ballast space provided:

Ore – 1,956,000 cu. ft.
Oil – 4,605,000 cu. ft.
Water Ballast – 585,000 cu. ft. (including fore and after peak tanks).

The firm of Turnbull Scott was established in 1872 and first operated ships in 1882. Since that time they have been prominent in the field of tramp shipping. Their first really large ship—the *Naess Parkgate*—was built in 1966. With the *Flowergate* Turnbull Scott became the owners of one of the largest cargo ships owned in this country or the Continent. It is an interesting fact that the previous *Flowergate*, built in 1952 and sold to Greek interests in 1967, had a deadweight tonnage of 9,450 and a diesel engine developing 3,300 b.h.p.

The *Flowergate* is on a 15-year time charter to Trafikakbolaget Grangesberg, and for the time being is scheduled to run on voyages between:

Buchanan (West Africa)–Japan with iron ore.
Japan–Persian Gulf in ballast.
Persian Gulf–U.K./Continent with oil.
U.K./Continent–Buchanan in ballast.

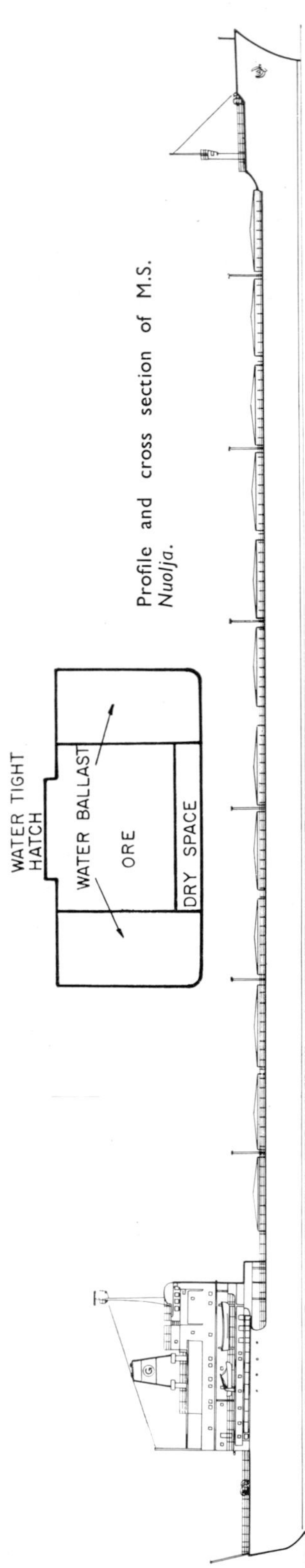

Profile and cross section of M.S. *Nuolja.*

M.S. NUOLJA (1967)

Owners: TRAFIKAKTIEBOLAGET GRÄNGESBERG-OXELÖSUND
Builders: A/B GÖTAVERKEN
Götaverken diesel, 17,600 b.h.p.
Single Kamewa propeller
Service speed 16 knots
Length overall 800 ft.
Beam 124 ft.
Deadweight tonnage 72,500

The M.S. *Nuolja* was built for the single purpose of carrying iron ore. Iron ore is one of the heaviest commodities carried in ships and presents certain difficulties of stowage—when loaded low in a ship it creates what is known as a stiff condition, resulting in very slow pitching and rolling, which, if not checked, can lead to serious damage and possible loss of the vessel. The sheer weight of the cargo, which nowhere fills the holds can also cause tremendous stresses on the structure. To overcome these problems ships such as the *Nuolja* carry the ore in narrow holds, the bottoms of which are raised up to 12 ft. above the keel. The surrounding spaces, known as side tanks, are subdivided and used for the carriage of water ballast. The centre of gravity of the ship is thus raised and the vessel, as a result, much more sea kindly. The *Nuolja* is strengthened throughout its length and when ore is loaded into each of the five holds, the ship remains in proper trim—fore and aft.

M.S. OBO PRINCE (1968)

Owners: SIGURD HERLOFSON & CO., A/S OSLO
Builders: A/B GÖTAVERKEN
Götaverken diesel, 19,800 b.h.p.
Single screw
Service speed 15·9 knots
Length overall 841 ft.
Beam 128 ft.
Deadweight tonnage 96,400

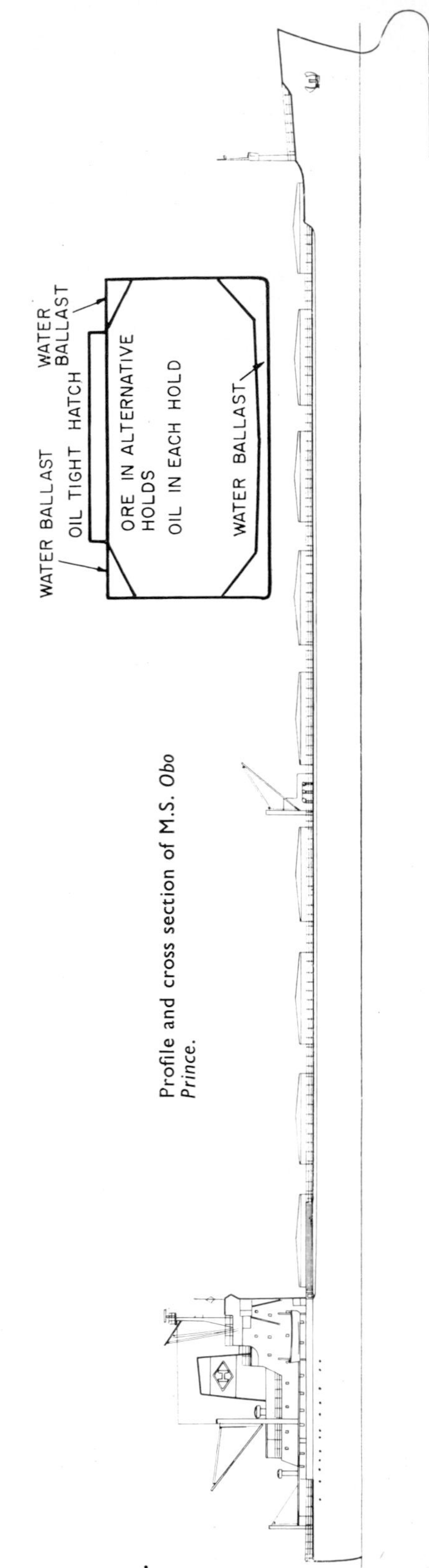

Profile and cross section of M.S. *Obo Prince.*

The *Obo Prince* is one of a class of vessels known as OBO (i.e. Ore–Bulk–Oil) and it is possible for these ships to operate in a wide variety of trades. Unlike the ore and the ore–oil carriers, the holds of these ships are not raised above the double bottoms. A further difference is that the holds extend the full width of the ship in order to facilitate the handling of bulk cargoes such as grain or coal. OBO ships have strengthened hulls, but because of the size of the holds and the need to maintain good stability alternate holds only are used for the carriage of ore. The double bottoms are used for water ballast and upper wing tanks are used for the same purpose. Oil is carried in all holds and a full pumping system is installed. It should, however, be noted that in some vessels of this type one or more holds have to be left empty when oil is carried.

The *Obo Prince* has the following cargo characteristics:

- Oil, nearly 4,000,000 cu. ft.
- Ore, just over 2,000,000 cu. ft.
- Bulk, nearly 4,000,000 cu. ft.
- Water ballast, just over 900,000 cu. ft.

Visually it is not possible to distinguish the pure ore carrier from any other type of bulk carrier which is not equipped with cargo handling gear. The ore-oil and the OBO type vessels can be identified by the midship deckhouse and the derricks or cranes used for handling hoses. In turn, all bulk carriers can be distinguished from tankers by the high hatch coamings, although at certain angles and in bad light some confusion can occur.

M.S. *Caledonia*, deadweight tonnage 58,902.
Photo courtesy: Uraga Heavy Industries Ltd.

Japanese Yards

At the end of the war in 1945, few Japanese shipyards remained undestroyed. From scratch the industry was rebuilt and for the last 14 years this country has produced the highest level of production in the world. The lead which has been established is such that Japan currently produces nearly half of the world's ships and the annual tonnage is six times that of the second largest producer. One company alone, Mitsubishi Heavy Industries Ltd., claims to produce 10% of the world's annual output.

A large proportion of Japanese production is for export, and the following table indicates the extent to which this business has been developed. The period covered is between January 1966 and December 1967.

M.S. *Doto* (1968), deadweight tonnage 62,334.
Photo courtesy: Uraga Heavy Industries Ltd.

Country	*No.*	*Deadweight tonnage*
Bermuda	8	640,380
Bahamas	4	211,790
Denmark	42	1,106,767
Finland	1	19,400
France	6	81,260
W. Germany	4	31,212
Greece	18	523,929
Italy	1	33,000
Norway	115	5,830,781
Netherlands	22	609,138
Portugal	4	186,294
Sweden	6	259,600
Switzerland	1	25,400
United Kingdom	41	1,763,118
Curacao	1	173,900
Ghana	16	39,900
Liberia	354	15,214,738
Egypt	1	650
S. Africa	7	76,329
Communist countries	104	2,197,373
S.E. Asia	197	1,650,000
Canada	5	276,435
U.S.A.	43	1,587,740
Brazil	24	146,320
Chile	6	63,794
Cuba	2	6,400
Mexico	6	82,350
Panama	258	7,883,719
Paraguay	6	5,620
Uruguay	1	28,267
Venezuela	4	128,000

The Liberty ship *Saint Oie*, built during the war as the *Isaac I. Stevens*. When these ships were taken over by private companies the gun emplacements were removed and the protected wheelhouses opened up. Sometimes, as in the case of the *Saint Oie*, a wheelhouse was constructed on the flying bridge and a few were lengthened. Otherwise the majority of these vessels traded without further modification.

Japanese shipyards have pioneered the development of giant tankers and bulk carriers and it has often been said that it is the European countries which have retained the market for high-class ships such as passenger liners, cargo liners and special vessels. Nevertheless, most of the leading cargo liner operators have now had ships built in Japan and one of the most powerful tugs in the world came from a Japanese shipyard.

Several completely new yards have been built in the last 15 years and the largest ships are now built in dry docks. This method, and that of building a ship in two sections, has led to a rapid increase in building rates. So, too, has the system of automation and prefabrication in which the ship or the dock is used for the minimum period possible. The overall speed at which ships can now be built is shown by Sasebo Heavy Industries Co. Ltd., who are currently building a series of 13 tankers, each of which will be built to a standard design and with a capacity of over 200,000 tons. One of these ships comes out of dock every three months. The M.S. *Bulford*, one of the series, was commenced at the end of 1967. She was launched in March 1968 and completed in June of the same year.

The latest yard at Tsu (Nippon Kokan) has building docks laid out parallel to the shore with entrances at either end. Each dock is also divided by a cofferdam so that ships of various sizes can be built at the same time, either complete or in sections.

Several Japanese yards now have facilities for constructing and repairing 500,000-ton ships.

The Japanese lead in shipbuilding is bound to continue for some years to come, but European yards have not failed to react. Both Sweden and Germany have, in fact, increased their annual output in the face of this competition and only the United Kingdom has regressed, 1968 being its worst year for launchings for a considerable period.

There are signs, however, that the U.K. industry, which for a period was threatened with near extinction, is now reviving. The reasons for the decline were many, but the overall effect was that U.K. tenders were uncompetitive or were secured in the knowledge that they would be unprofitable. In addition there was no guarantee that delivery dates could be met. Following the publication of the Geddes Report, the principal yards have merged so that on the Tyne there is now just one company controlling the several yards. The Clyde has reorganised into two large groups and there is a body of opinion which considers that a further merger of these two groups would ultimately lead to greater efficiency. For geographical reasons Harland and Wolff Ltd. have remained unaffected and several other much smaller companies who are similarly isolated will carry on as single units. Mergers in themselves, produce nothing, but the U.K. shipbuilding indus-

The S.S. *Baron Douglas* of 6,300 deadweight tons.

SAKAIDE WORKS OF THE KAWASAKI DOCKYARD CO. LTD.

Key: **1.** Fabrication Shop. **2.** Assembly Shop. **3.** Painting Shop. **4.** Pre-erection Yard. **5.** Building Dock. **6.** 200-ton Gantry Crane. **7.** 120-ton Jib Crane. **8.** 30-ton Jib Crane. **9.** 10-ton Jib Crane. **10.** Ship Repair Office. **11.** Repair Dock. **12.** 80-ton Jib Crane. **13.** 3-ton Jib Crane. **14.** Platers Shop. **15.** Overhaul Shop. **16.** Warehouse. **17.** Dock. **18.** 15-ton Jib Crane.

Principal particulars of Docks:

	Building Dock	*Repair Dock*
Capacity	350,000 dwt	500,000 dwt.
Length	1,247 ft.	1,476 ft.
Breadth	203 ft.	236 ft.
Depth	33 ft. 10 in.	40 ft. 4 in.
Cranes	200-ton gantry cranes × 2	80-ton jib cranes × 2
	120-ton jib crane × 2	3-ton jib crane × 1
	30-ton jib crane × 1	

try is undergoing a rigorous self-imposed shake up, and the facilities, which have always been as good—if not better—than those of any other country, are now beginning to be used to greater effect. The Government has also assisted by making it possible for U.K. shipyards to offer credit facilities more in line with those of other countries, and it is significant that orders are now being won which a year or two ago would almost automatically have been taken by Japanese yards.

Harland and Wolff Ltd. have built a new dock in the old Musgrave channel, Belfast, and, whereas the most modern yards elsewhere are limited to handling prefabricated units of about 200 tons, the new gantry crane at Queen's Island will have a capacity of 800 tons. Already the yard has booked orders for a series of 200,000-tons-plus tankers, and the building dock and the yard facilities will be able to build the largest ships which are ever likely to be ordered. Other companies, both British and Continental, can either build ships up to 300,000 tons or are in the process of providing the necessary docks and facilities. Japan's shipbuilding costs are believed to be increasing at a faster rate than elsewhere and several other factors, including, ironically, their long order books, are beginning to change the world pattern. The Japanese will obviously hold their position for some time to come, but the next few years will show whether their dominating ascendancy will be continued, or whether once again the European yards will regain the position which they held for so many years prior to about 1955. It also has to be remembered that the world's shipbuilding potential considerably exceeds world demand and a recession in world trade could create a situation in which only the most efficient yards even within the Japanese complex would be able to continue on a profitable basis.

Uraga Heavy Industries Ltd. is a typical Japanese yard which has tendered successfully not only for bulk carriers and tankers, but also for cargo liners, passenger and car ferries (mainly for domestic use), naval vessels and a variety of small specialised craft. Facilities include five shipbuilding berths, the largest of which can accommodate a ship of 105,000 tons deadweight. Sulzer diesel engines are manufactured under licence as are Stal-Laval turbines.

Much of the yard's output is for export and the photographs illustrate two typical products which have been built for companies operating under the "flags of convenience" (principally Liberia and Panama).

The *Caledonia*, delivered in 1968, is an OBO type vessel with a deadweight tonnage of 58,902. A particular feature of this ship is the double-hull construction. All the faces of the holds are flush and tank cleaning has been made much easier as a result. The *Caledonia* is owned by Nueva Valencia Compania Naviera, S.A., an affiliate company of the N. J. Goulandris Group, and is registered under the Liberian flag. A sister ship, the *Makedonia*, is owned by the Hellenic Bulk Transport, S.A. of Panama and registered in Greece.

The *Doto* was also completed in 1968 and is a bulk carrier of 62,334 tons deadweight. She is powered by a Sulzer diesel of 16,000 b.h.p. and attained a speed of 17·12 knots on trials. The *Doto* is owned by the Vitasa Steamship Company, S.A. of Panama and is registered in Liberia.

Some idea of the tempo of modern shipbuilding is indicated by the following figures:

	1968
Keel laid	27th May

Launched 19th August
Delivered 27th November

One interesting fact about the Japanese shipbuilding industry is that little success has been achieved with the marketing of their own propulsive units. Almost all of the ships built for export have been equipped with European-designed engines either imported or built under licence in Japanese engine shops. This is particularly the case with diesel engines in which field a handful of companies, such as Sulzer, Pielstick, M.A.N., B. & W., Götaverken and Doxford, have become household words.

M.V. STONEPOOL (1966)

Owners: SIR R. ROPNER & CO. LTD.
Builders: CHARLES CONNELL & CO. (SHIPBUILDERS) LTD.
6RD 90 Sulzer diesel, 13,000 b.h.p.
Length overall 718 ft.
Beam 90 ft.
Load draught (summer) 34 ft.
Deadweight tonnage 45,027

The *Stonepool* is designed to carry all kinds of bulk cargo including ores. The double-bottom tanks are carried up the side of the vessel forming hopper sides to aid the discharge of cargo by grabs. Topside tanks are fitted for grain carriage. Grain is discharged from these tanks via small ports into the holds. Loading to the tanks is through small watertight hatches, the main holds being covered by MacGregor single-pull watertight steel hatch covers.

There is no cargo-handling gear, but a stores derrick is arranged on the poop. Two 3-ton derricks are fitted at the bridge front for engine room spares, etc.

The foremast is fitted with an observation house, equipped with swivel seat, desk, telephone and heater.

The accompanying plan shows officers' and crews' accommodation.

All crews' cabins are lined with Formica plastic and the public rooms and officers' cabins are panelled with various wood veneers.

Two recent voyages were:
Seven Islands to Baltimore with 42,710 tons of iron ore. 1,489 miles in 4 days, 16 hours.
Norfolk (Va.) to Sakai (Japan) with 41,096 tons of coal. 10,172 miles in 29 days, 5 hours.

The *Stonepool* then sailed in ballast to New South Wales to load for Amsterdam.

M.S. WEARFIELD (1964)

Owners: HUNTING AND SON LTD.
Builders: AUSTIN AND PICKERSGILL LTD.
6 cylinder Clark-Sulzer diesel, 8,640 b.h.p.
Single screw
Service speed 14·5 knots
Length overall 466 ft.
Beam 61 ft.
Deadweight tonnage 26,250

The M.S. *Wearfield* is the largest bulk carrier in the Hunting fleet, although the largest tanker has a deadweight tonnage of 60,600.

Recently four cranes have been fitted to the *Wearfield*, which has eight hatches and is able to carry many types of bulk cargo.

Huntings have now adopted the system of integrated manning pioneered by the major oil companies.

The system has two chief aims: the most economical use of manpower and the improvement of the work content of the crew's duties, coupled with continuing employment and increasing opportunities for advancement.

To work efficiently under the new system, the crew of a ship, from captain downwards, must discard long-standing traditions and demarcations between departments and regard the ship as a single unit operated by a work force with a single purpose—the efficiency of the ship.

Under the new system, the captain acts as a general manager with a management team comprising the chief officer, chief engineer and second engineer. At weekly meetings of the team, members plan the short- and long-term operational and maintenance requirements based on a work plan prepared in advance by the chief engineer in co-operation with the chief officer and second engineer. The meet-

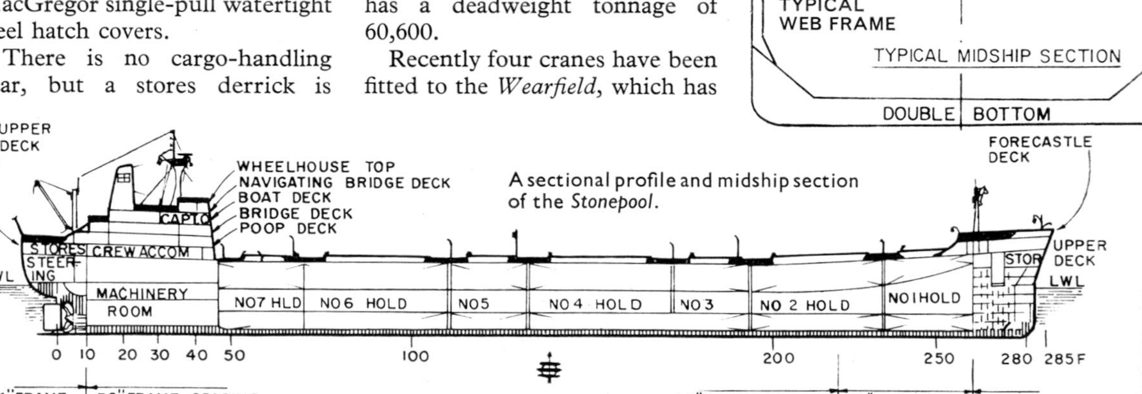

A sectional profile and midship section of the *Stonepool*.

ing also discusses the effectiveness of previous plans and measures to overcome difficulties. The team may also co-opt any other staff member for any particular meeting or subject.

Once a programme has been agreed, the chief engineer instructs the chief petty officer regarding each day's duties. The chief petty officer details and supervises members of the work force, each of whom has been trained in engine room, catering and deck work. The only exception to this will be when the work force is engaged in engine room tasks, when the watchkeeping engineers will be responsible for technical supervision. In the event of an emergency or unexpected maintenance demands, the chief officer or second engineer requests assistance through the chief engineer and, if necessary, a special meeting of the management team will be called. Minutes are kept of all weekly meetings to ensure continuity in the event of staff changes, and regular ship inspections are carried out to check on progress or to assess the need for amendments to the plan. To maintain uniformity between ships the company has drawn up a standard code for operational assignments, but the captain has discretion to increase the strength of a watch. Departure from the work plan may also occur during adverse weather or extreme heat.

Under the new scheme the chief officer becomes the commercial manager. Apart from normal cargo and watch-keeping duties, he is responsible for all safety and security measures throughout the ship. He looks after the medicine chest and first-aid and organises the training and work activities for the deck apprentices. He also understudies the captain so as to be conversant with all aspects of the latter's work when he is himself promoted.

The second officer assists the chief officer in all commercial work in addition to his normal duties, and the third officer will look after safety records and assist the chief officer with welfare and deck safety equipment. The radio officer assists the master as needed on paper work.

The chief engineer becomes the ship's technical officer and works manager. He is responsible for the maintenance and repairs to the vessel's structure, machinery, equipment, fittings and engine room maintenance. He is also in charge of apprentice engineers—when carried—for training and work activities. Maintenance of the vessel's structure includes such items as painting and upkeep of decks and superstructure, deck gear and gangways.

The second engineer, in addition to his normal duties, arranges for technical supervision by watch-keeping engineers of machinery maintenance when this is undertaken by the general purpose work force.

M.S. *Wearfield.*
Photo courtesy: The Hunting Group of Companies

During the period of change-over to integrated operations, an additional engineer officer is appointed to the ship as training officer for a period of three to four months. He is a day worker and responsible for training the crew in multi-purpose duties and, in particular, in the operation and upkeep of all deck and engine room equipment.

The chief petty officer, who is a bosun, in addition to his normal duties assists in the training of engine ratings in deck duties.

Acknowledgement for this information is made to the Hunting Group Review.

M.S. *Sigsilver*.
Photos courtesy: Silver Line Ltd.

M.S. SIGSILVER (1967)

Owners: SILVER LINE LTD.
Builders: ISHIKAWAJIMA HARIMA HEAVY INDUSTRIES CO. LTD.
Sulzer diesel, 23,000 b.h.p.
Single screw
Service speed 15·5 knots
Length overall 820 ft.
Beam 134 ft.
Deadweight tonnage 105,780

One of the largest ships of its type in the world, the *Sigsilver* can carry any type of bulk cargo. She has 11 holds with hopper sides and wing tanks. No cargo handling gear has been fitted since her size limits her to operating between ports with shore facilities. The total complement of this vessel amounts to 36, including four stewardesses.

The main engine can be controlled from the bridge and also from a console in the engine room. Because of extensive automation and alarm systems, it is unnecessary to have more than one engineer taking charge of the engines.

M.S. SUGAR PRODUCER (1968)

Owners: SUGAR LINE LIMITED, LONDON
Builders: LITHGOWS LTD.
Kincaid-B. & W. diesel, 5,000 b.h.p.
Single screw
Service speed 15·5 knots
Length overall 550 ft.
Beam 73 ft.
Deadweight tonnage 20,700

Primarily built for the carriage of bulk sugar, this ship can also be used for the carriage of other bulk commodities such as ores, grain, sulphur, etc. When carrying sugar the *Sugar Producer* works between ports with shore installations, but a full set of derricks and winches is fitted so that voyages can be undertaken in the bulk cargo tramp trade.

This ship is also fitted with a ram bow which increases speed, especially in a light condition.

The *Sugar Producer* normally works between the West Indies and Messrs. Tate and Lyle's London refinery. Owing to draft limitations at the U.K. discharging ports the weight of cargo is limited to 17,500 tons on a draught of about 29 ft. 6 in.

A round voyage from London to Point Lisas (Trinidad) with completion of loading and discharging operations would normally take about one month.

The *Sugar Producer* is also designed to load sugar from Queensland, Australia.

The Sakaide Works of the Kawasaki Dockyard Co. Ltd. were completed in 1967 and 1968 (the repair dock), and have an annual production of 900,000 tons. All ships are built in the 350,000-ton capacity building dock, and the various assembly shops are

M.S. *Sugar Producer*.
Photo courtesy: Tate & Lyle Ltd.

M.S. *Cotswold*.
Photo courtesy: B.I.S.N. Co. Ltd.

planned to provide a continuous flow of prefabricated units to the wide areas surrounding the dock. As is the case with many modern shipbuilding establishments, the prefabricated units are painted and fitted-out to varying degrees before leaving the shops. The travelling gantry cranes which span the dock are now a feature of all modern yards, where they have superseded the conventional jib crane.

M.S. COTSWOLD (1966)

Owners: BRITISH INDIA STEAM NAVIGATION CO. LTD. (Managed by Hain Nourse Management Ltd.)
Builders: FURNESS SHIPBUILDING CO. LTD.
B. & W. diesel, 16,000 b.h.p.
Single screw
Service speed 15·5 knots
Length overall 675 ft.
Beam 90 ft.
Deadweight tonnage 43,000

The *Cotswold* is typical of bulk carriers generally. She has no cargo handling gear and is therefore limited to voyages between ports with shore facilities.

Many bulk carriers in the 35–45,000 ton range are now being built. The *Sigsilver* (page 30) is very much larger, but in general is similar in construction and hold arrangement. One or two ships of this type are now on order or in service with deadweight tonnages above 150,000.

M.S. VESTAN (1967)

Owners: SMEDVIGS TANKREDERI A/S (NORWAY)
Builders: HITACHI SHIPBUILDING AND ENGINEERING CO. LTD.
B. & W. diesel, 20,700 b.h.p.
Single screw
Service speed 15·2 knots
Length overall 827 ft. (approx.)
Beam 128 ft. (approx.)
Deadweight tonnage 91,800

The *Vestan* was, at the time of her completion, one of the largest ore–oil carriers in the world. The tonnage of 91,800 has, however, since been passed and as in the case of ordinary bulk carriers a ship of 160,000 tons deadweight is now in service.

The *Vestan* was the first ship to be classified as E–o (Engine Room Zero) by the Norske Veritas and it is the intention of the owners to operate the vessel with an unattended engine room for periods of up to 24 hours. Bridge or engine room remote control consoles can operate independently of each other and alarm signals are given by a red light (major defect), orange light (abnormality in the electrical system) or yellow light (general abnormality in the main engine).

In the case of "Red" alarms, such as the abnormal drop in pressure at the lubricating oil inlet of the main engine or of excessive speed because of governor trouble in the main engine, the engine is automatically stopped. "Yellow" alarms, which do not involve immediate stoppage of the main engine include the detection of abnormal temperatures and abnormal liquid levels. The main and auxiliary machinery is monitored at 345 points and alarm systems are installed in the day room of the duty engineer and on the bridge. Extensive precautions are installed against the misuse of the main engine whilst on bridge control and, in the event of an emergency, the engineer on duty can switch immediately from bridge to engine room control.

All oil loading and discharge operations are remotely controlled.

The diagram overleaf illustrates the way in which a bulk carrier is loaded to obtain correct stability. The density of iron ore is such that four holds partly loaded will take the ship down to its load line. One advantage arising from the installation of upper wing tanks is that the free surface area of grain is limited and can therefore be carried without portable bulkheads.

The *San Juan Trader* has a deadweight tonnage of 63,391. She was built in 1966, is owned by San Juan Carriers Ltd., and is employed carrying iron ore from the Marcona mines in Peru to Japan, U.S.A. and Europe. On the return journey coal or other bulk cargo is loaded.

"SAN JUAN TRADER" LOADING CONDITIONS

HOLD NO.
ORE
OIL
COAL/GRAIN
BALLAST
1
3
2
4
5
6
7

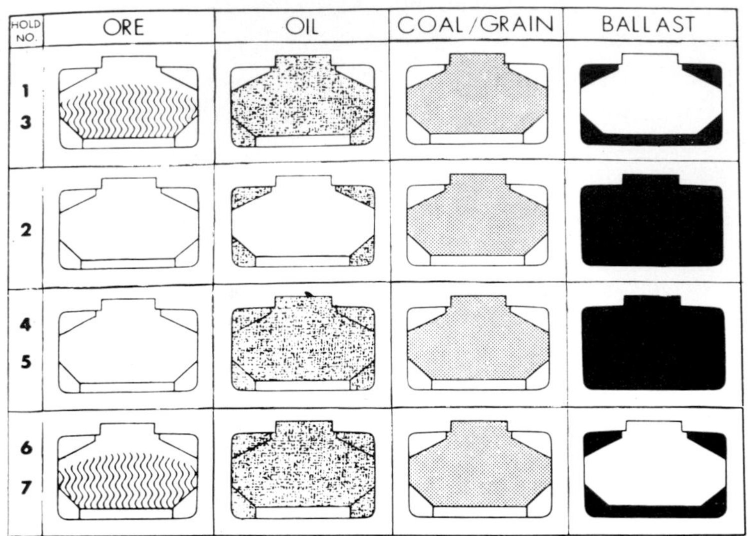

Table from Shipbuilding & Marine Engineering in Japan.

S.S. CEDROS (1966)

Owners: SEA TANKERS INCORPORATED
Builders: THE KURE SHIPBUILDING AND ENGINEERING CO. LTD.
General Electric turbine, 27,500 s.h.p.
Single screw
Service speed 15·1 knots
Length overall 998 ft. (approx.)
Beam 142 ft. (approx.)
Deadweight tonnage 146,218

The *Cedros* was the largest bulk–oil carrier at the time of her completion. She is double-hulled and all the faces of the holds are flush.

The *Cedros* transports industrial salt from Mexico to Japan and crude oil from the Persian Gulf to the U.S.A. It is in ways such

Drawing of M.S. *Vestan* from Shipbuilding & Marine Engineering in Japan.

BOAT DECK
A-DECK
FIDDLEY TOP
BRI. DECK
(B-DECK)
UPPER BRI.
DECK
(C-DECK)
CAPT. BRI.
DECK
(D-DECK)
NAV. BRIDGE
COMP.
FLAT
F'CLE DECK
UPPER DECK
HOLD

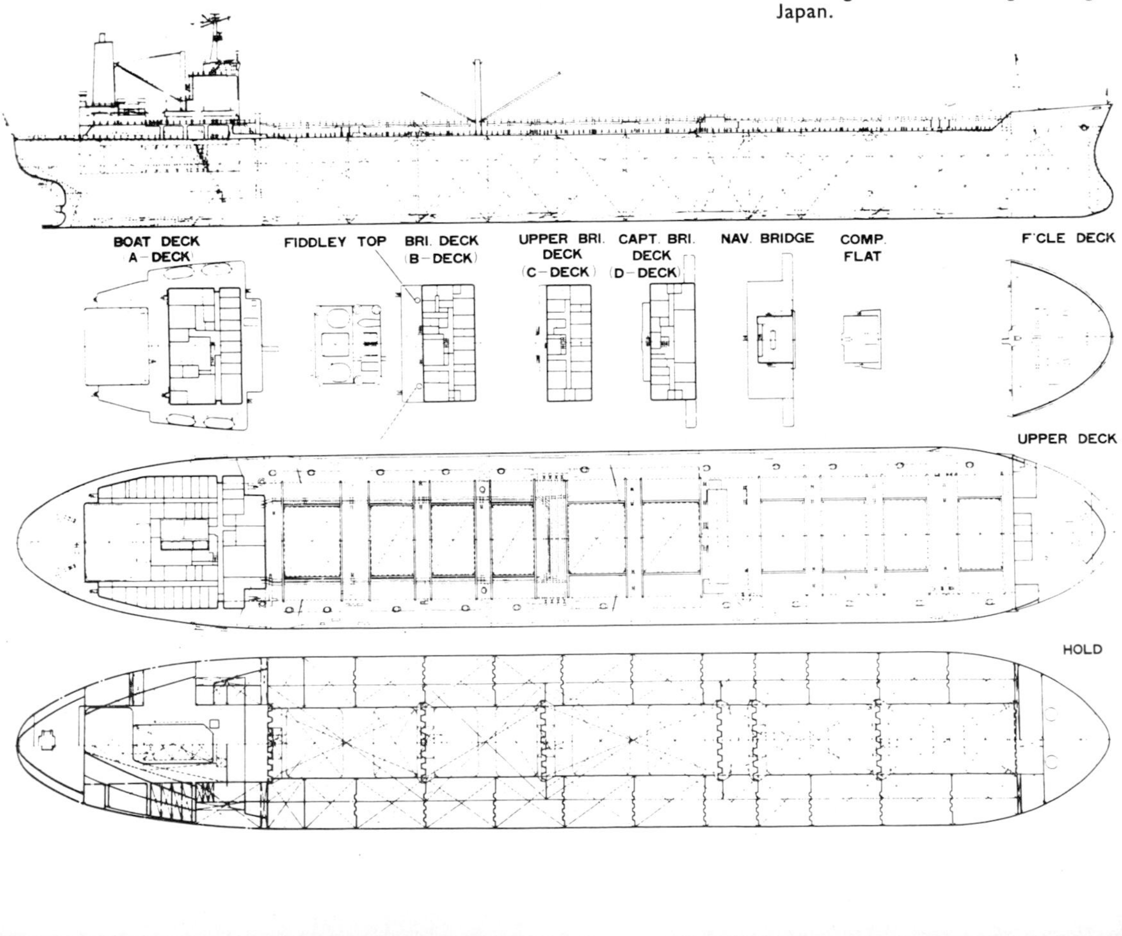

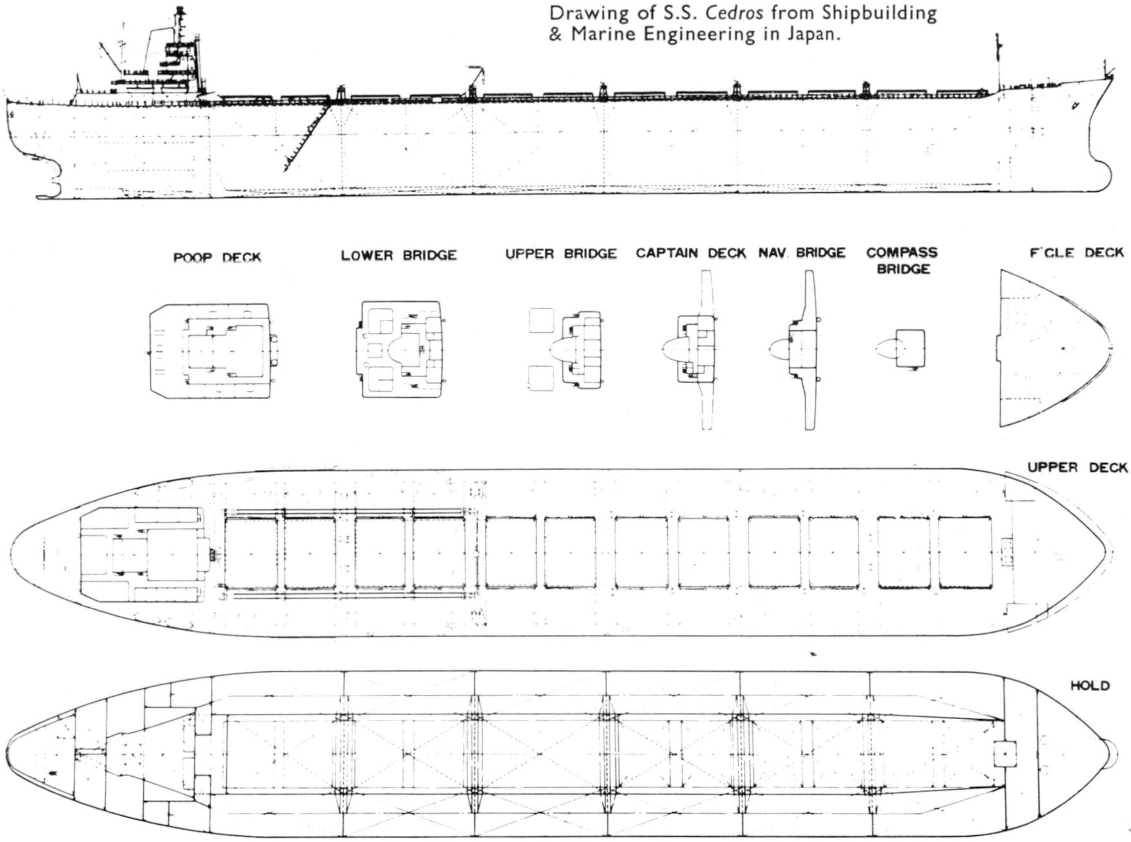

Drawing of S.S. *Cedros* from Shipbuilding & Marine Engineering in Japan.

POOP DECK LOWER BRIDGE UPPER BRIDGE CAPTAIN DECK NAV. BRIDGE COMPASS BRIDGE F'CLE DECK

UPPER DECK

HOLD

as this that combination ships are able to cut out or reduce the time spent on ballast voyages. The cruising range of this ship is 29,135 miles at the service speed of 15·1 knots.

M.S. SKAUFAST (1968)

Owners: I. M. SKAUGEN, OSLO
Builders: HARLAND AND WOLFF LTD.
B. & W. diesel, 20,700 b.h.p.
Single screw
Length overal 855 ft.
Beam 133 ft. 6 in.
Draught 46 ft. 4 in.
Deadweight tonnage 100,000 (approx.)

The *Skaufast* is the last of a group of four bulk carriers built by Harland and Wolff Ltd. for Norwegian Bulk Carriers (N.B.C.)

The M.S. *Atlantic City* owned by the Reardon Smith Line Ltd. With a deadweight tonnage of 41,250 this vessel is typical of the large bulk carriers which are being built for British owners. The combined derrick port/ventilators are unusual and there are few vessels of this size equipped with their own cargo handling gear.

Until 1960 the largest vessel in the Reardon Smith fleet was the *Orient City*, with a deadweight tonnage of 14,490 tons. In 1964 the *Australian City* entered service with a deadweight tonnage of 27,000.

This remarkable development is reflected in the fleets of most of the British tramp shipping companies who have been able to stay in business.

Photo courtesy: Reardon Smith Line Ltd.

M.S. *Skaufast.*
Photo courtesy: Harland & Wolff Ltd.

of Oslo. This group is one of many which have been set up in recent years to finance the purchase of these big ships and to secure more efficient management and operation. An example of a British consortium is Seabridge Shipping Ltd., which is financed by the Bibby Line, Hunting & Son Ltd., Furness Withy & Co. Ltd. and H. Clarkson & Co. Ltd. This group already owns and operates 15 large vessels and orders have been recently placed for four OBO ships; three of these vessels will have deadweight tonnages of 135,000.

The *Skaufast* is the largest bulk carrier built by Harland and Wolff and is also believed to be the largest ship of this type so far built in Europe. The hull is divided into nine cargo holds, all of which are suitable for the carriage of grain. When carrying ore only holds number 1, 3, 5, 7 and 9 are used. No cargo handling gear is carried. The accommodation for officers and crew is of a very high standard and provision has been made for stewardesses. The crew has the use of a swimming pool and a gymnasium, which is a facility so far provided in very few cargo ships. Communal aerial sockets and shaving points are fitted in every cabin, and the whole of the accommodation is air conditioned.

Replacing the Liberty Ships

STANDARD ships were built in large numbers during the war to replace the enormous losses and to provide the additional tonnage required to back up the seaborne operations which commenced in North Africa in 1942. Of all the classes built, the "Liberty" was undoubtedly the most famous, and even now it is a familiar name to many people who know little about shipping.

After the war the "Liberties" were purchased in their hundreds by shipping companies anxious to take advantage of the high freights then obtaining. Even cargo liner operators used them to maintain their services until new replacement tonnage became available. Eventually all the "Liberties" found themselves tramping, and for some years they traded profitably. Recessions, however, led to many of them being laid up, to resume trading when cargo rates rose above the break-even point. Nevertheless, each period of lay-up inevitably meant that some ships went to the breakers and numbers gradually dwindled. From time to time it was forecast that the day of the "Liberties" was over, but they have always come back and only now is old age removing them from the tramping routes.

Despite the unprecedented rise in the capacity of bulk carriers, trading conditions for smaller ships have remained buoyant, and there are many owners who consider that the demand will persist for many years to come. Many shipbuilders therefore saw a lucrative source of business in replacing "Liberties", and during the last few years up to 20 designs

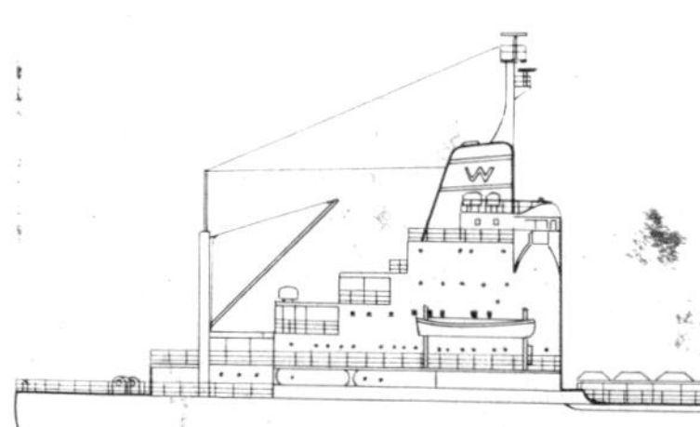

M.S. WORLD SOYA (1966)
Owners: World Magnate Shipping Ltd.
(Managed by World-Wide (Shipping) Ltd., Hong Kong)
Builder: Sasebo Heavy Industries
Sulzer diesel, 18,400 b.h.p.
Single screw
Trial speed 17·84 knots
Length overall 800 ft.
Beam 105 ft.
Deadweight tonnage 69,000

A large bulk carrier built for world wide trade. This vessel is at present chartered by O. Wallenius and has already completed several voyages between Peru and Japan, Brazil and Japan with iron ore, and between the U.S.A. and Europe. In 1966 the *World Soya* was the largest bulk carrier to enter Rotterdam and established a record for the tonnage of grain then discharged.

The M.S. *Athelknight* is owned by the Athel Line Ltd. of London. This vessel, which has a deadweight tonnage of 17,610, was built by Uddevallavarvet A/B, Sweden, and is designed to carry oil, molasses and liquid chemicals. A B. & W. diesel engine, which develops 9,000 b.h.p., gives a service speed of 16·1 knots.
Photo courtesy: Athel Line Ltd.

for standard ships have been produced. All of them are for ships in a limited tonnage range. Speeds are similar as are costs, and each design claims specific advantages, particularly in connection with the type of engine selected. Bids for orders of this nature have never been made before and shipowners are faced with a bewildering choice. Even so, the majority of shipbuilders are prepared to incorporate modifications to suit particular needs.

Initially, the Japanese "Freedom" ship attracted much attention and many orders were placed. The British "S.D. 14" type was slower off the mark, but by January, 1970 it had overtaken the "Freedom", and Austin and Pickersgill had 60 vessels either built or on order. A proportion of these were being built under licence at the Skaramanga yard in Greece.

The M.S. *Bishopgate*. A "handy-sized" bulk carrier of 18,220 tons deadweight owned by the Bishopgate Shipping Co. Ltd.
Photo courtesy: Silver Line Ltd.

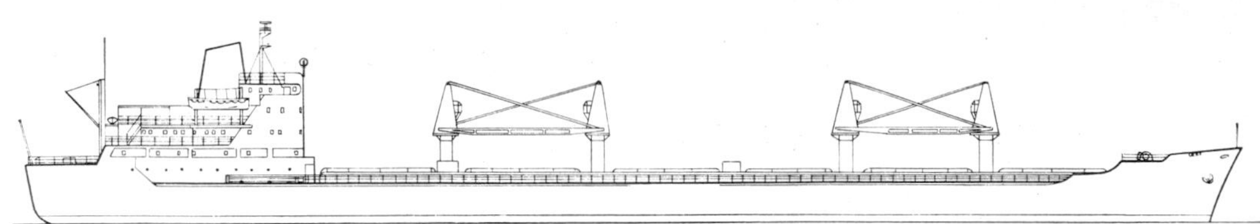

M.S. BARON CAWDOR (1968)
Owners: H. Hogarth & Sons Ltd.
Builders: Marinens Hovedverft
Horten diesel, 9,600 b.h.p.
Single screw
Service speed 15 knots
Length overall 527 ft. 8 in.
Beam 75 ft.
Deadweight tonnage 21,340
The *Baron Cawdor* is typical of many of the relatively small bulk carriers still being built in considerable numbers. Cargo is carried in six holds and continuous upper wing tanks can be used, obtaining stability when carrying very heavy cargoes. An unusual feature of this vessel is that although cranes are carried they are arranged so that each one can serve two hatches.

A pronounced ram bow increases the speed of the ship when in ballast.

The George N Papalios. The second "S.D.14" type ship to be built.
Photo courtesy: Austin and Pickersgill Ltd.

"S.D.14 TYPE"

Owners: VARIOUS
Builders: AUSTIN AND PICKERSGILL
Sulzer diesel, 5,500 b.h.p.
Single screw
Service speed 14 knots
Length overall 462 ft.
Beam 67 ft.
Deadweight tonnage 14,200

This type of vessel, which is equipped with 'tween decks, is a versatile ship in which the cost of maintenance has been carefully considered. It is able to carry a wide range of bulk and unitised cargoes and, with a full set of derricks and winches and a draft of about 28 ft., is able to operate to many ports. This class of ship is an example of modern functional design. Combined with standardisation it allows the shipbuilder to offer a price considerably lower than that for a "one off" ship.

"FREEDOM" CLASS

Owners: VARIOUS
Builders: ISHAKAWAJIMA-HARIMA HEAVY INDUSTRIES LTD.
Pielstick diesel up to 6,850 b.h.p., dependent upon engine installed
Single screw
Service speed 14 knots
Length overall 465 ft.
Beam 65 ft.
Deadweight tonnage 13,800

The "Freedom" class ships are able to carry bulk cargoes of grain without the fitting of shifting boards, bauxite, packaged timber and iron ore. In addition cars can be carried and provision is made for the stowage of containers in the hatches (five in tiers) and a single tier on the upper deck hatch covers. The draft of 28 ft. is similar to that of the "S.D.14" and the

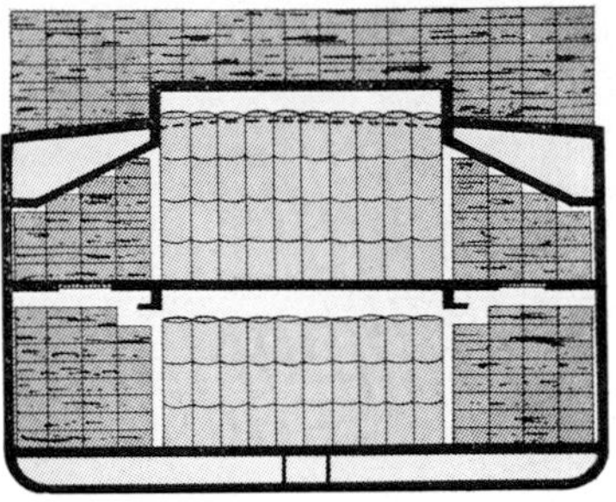

MIXED CARGO
(Newsprint and packaged lumber)

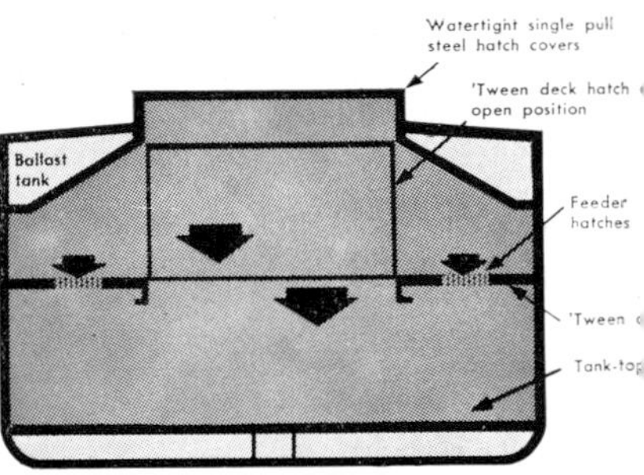

GRAIN CARGO

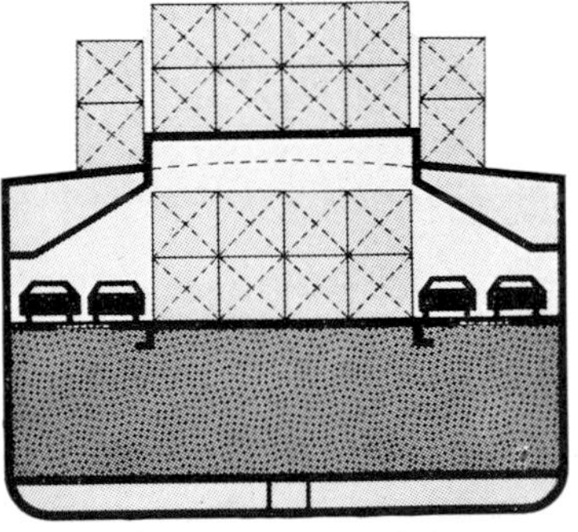

MIXED CARGO
(Containers, automobiles and bulk cargo)

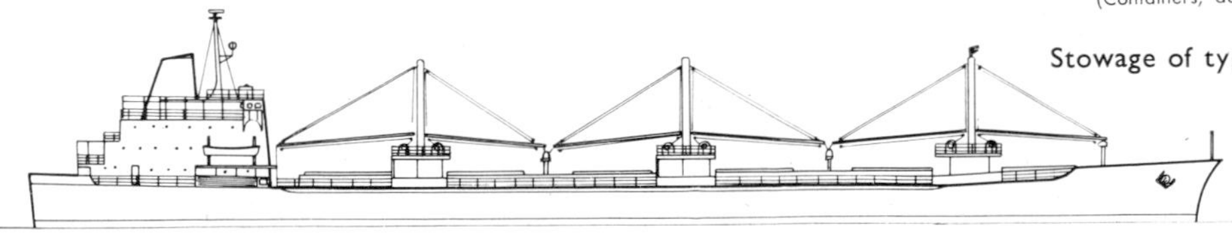

Stowage of typical cargoes in the "Freedom" ship.
Photo courtesy: Ishakawajima-Harima Heavy Industries Ltd.

derricks are similarly rigged to handle loads of up to 10 tons. "Freedom" class vessels are built with minor variations and the profile should not therefore be taken as representative of them all.

The *Universe Aztec*, which is owned by Sea Tankers Company, is the world's largest bulk carrier and likely to retain this distinction for some time to come. This vessel has a deadweight tonnage of 160,242, a length of 991 ft., a beam of 140 ft., and a fully loaded draft of 57 ft. The *Universe Aztec* can carry a wide variety of bulk cargoes, including ores, but for the time being will be employed carrying salt from Mexico to Japan.

The wheelhouse. This is typical of modern practice and shows clearly the extensive controls and aids which are now used. Visible in this photograph are the wheel and automatic pilot, radar screens, gyro repeaters and magnetic compass, engine controls, monitor alarms and fire alarms. The wheelhouse is heated and anti-glare windows and a clear vision screen assist the watchkeeping officers.

The partly opened hatch covers. Hatch covers which slide athwartships are now almost standard equipment for large bulk carriers. The wide openings make for speed in loading and unloading. In ships such as the *Universe Aztec* bulldozers are lowered into the holds to shift the cargo from the wings. In container ships the hatch cover sections, which can weigh up to 30 tons apiece, are often handled by shore cranes. Other types of hatch covers illustrated in other chapters.

The turbines of the *Universe Aztec*. It can be seen from the illustrations in this chapter just how little space is occupied by engines and boilers. These particular turbines produce a power of 25,000 s.h.p. and drive a single propeller at 95 revolutions per minute, giving a service speed of about 16 knots.

Photos courtesy: Ishakawajima-Harima Heavy Industries Ltd.

The S.S. *Encounter Bay*.
Photo courtesy: Overseas Containers Ltd.

CHAPTER 3 Container Ships

In Chapters 6 and 10 an account is given of the various steps taken to improve the efficiency of cargo liners. Unfortunately, many of the causes of delay mentioned have been beyond the control of the shipping companies. Shippers have, for instance, always demanded a full range of loading ports, both here, on the Continent and overseas. As a result cargo liners have been required to spend up to a month "doing the rounds" between arrival and departure on the next voyage.

It is hard to determine exactly when the revolution against this form of transport occurred but for many years American shipowners have been experimenting with and developing domestic seaborne container ship services. In this country the change came later, but has been more rapid, for it was only in 1965 that moves were made towards the development of this radically different and completely integrated form of transport across land and sea. In simple terms "containerisation" works as follows:

Containers are loaded either at factories or at depots set up in industrial and commercial areas. At the depots small parcels of goods for similar destinations are made up into container loads. These are conveyed by road or rail to the dockside where they are loaded into the ship. Less than 48 hours is required to load a full cargo. At the completion of the ocean passage, containers are either delivered direct to the consignee or sent to depots where the contents are broken down and the smaller parcels delivered.

The saving in time and effort is enormous. At one stroke the need for dockworkers and stevedores is almost eliminated, although it has to be remembered that new labour forces are required at factories and depots. Because the goods are virtually encased in metal the problems of hold stowage are removed. Damage to goods in transit is minimised and restricted to individual containers, and the risk of pilfering has also been reduced. Delivery times have been cut and charges possibly reduced.

It is estimated that by 1970, up to 90% of cargo hitherto carried in cargo liners will be containerised. Already for example there are container services between Japan and the West Coast of the United States, and a joint Australian/Japanese service has started between the two countries. By 1970 the N.Y.K. and the Mitsui O.S.K. Lines will have a container service between the Far East and Europe; OCL has ordered ships for this run. Plans are also being made for a Europe-New Zealand container service.

By the mid-'70s a network of services will cover the oceans of the world and the majority of shipowners will be fully committed to this form of transport. Second generation ships incorporating the experience gained from earlier ships are now operational, and an enormous step forward will be taken when Sea-Land Services Inc. take delivery of five ships at present on order in Germany and Holland. Each ship will have a deadweight tonnage of 43,000 and a service speed of 33 knots. The cost of these vessels will be about £16,000,000 and will presumably force competitors to build similar ships. Further examples of container ships at present on order are:

Scanservice (W. Wilhelmsen, The East Asiatic Co. Ltd., Swedish East Asiatic Co.), four vessels, 29,000 tons deadweight, 26 knots, capacity 1,700 20-ft. containers. Seatrains Pty., Ltd. (Messageries Maritimes, Hamburg-Amerika Line, Norddeutscher Lloyd, Lloyd Triestino, Holland Australia Line), five vessels, 30,000 tons deadweight, 21·5 knots, 1,300 20-ft. containers. Orient Overseas Line, five vessels, 18,750 tons, 22 knots, up to 900 20-ft. containers. Ben Line, two vessels, 34,000 tons deadweight, 26 knots, capacity 1,800 20-ft. containers.

The OCL terminal at No. 39 berth, Tilbury, has an overall area of 19 acres. There is parking space for 100 vehicles and trailers and the stack capacity is 1,640 general cargo containers and 360 refrigerated containers: these will be stacked five high. The refrigerated end of the stack is roofed over to give protection from solar radiation and to protect refrigerated containers and refrigeration equipment against the weather.

The equipment for handling the containers consists of one ASEA quay crane of 45 tons capacity, two ASEA stack cranes with a similar capacity, six internal motive vehicles, six 40 ft. twin-lift trailers, two washing plants and two 60 ton weighbridges.

Shore operations are controlled by a DDP/516 computer. Centralised decision making is essential and each container must be stacked so that it comes forward at the moment for loading; similarly ease of access is vital so that incoming containers can be forwarded by road or rail without delay. At the same time as loading proceeds containers are continually being received and despatched.

The five container ships, the shore facilities in this country and in Australia, the containers and the vehicles represent an investment of £50,000,000.

The maiden voyage of the *Moreton Bay* was typical of the operations now in full swing. Owing to a dispute at Tilbury loading took place in Antwerp. The ship sailed on 26th June, 1969 with a full cargo and then followed this itinerary:

Arr.	Fremantle	18th July, 1969
,,	Sydney	23rd July, 1969
,,	Melbourne	28th July, 1969
,,	Fremantle	2nd Aug. 1969
,,	Antwerp	24th Aug. 1969

The round voyage is about 26,500 miles. Each ship will be able to carry out more than five round voyages each year in comparison with conventional cargo liners which can normally complete two to three voyages during the same period, but with smaller tonnages of cargo.

The commodities carried by OCL ships vary enormously and are those previously carried by cargo liners and mentioned elsewhere in this book. Specific examples recently carried are:

Wallpaper. 100,000 rolls in eight containers. Considerable savings resulted through the use of lighter packing materials.

Apples. The first container shipment of apples was carried in refrigerated units. Grapes and pears were also included in the 190 container shipment. The second half of 1969 also saw the arrival of the first container consignment of oranges and lemons. It is believed that the lemons were the first ever to arrive from Australia.

Wool-washing machine. This machine was broken down into four units and loaded into a single container. The remaining empty spaces were filled with feeding equipment wrapped in wood wool. This method of transport eliminated the use of specially built wooden crates, and the time needed to reassemble the machine was shortened.

Wire-drawing machine weighing 110 tons. Was broken down into units and stowed in three 20 ft., one 20 ft. top loading and two 40 ft. containers.

Biscuits and shortbread. 98,000 pounds were packed into ten containers. Considerable savings resulted from the elimination of the export boxes into which the biscuits had previously been packed.

Sherry. 12,000 gallons were brought from Australia in a single bulk liquid container. Previously sherry had been transported in 535 gallon capacity metal containers.

Gin. 3,700 gallons were carried in a bulk liquid container. 78 drums had previously been needed.

1,000 tons of trucks and vans were broken down and loaded into containers at a base. The spare spaces in the containers were filled with suitable less-than-container load cargo.

The carriage over a period of time of 140,000 procelain insulators in 140 containers.

The complete hull of a new three-berth fibreglass sailing cruiser, 80,000 books, 40 hogshead of Scotch, and racing cars are further examples of recent consignments.

S.S. ENCOUNTER BAY (1969)

Overseas Containers Ltd. (OCL) is a consortium of the British and Commonwealth Shipping Co. Ltd., Furness Withy & Co. Ltd., the Ocean Steam Ship Co. Ltd. and the P & O Line.

OCL was formed in 1965 and immediately commenced investigations into the requirements of a container service. Eventually the point was reached when experimental cargoes were carried in conventional cargo liners. Consignments included vacuum flasks, tumbler driers, tinned fruit and books. The lashing of containers on deck was also the subject of careful investigation and experiment. The Ocean Steam Ship Co.'s *Priam* carried a stack of 12 loaded containers on several voyages to Japan. Each container was lashed with a different system of wires, and instruments were carried to measure stresses and forces. At one point it became necessary to test in racking a series of actual containers to determine how much load could be absorbed by them and how much by the lashings. The outcome was a diagonally arranged wire and rod system, easily set up and dismantled, which will have the strength to hold three tiers of containers in place through the worst of weather.

Considerable research, including the testing of models, was undertaken to evolve a hull which would throw water clear of the upper deck and containers. The first ship was launched in June 1968 and entered service in 1969, although labour disputes in the Port of London made it necessary to load and unload the first cargoes on the Continent.

The characteristics of the *Encounter Bay* are:

Builders: CONTAINER SHIP CONSORTIUM, HAMBURG

Two cross compounded turbines developing 32,000 s.h.p.

Single screw

Service speed 22 knots

Length overall 745 ft. 9 in.

Beam 100 ft.

Deadweight tonnage 29,150 (approx.)

Cargo capacity 1,300 20 × 8 × 8 ft. ISO containers, including 304 insulated.

Because of the width of the triple hatches and the high loading factor upon them, the main strength members and the hatch covers are constructed of higher grade tensile steel. No. 1 hold is reserved for containers carrying hazardous substances and is specially ventilated. In order to avoid the jamming of containers whilst loading and unloading, cross pumping facilities can move water ballast from one side of the ship to the other at a rate equivalent to the movement of containers in and out of the ship. Four passive anti-rolling tanks of Flume design steady the ship's movement at sea and reduce the strain on deck container lashings. Four automatic constant tension winches moor the ship securely during the movement of containers.

The ships of this class will spend the majority of their time at sea and officers and all members of the ship's company will be permitted to take their wives to sea on a limited number of voyages. Each member of the crew has a single air conditioned cabin.

The engine room is designed for control by one officer at sea and unattended in harbour. Systems developed by the Ocean Steam Ship Co. have been used extensively, and machinery and refrigeration plant are controlled automatically and by remote control from an air conditioned control room. Data logging devices record all information relevant to the operation of the machinery.

The ocean section of the OCL container service is run in co-operation with Associated Container Transportation, who have built three ships for the purpose.

The nine ships are able to maintain a weekly service between Tilbury and Sydney, Melbourne and Fremantle. Depots have been established at Glasgow, Leeds, Manchester, Liverpool, Birmingham and London (Orsett). In Australia depots have been established at Sydney, Melbourne, Fremantle, Adelaide and Brisbane.

ACT (Associated Container Transportation) which also runs its own integrated services is a consortium of the following lines: Blue Star Line Ltd., Ellerman Lines Ltd., Port Line Ltd., Ben Line Ltd. and T. and J. Harrison Ltd.

S.S. *American Lancer.*
Photo courtesy: United States Lines

S.S. AMERICAN LANCER (1967)

Builders: SUN SHIPBUILDING AND DRY DOCK CO., CHESTER, PA.
Steam turbines, 27,300 h.p.
Single screw
Service speed 22 knots
Length overall 700 ft.
Beam 85 ft.
Load displacement 31,987 tons
Four passengers
Crew 40, excluding apprentices
Container Capacity
Stowed maximum below decks six high

Below Deck

20-ft.	212
40-ft.	222

On Deck	*Two High*	*Three High*
Maximum 20s	368	552
Maximum 40s	184	276

Total 20-ft. Equivalents

Two-high on deck	1,024
Three-high on deck	1,208

Maximum Total 40-ft. Containers
Two-high on deck, 406 40s plus 212 20s
Three-high on deck, 498 40s plus 212 20s

The *American Lancer* and five sister ships operate the United States Lines' North Atlantic Container Service. Sailings are weekly from Europe and North America, and the ships operate on a 21-day turn-round. The two services provided are:

(*a*) Rotterdam, London and Hamburg to New York, Baltimore and Norfolk.
(*b*) Le Havre, Antwerp, Liverpool and Greenock to New York, Baltimore and Norfolk.

The United States Lines' container service to Western Europe was preceded by the conveyance of experimental and limited consignments in ordinary cargo liners. In 1966, the fully integrated service was inaugurated when the S.S. *American Racer* sailed from New York for Antwerp and Rotterdam in March of that year. This ship and three sister ships had previously undergone conversion to provide cellular stowage in holds nos. 2 and 3. Break bulk cargo was also carried. As ships of the "Lancer" class were placed in service the ports of call were increased. Eventually the six ships were running and the *American Racer* and her sister ships were sold in the summer of 1969 to the Farrell Lines for service from the U.S.A. to Australia.

The *Manchester Port*.
Photo courtesy: Manchester Lines Ltd.

The 20-ft. containers used by the United States Lines are constructed of polypanel fibreglass and aluminium, with a double door at the rear of each container. They can be lifted by large fork lift trucks or by a crane equipped with a spreader.

The 40-ft. containers are constructed entirely of aluminium and also have a double door at the rear of each container. In addition, a few are provided with a side door.

The gross carrying capacity of these containers is 44,800 and 50,000 lb. respectively.

The service is provided and controlled by the company on a door-to-door basis, and by July 1968 3,600 vehicles for the conveyance of containers were in operation.

M.S. MANCHESTER PORT (1967) AND MANCHESTER CHALLENGE (1969)

Manchester Port
Builders: SMITH'S DOCK CO. LTD.
Two 14-cylinder Crossley-Pielstick diesels, 12,500 s.h.p.
Single screw
Service speed 19 knots
Length overall 502 ft.
Beam 62·3 ft.
Deadweight tonnage 12,000
Strengthened for navigation in ice (Class I)

Manchester Challenge
Builders: SMITH'S DOCK CO. LTD.
Two 14-cylinder Crossley-Pielstick diesels, 15,000 s.h.p. Service speed 21 knots.
Geared to single screw Kamewa propellers
Length overall 530 ft.
Beam 63·6 ft.
Strengthened for navigation in ice (Class I)

Manchester Liners Ltd. have maintained services to Canada and the U.S.A. for more than 70 years, and in 1952 they were the first British company to provide a direct ocean service to the Great Lakes. Manchester Liners Ltd. were also early in the field of containerisation and the *Manchester Port* was the first ship in the company to be designed for combined container and general cargo work.

Owing to the rapidly increasing demand for container space, three further ships were built and in March 1969 a fully containerised service was put into operation. At Manchester and Montreal special berths have been prepared with adequate space for handling and storing containers. A 25-ton transporter crane has been installed at each port. The majority of containers will be loaded at factories, but depots have been provided at both ends for making up complete container loads. The time taken from Manchester to Montreal is 6½ days with a turn-round time at each end of between 36 and 48 hours. The service will operate for 52 weeks of the year.

Unlike the operators of several other container services, the company have no immediate intention of withdrawing their conventional cargo liners, and in order to achieve a smooth changeover to containerisation and to deal with cargoes which are not suited to this form of transport, a weekly service by conventional ships will be maintained to Montreal, Toronto, Hamilton, Detroit and Chicago. Duluth and Port Arthur (with calls at Buffalo, Cleveland and Toledo if required) have a monthly service. Thus Manchester Liners are able to offer one of the most frequent and comprehensive cargo services from the U.K. to Canada and the Great Lakes ports.

The *Manchester Challenge* is smaller than many container ships, but like other ships in the fleet, her size is limited by the depth and breadth of the 36-mile long Manchester Ship Canal. Stabilisers have been fitted to reduce strain on containers, all of which are stowed below decks. The engines and auxiliary services are monitored by data logging equipment and sophisticated systems which will enable the engine room to be operated under unmanned conditions and thus relieve the watch keepers of all routine duties.

The maximum capacity of the

Manchester Challenge is 500 containers of standard 20×8×8 ft. size. Half-size containers and refrigerated units are also available.

Manchester Liners Ltd. also maintain services from Manchester and Glasgow to ports between Baltimore and Miami. During the winter months there is also a service to Halifax and St. John, N.B., and sailings to Baltimore are increased to provide continuity of service for U.S. Great Lakes shippers.

Sea-Land Incorporated is a company which carried out much pioneer work in the carriage of containers. They established the first transatlantic container service with fully containerised ships and other services are in operation between New York (Elizabeth, N.J.) and the Caribbean.

Marshalling yard and containers at Elizabeth, N.J.
Photo courtesy: Ferry Masters Ltd.

This photograph shows the extensive installations at Elizabeth. It covers an area of 98 acres of a 203-acre harbour development scheme. It incorporates two container cranes and berths for six vessels. There is a three-storey office building, a truck operation centre where the movement of

The *Manchester Challenge*.
Photo courtesy: Smith's Dock Co. Ltd.

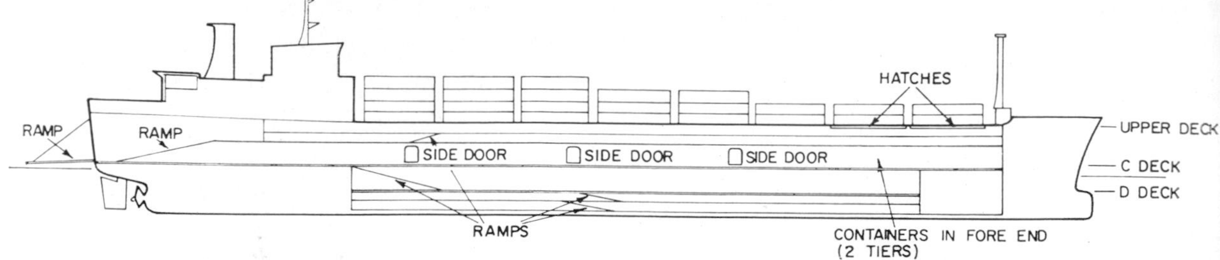

Longitudinal section of M.S. *Atlantic Span* showing six cargo decks, ramps, deck stowage of containers.

any trailer in the system can be plotted by computer, a Marine Operations building, a truck maintenance garage and an 1,100-ft. general cargo warehouse. In addition there is a special terminal for perishable cargo with special outlets to maintain refrigeration in parked trailers.

The 61-acre marshalling yard can accommodate 2,600 trailers—just a proportion of the total number involved—and daylight brightness can be maintained throughout the night.

In the past, general cargo ports have varied considerably in their facilities. In New York all cargo is handled by ships' gear and American ports generally follow this principal. Now, however, container ports are assuming an international character, and it will be seen from this photo and those of Tilbury that differences are minor and solely related to the shore movement of containers.

M.S. *Atlantic Span*.
Photo courtesy: D. W. A. Mercer

M.S. ATLANTIC SPAN (1967)

Owners: REDERI A/B TRANSATLANTIC (ATLANTIC CONTAINER LINE)
Builders: RHEINSTAAL NORDSEE-WERKE
Krupp-Burmeister & Wain, 20,700 b.h.p.
Single screw
Trial speed 21·5 knots
Length overall 647 ft.
Beam 87 ft.

The Atlantic Container Line is a consortium of the Wallenius Group, the Rederi A/B Transatlantic, the Cunard Line, the Holland America Line, the French Line and the Swedish America Line. Four ships of one class have been built and a further six ships are either completed or on order. Regular services are maintained between Gothenburg, Bremerhaven, Rotterdam, Antwerp, Southampton, Liverpool and New York, Baltimore and Portsmouth (Va.).

Unlike the ships described earlier in this chapter, the ACL ships are designed primarily to carry vehicles and general cargo, although considerable stowage space has been provided for containers. The service is a completely new concept of transocean cargo carrying and, should trading conditions so demand, the present container stowage can be extended by cutting additional hatches in the upper deck and fitting guide rails.

Six decks are available for export cars, commercial vehicles, cargo on trailers, general cargo and containers, whilst the upper deck is fitted for container stowage for more than three-quarters of the length of the ship. Access is gained via stern door and ramp, six side hatches and hatches in the upper deck. Ramps interconnect the vehicle decks.

A wide permutation of cargoes can be carried, a typical example being 74 trailers, 1,090 cars, 212 containers (ISO 20 ft. type) on C deck and 250 on the upper deck.

The *Atlantic Span* has a comprehensive outfit of navigational aids, including two Decca radars and a Decca Navigator, autopilot and echo sounder. A Kamewa bow thruster with bridge control is fitted to assist in mooring. The main engine is remotely controlled from a control room in the engine room.

The ACL has established several container assembly depots

in the U.S., and all aspects of cargo control, including bookings, cargo documentation and daily statistical summaries are controlled by a computer located at the New York terminal. Agencies and depots are linked to the computer by teletypewriters and telex dial network.

The sister ships of the *Atlantic Span* are the *Atlantic Song*, *Saga* and *Star*, but they vary slightly from each other in details of superstructure, stern ramps and ventilating machinery on the upper deck.

The Lash System

The Americans conceived the idea of container ships—and proved their practicability, and, whilst the majority of cargo lines are in the throes of converting to this system, a further and still more revolutionary system of sea transport has been developed by the American LASH Systems Incorporated of New Orleans; this is the LASH (Lighter Aboard Ship) cargo vessel.

The ship is essentially a bulk carrier, but it is equipped with a gantry crane which can lift floating containers (lighters) from the water and stow them in any position within the holds or on the hatch covers. At the same time conventional containers can be carried, either loaded by ship or shore crane. In addition the construction of the ship is such as to permit the carriage of general break bulk, palletised and bulk cargoes. Liquid cargoes can be loaded in the wing and deep tanks. The advantages which are claimed over and above those of the container ship are:

1. The turn-round time in port is reduced considerably. A LASH ship can load at a rate of about 1,500 tons of cargo an hour; a complete loading cycle for one fully loaded lighter takes 15 minutes.
2. The lighters can be loaded in shallow water by mobile cranes and fork lift trucks. No expensive dock facilities are required.
3. Advantage can be taken, when necessary, of existing container quays, lighters being loaded simultaneously with containers.
4. Any sheltered waters will serve as a mooring for the LASH ship. Because of this, port congestion (waits of up to 14 days or more for a berth in some ports are not unusual) does not affect the sailing schedules.
5. In its ability to load bulk cargoes, the LASH ship has an additional trading outlet.
6. Liquid cargoes can be carried at the same time as lighters.
7. Any combination of bulk cargoes (either in lighters or hold), lighters and containers can be carried according to need.

There are now more than a dozen LASH ships on order, 11 of these with the Avondale Shipyards Inc., of New Orleans, for the Pacific Far East Line Inc. and the Prudential Lines Inc., and one with Uraga Heavy Industries Ltd. for the Central Gulf Steamship Corporation Inc. The American Lykes Line have also placed orders for these ships.

The characteristics of the Avondale ships are as follows:

Length overall 772 ft.

Beam 100 ft.

Single screw, 32,000 h.p. turbines giving a service speed of 23 knots.

Capacity 54 lighters (Prudential), 49 lighters (Pacific Far-East).

The lighters are 61 ft. 6 in. long, 31 ft. 2 in. wide and 13 ft. deep, with 18,500 cu. ft. bale stowage.

In addition 150 (Prudential), 204 (Pacific Far-East) containers can be stowed.

One of two Paceco-Vickers Portainer cranes installed at No. 40 Berth at Tilbury. Costing £200,000 this crane can lift containers up to 30 tons in weight. A container can be loaded in about $2\frac{1}{2}$ minutes. The vessel alongside is the *American Lancer*. Frames across the hatches ensure level stowage for the containers.

Photos courtesy: Port of London Authority

Total container capacity is about 1,400.

Up to 10,000 tons of liquid cargo can be carried in wing tanks and deep tanks.

The lighters are positioned in the holds by vertical guides.

Connections are provided for refrigerated lighters.

In addition to the lighter crane, the Avondale ships are equipped with a 30-ton container gantry crane.

The Uraga ship is slightly larger and has a capacity of 73 lighters, of which over 200 are required to maintain the service between U.S. Gulf and S.E. Atlantic ports to the U.K. and Rotterdam. The round voyage takes about 30 days and will call at more ports than would a container ship.

The Central Gulf ship, the *Arcadia Forest*, operates as a lighter ship only and no container crane has been fitted.

M.S. *Hakone Maru*.
Photo courtesy: Mitsubishi Heavy Industries Ltd.

M.S. HAKONE MARU (1968)

Owners: NIPPON YUSEN KAISHA
Builders: MITSUBISHI HEAVY INDUSTRIES
M.A.N. diesel, 27,800 b.h.p.
Single screw
Service speed 22·6 knots
Length overall 610 ft. (approx.)
Beam 85 ft. 4 in.
Deadweight tonnage 16,300

The first Japanese cellular container ship, the *Hakone Maru*, has stowage for 752 20-ft. units, of these, 266 are carried on deck in two tiers between the forecastle and superstructure.

The extensively automated main and auxiliary engines are monitored and controlled from a control room in the engine room. On trials the *Hakone Maru* attained a speed of 26 knots.

Several more container ships for Japanese owners have been completed or are under construction. Services have been established on the Pacific Ocean, and both the N.Y.K. and the Mitsui-O.S.K. Lines plan to introduce similar services to Europe in 1970.

The effect of container ships upon conventional cargo liners cannot yet be assessed, but if a container ship can carry out the work of four or five conventional ships, and if the range of products which can be containerised can be widened there is little doubt that many ships will become surplus to requirements. The United States Lines, for instance, sold their extremely modern cargo liners on the Atlantic run when the final container ship entered service. Other lines have used their conventional ships to provide improved services for break bulk cargo, but it remains to be seen whether these ventures will be profitable or whether the container ships will be required to subsidise the supporting services.

In the short-sea trade conventional cargo liners have been largely eliminated, and many ships have been sold to companies who are using them for tramping. Such a ship is the *Evdelos*. The *Evdelos* was built in 1955 for Coast Lines Ltd. and was employed for many years on scheduled services. This ship is now owned by a Greek company and is registered under the Panamanian flag. The *Evdelos* will go wherever profitable cargo offers, and the photograph shows her unloading a cargo of wine. The cargo is being handled by "can hooks". These are made of flat steel plate and are secured to chain slings. The hooks grip under the rim of the cask or drum, and the upward pressure exerted as the slings are raised ensures a firm grip. When used with powerful cranes, additional slings and hooks are secured to the cargo runner and several casks are lifted at the same time.

M.S. *Evdelos*.

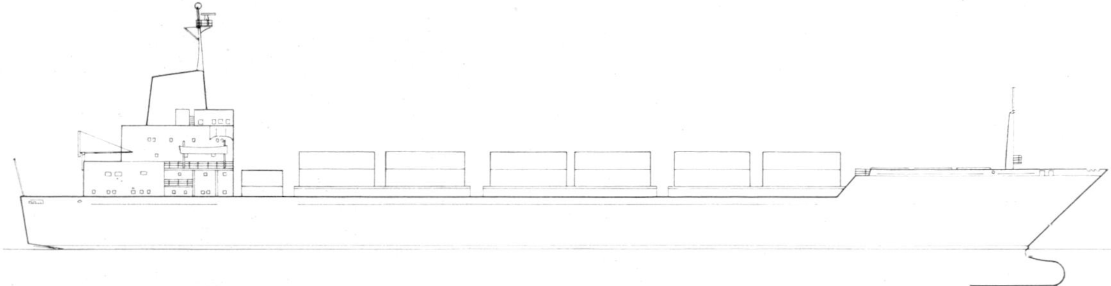

M.S. ELBE EXPRESS (1968)
Owners: Hapag-Lloyd
Builders: Blohm and Voss
M.A.N. diesel, 15,750 b.h.p.
Single screw
Service speed 20·6 knots
Length overall 560 ft.
Beam 80 ft.
Deadweight tonnage 10,800. (approx)

The *Elbe Express* was the second of four similar cellular container ships ordered by the Hamburg-Amerika Line and the Norddeutscher Lloyd for their joint Hapag-Lloyd Container Line. A service is provided on a weekly basis between Antwerp, Rotterdam, Bremerhaven and Hamburg to Norfolk (Va.), Baltimore and New York.

Both of these lines have had extensive experience of carrying containers in semi-container ships and the new vessels incorporate this experience.

The *Elbe Express* can load 728 20-ft. containers in seven holds. They are stowed on deck in two tiers between the forecastle and superstructure. The inauguration of the Hapag-Lloyd service and the decision of the Bristol City Line and the Belgian Armement Deppe S.A. to join together to provide a fully containerised service means that the great majority of companies on the North Atlantic are now committed, either individually or in consort, to container services. It should be noted that the Armement Deppe are already conveying containers in converted cargo liners, and were the first company to use the new facilities at Southampton.

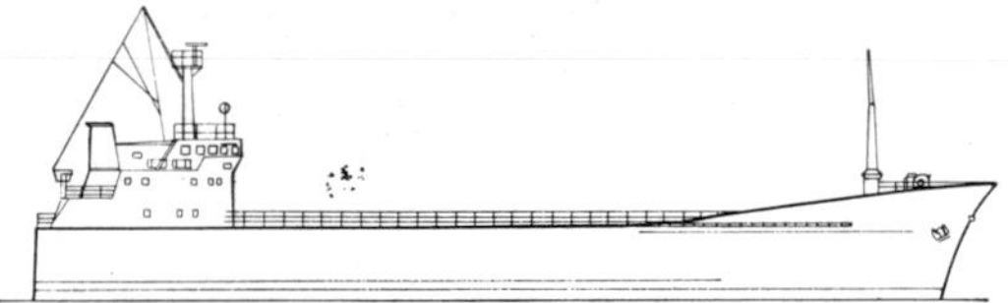

M.S. ARCTURUS (1967)
Owners: Argo Reederei Richard Adler und Sohne
Builders: Busumer Werft
M.A.N. diesel, 2,200 b.h.p.
Single screw
Service speed 14 knots
Length overall 251 ft
Beam 43 ft

The *Arcturus* runs between Bremen, Hamburg and Hull on the joint service of Argo Reederei and Associated Humber Liners Ltd., Cargo can be carried on three decks and the main access is via a stern door which is large enough to allow the passage of the largest commercial vehicles. Palletised cargo is loaded by fork lift trucks. A ramp leads to the upper deck hatches which serve the shallow hold. Cargo can be lowered to the hold or raised to the main deck by fork lift truck. Additional hatches in the upper deck permit loading and discharge by shore crane. The ship has also been designed for the carriage of containers and up to 70 standard 20-ft. units can be stowed below decks.

M.S. IMPALA (1968)
Owners: Peter Dohle, Hamburg
Builders: J. J. Sietas Shipyard
Deutz diesel, 1,350 b.h.p.
Single screw
Service speed 12½ knots
Length overall 250 ft.
Beam 35 ft. 6 in.
Deadweight tonnage 1,500

A standard Sietas coaster adapted to carry containers, both in the hold and on deck. The total capacity is 36 standard ISO 20-ft. containers.

The *Impala* is on long-term charter to European Unit Routes Ltd., and is in service between Tilbury and Rotterdam. There is now a crew of eight, but in view of the extensive engine automation it is intended at a later date to run the engine room unattended and to dispense with the services of the engineer.

The LASH ship *Acadia Forest*. Although operated by the Central Gulf Steamship Corporation this vessel is owned by A/S Moslash Shipping Co. of Norway.
Photo courtesy: Central News Agency

The M.S. *Winston Churchill*, flagship of the United Steamship Company of Copenhagen and the largest Danish passenger ship.
Photo courtesy: D.F.D.S.

CHAPTER 4

Vehicle Ferries & Short Sea Cargo Ships

THE conventional cargo ship has almost disappeared from the routes serving the U.K. and the Continent. So, too, the purely passenger cross-channel ship remains in service on very few routes. In less than a decade the position has been reached in which practically all cargo is either palletised, containerised or conveyed in roll on/roll off ferries. Cross-channel passengers go in ships especially designed for the carriage of cars.

In 1939 there were just a few little ships, including the *Autocar* of the Southern Railway, which had been adapted for the primary purpose of carrying vehicles. Few people took their cars to the Continent, and those that did suffered agonies while their cherished possession was slung aboard by crane. The post-war story is too well known to need elaboration, but it is worthwhile remembering the pioneer work which was carried out from Dover by Townsend Ferries and the Southern Region of British Railways.

On the commercial front vehicle ferries were first put into service by the Atlantic Steam Navigation Co. Ltd. They chose L.S.T.s, adapted to conform with Board of Trade Regulations and the needs of civilian passengers. The company prospered and the blue, white and black funnel is now well known around the coast.

Since the introduction of these few ships services have proliferated and trade has increased considerably. For container service adapted cargo ships have been widely used. Many of them remain in service, but new, specially designed cellular ships have now arrived on the scene. Their capacity is such that fears are being expressed lest the total tonnage now available has outstripped the demand—a situation which could well lead to a rate-war and the elimination of some of the companies at present engaged in the trade.

The M.S. *Europic Ferry.*
Photo courtesy: D. W. A. Mercer

M.S. EUROPIC FERRY (1968)

Owners: THE TRANSPORT FERRY SERVICE (ATLANTIC STEAM NAVIGATION CO. LTD.)
Builders: SWAN HUNTER (SHIPBUILDERS) LTD.
Two S.E.M.T. Lindholmen-Pielstick diesels, 13,560 b.h.p.
Twin screw
Service speed 18 knots
Length overall 450 ft.
Beam 66 ft. 6 in.

The *Europic Ferry* is a stern loading vehicle ferry, with a clear upper deck for the stowage of containers and flats.

The main vehicle deck has sufficient clearance to accommodate the largest commercial vehicles. A lower vehicle deck aft of the engine room, with a hydraulic ramp from the main deck, is used for the conveyance of export cars.

The ship is fitted with twin rudders aft, Denny-Brown stabilisers and a Kamewa bow thrust unit. The main engines are bridge controlled.

The *Europic Ferry* maintains a daily service for road freight and private cars between Felixstowe and Europoort. The crossing takes six hours, leaving Felixstowe

The cabin-de-luxe on board the *Europic Ferry.*
Photo courtesy: The Transport Ferry Service

Loading of containers and trailers proceeds simultaneously. The large crane can place containers on any part of the upper deck and the ramp can be lowered or raised to suit any tidal conditions.
Photo courtesy: The Transport Ferry Service

at 23.30 hours and Europoort at 12.00 hours.

Accommodation is provided for 44 drivers and passengers in two- and four-berth cabins; there is a crew of 52. The passenger accommodation is of an unusually high standard and matches that provided in many liners.

The Atlantic Steam Navigation Co. first started commercial operations in 1948 with a service between Preston and Larne, and during the first year 5,000 vehicles, containers and trailers were carried. Later, services were opened to Antwerp and Rotterdam. The first three ships were L.S.T.s (Landing Ship Tanks) which had provided the main support and vehicle supply services through all the landings subsequent to the occupation of North Africa. They were highly efficient ships and were easily convertible to Board of Trade requirements.

The lounge of the *Europic Ferry.*
Photo courtesy: The Transport Ferry Service

M.S. *Ulster Queen.*
Photo courtesy: Belfast Steamship Co. Ltd

M.S. ULSTER QUEEN (1967)

Owners: BELFAST STEAMSHIP CO. LTD.
Builders: CAMMELL LAIRD & CO. (SHIPBUILDERS & ENGINEERS) LTD., BIRKENHEAD
Twin screw. Two Crossley-Pielstick diesels, 7,200 b.h.p.
Fitted with stabilisers
Length overall 377 ft.
Beam 54 ft. 1 in.
Gross tonnage 4,478
Deadweight tonnage 1,390

The *Ulster Queen* was built in 1967 for a new car ferry service between Liverpool and Belfast. With a sister ship, the *Ulster Prince,* nightly sailings are maintained between the two ports. Between 30th June and 15th September additional Sunday sailings are provided. Reduced winter sailings are maintained by one ship. Passage time is 9¼ hours outwards, and 10½ homewards. The *Ulster Queen* is licensed to carry up to 1,000 passengers. The car deck has space for 120 vehicles and one part is designed with additional height for caravans and coaches.

Accommodation for 280 First Class passengers is provided in single- and double-berth cabins. There are also four double cabins-de-luxe. Two-, three- and four-berth cabins are available for 140 Second Class passengers. Ample seating is provided for other passengers.

First Class public rooms: lounge, writing room, smoke room, main restaurant and self-service cafeteria.

Second Class public rooms: lounge, smoke room–bar and self-service cafeteria.

M.S. DANMARK (1968)

Owners: DANISH STATE RAILWAYS
Builders: ELSINORE SHIPBUILDING & ENGINEERING CO. LTD.
B. & W. V 45 diesels, 5,500 b.h.p.
Twin screw
Service speed 19 knots
Length overall 474 ft. (approx.)
Beam 55 ft. (approx.)
Gross tonnage 6,300

The M.S. *Danmark* is fitted with a rail deck and a car deck with the following capacities: 12 large railway carriages (on 1,015 ft. of track) and 150 vehicles or 30–35 goods wagons and 150 vehicles, or 310 vehicles on car and rail decks—350 if movable platform is fitted in rail deck. Accommodation is provided for 1,500 passengers, public rooms include two large restaurants, a saloon and a bar. A la carte, Danish hors d'oeuvres and buffet meals are served. In addition, a large duty-free shop sells a wide variety of goods.

The main engines are remotely controlled from a control room. To assist manoeuvring twin rudders, a bow rudder and a bow thrust unit are provided. When running astern the ship is controlled from an after wheelhouse and duplicate sets of radar equipment have been installed.

The M.S. *Danmark.*
Photo courtesy: Danish State Railways

The *Danmark*, together with the *King Frederik IX*, the *Deutschland* and the *Theodor Heuss* maintain up to 28 services a day between Rødby Fœrge and the German port of Puttgarden, a distance of 11 miles. It would therefore appear to be a very large ship for such a short voyage, but the Rødby–Puttgarden ferry is the main link between Germany and Denmark. All of the international expresses to and from Copenhagen cross by this route and the car traffic is very heavy. When not carrying passenger trains, goods wagons are carried.

The service was opened in 1963 to run parallel to the much older Gedser–Warnemünde ferry and in its first year three vessels in 4,955 round voyages carried 2,363,000 passengers, 275,880 passenger carriages and wagons, and 304,082 vehicles. By early 1968, 12,000,000 passengers had been carried and cargo showed proportionate increases. The *Danmark* is needed to deal with rises in traffic and the passage time has been reduced to 1 hour and 5 minutes.

The first British train ferries entered service in 1860 between Granton and Burntisland ($5\frac{1}{2}$ miles) and at Dundee ($\frac{7}{8}$ mile across the River Tay). Both services were superseded by bridges. In 1916 train ferries were built to carry ammunition and stores from Richborough to France. After the war the three ships T.Fs. 1, 2 and 3 began a new service between Harwich and Zeebrugge. A series of new vessels was built in recent years to carry on the service which is for freight only.

The first British passenger train ferry service was established in 1934 to work a new London–Paris overnight sleeper express. This service remains in operation with the *Twickenham Ferry*, *Hampton Ferry*, *Shepperton Ferry* and the *Saint Germain*, and sleeper carriages are also carried for the post-war London–Brussels express. The ships sail between Dover and Dunkirk and carry goods wagons and vehicles when not required for the passenger trains.

A new vessel the *Vortigern* which can be used as either a train ferry or a commercial and private vehicle ferry entered service in 1969.

The boat deck of the *Danmark*. Because of the restricted limits of the ship's operations the lifesaving regulations allow the substitution of life rafts in place of lifeboats. The life rafts inflate on contact with the water and embarkation is by the rope ladders which are ready for instant release. Although life rafts form an excellent method of abandoning ship, they cannot be manoeuvred and drift with wind or current. On the opposite quay is one of many small car ferries which operate in Denmark.
Photo courtesy: Danish State Railways

The insulated control room in the engine room. Instructions are received from the bridge by telegraph.
Photo courtesy: Danish State Railways

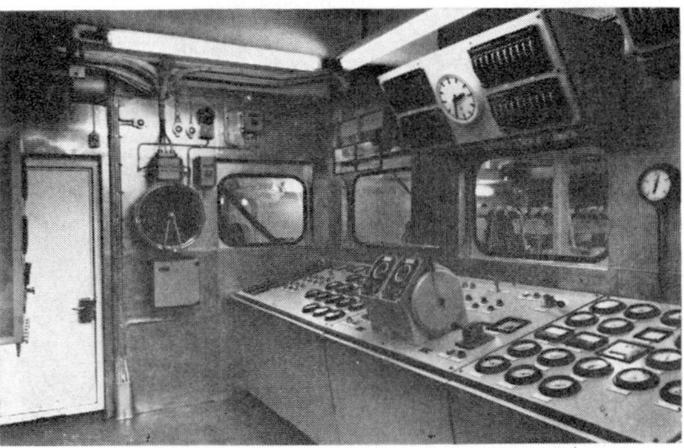

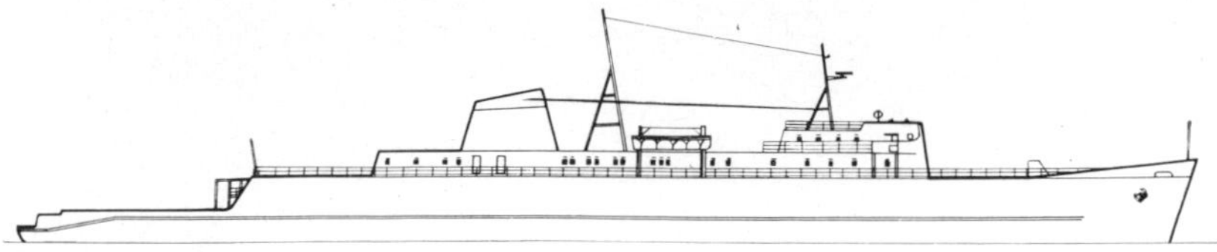

M.S. CAMBRIDGE FERRY (1964)
Owners: British Rail
Builders: Hawthorn Leslie (Shipbuilders) Ltd.
Mirrlees diesels, 3,720 b.h.p.
Twin Stone-Kamewa-type controllable-pitch screws
Service speed 13½ knots
Length overall 406 ft.
Beam 58·6 ft.
Gross tonnage 3,160

(Sister ships—*Suffolk, Norfolk* and *Essex Ferry*)

Train ferry operating between Harwich and Zeebrugge. Capacity 35 Continental-type wagons on four tracks. Rails recessed into deck to allow carriage of vehicles. Travelling gantry cranes fitted to handle containers. Flume stabilising system. Bridge or engine room control of propellers.

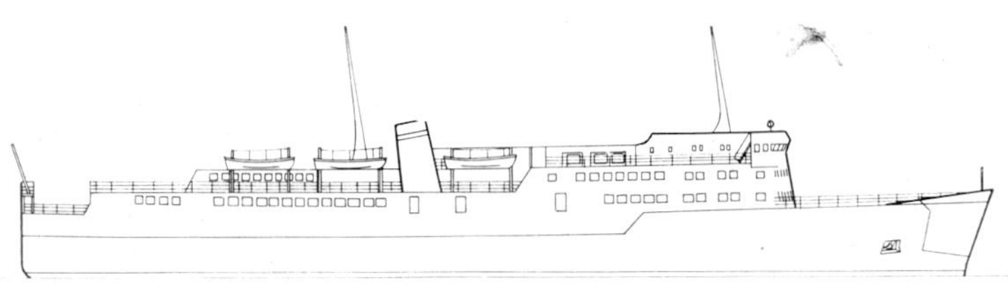

M.S. LION (1968)
Owners: Burns and Laird Lines Ltd.
Builders: Cammell Laird & Co. Ltd.
Two Crossley Pielstick diesels
Twin screw (controllable pitch)
Service speed 21 knots
Length overall 365 ft.
Beam 56 ft.

The *Lion* is employed on the Ardrossan–Belfast daily service. Bow and stern doors allow rapid loading and discharge of 170 cars. One-class accommodation for 1,200 passengers includes four de-luxe cabins, day cabins, restaurant and lounges. Stabilisers and twin rudders are fitted. The propellers are controlled from the bridge and a bow thrust unit permits easier manoeuvring in confined waters.

The voyage between Scotland and Northern Ireland takes 4½ hours.

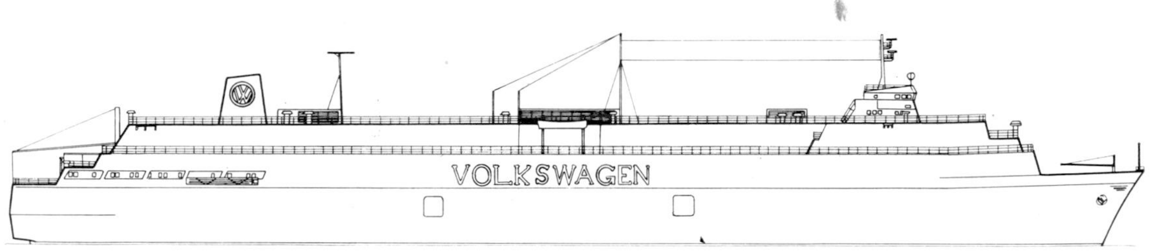

M.S. DYVI OCEANIC (1968)
Owners: Jan-Erik Dyvi, Oslo
Builders: A/S Tangen Verft and Nylands Verksted
Diesel
Length overall 576 ft. 9 in.
Beam 74 ft.
Deadweight tonnage 6,000.
Flume stabilising system

The *Dyvi Oceanic* is one of the first, and probably the largest, purpose-built car carrier. She has stowage space for the equivalent of 2,500 standard-sized Volkswagen cars and these are carried on nine decks. In the main hull, cars are stowed 13 abreast. Loading and discharge is via two doors on each side of the hull whence the cars move to various decks by means of ramps. A fifth door is located in the stern of the ship.

In addition, the *Dyvi Oceanic* has been designed to carry a number of containers. These are smaller than the standard ISO units and are loaded and stowed by fork lift trucks.

Crew accommodation is fully air conditioned and the equipment is designed to cope with extremes of temperature.

The *Dyvi Oceanic* is on long-term charter to Volkswagen and makes frequent transatlantic voyages.

M.S. SEA FREIGHTLINER I (1968)

Owners: BRITISH RAIL
Builders: JOHN READHEAD & CO. LTD.
Mirrlees National diesels, 4,200 b.h.p.
Twin screw
Service Speed 13·5 knots.
Length overall 388 ft.
Beam 55 ft.

The *Sea Freightliner I* is a cellular container ship, and with another similar vessel maintains a regular service between Parkeston Quay, Harwich, and Zeebrugge. Passage time is just over 7 hours with a 5-hour turn-round period at both ports.

148 ISO standard 30-ft. containers can be carried, 38 of these being stowed on deck. Refrigerated containers can also be accommodated.

Containers are guided into the cellular holds by steel guide rails. Once in position no further securing is required. On deck the containers are held in position by simple locking devices.

Three steel hatch covers move fore and aft and act as carriers for the other hatch covers, which are first jacked-up to allow the moving hatch to be placed in position underneath.

Automated control of the engines permits the engine room to be unoccupied for periods of up to 12 hours. Alarm systems are fitted on the bridge, in the Chief Engineer's cabin and in the engine room console, from which the engines are controlled.

M.S. *Sea Freightliner I.*

A container being lowered in a cellular hold. The containers are guided by vertical rails and each container rests on the top of the one below.
Photo courtesy: British Rail

A shore container crane loading the *Sea Freightliner I.* This British Rail service carries containers received from many firms who arrange their conveyance from factory to ship, and ship to customer at the other end. It will also be noted that although of standard size, the containers are of different construction.
Photo courtesy: British Rail

M.S. FREE ENTERPRISE III (1967)

Owners: TOWNSEND THORENSEN CAR FERRIES LTD.
Builders: WERF "GUSTO," SCHIEDAM
Four Smit-M.A.N. diesels, 11,550 b.h.p.
Twin screw
Service speed 21 knots
Length overall 385 ft. 6 in.
Beam 61 ft.
High clearance on main car deck (13 ft. 2 in.) to allow carriage of commercial vehicles
Fitted with "Flume" stabiliser

The *Free Enterprise III* cost

M.S. *Free Enterprise III.*
Photo courtesy: Townsend Car Ferries Ltd.

£2,000,000 to build, and until recently was the largest car ferry to operate across the English Channel.

Using side platforms this ship can carry 250 cars. Accommodation is also provided for 1,200 passengers with 14 four-berth and 9 two-berth cabins, all of which can be converted into day rooms. The public rooms are on the open-plan system with bars, shop and a dining saloon for 150.

The Townsend ferries are hard pressed during the season and in order to reduce to the minimum time spent docking and undocking the *Free Enterprise III* is fitted with a bow rudder and a Kamewa controllable-pitch bow propeller. This propeller, together with the main propellers which are of a similar design can be controlled from either the forward or after wheelhouses. The vessel also has an exceptionally high astern speed of 16 knots.

The main engines are operated on the "father" and "son" principle so that the minimum power is used. The "father" engines (3,850 h.p. each) are directly connected to the shafts. The "son" engines (1,925 h.p. each) are connected by gearboxes and fluid couplings, and speeds of 21 and 19 knots are possible using full power and two-thirds power respectively.

Although only engaged on short duration voyages, a full range of radio and navigational aids is fitted, including VHF equipment for passenger ship-to-shore telephone calls and for the maintenance of communications between the ship, the harbour board control and the Automobile Association's ship and shore offices.

A public address system covers crew, passenger and car spaces, and a special tape recorder reproduces pre-recorded messages in several languages.

The development of cross-Channel vehicle ferries can be seen from the history of Townsend Car Ferries.

In 1928 one ship, the *Artificer*, carrying 15 crane-loaded vehicles operated between Dover and Calais. Passengers in excess of 12 had to cross separately by passenger ship (a similar service operated between Newhaven and Dieppe until the introduction of car ferries on this route).

Two later ships the *Royal Firth* and the *Forde*, worked the Dover crossing and by the outbreak of war in 1939 the potential of this kind of service was already recognised.

In 1950 the *Halladale*, a converted frigate, entered service as the first ramp-loaded vessel, and

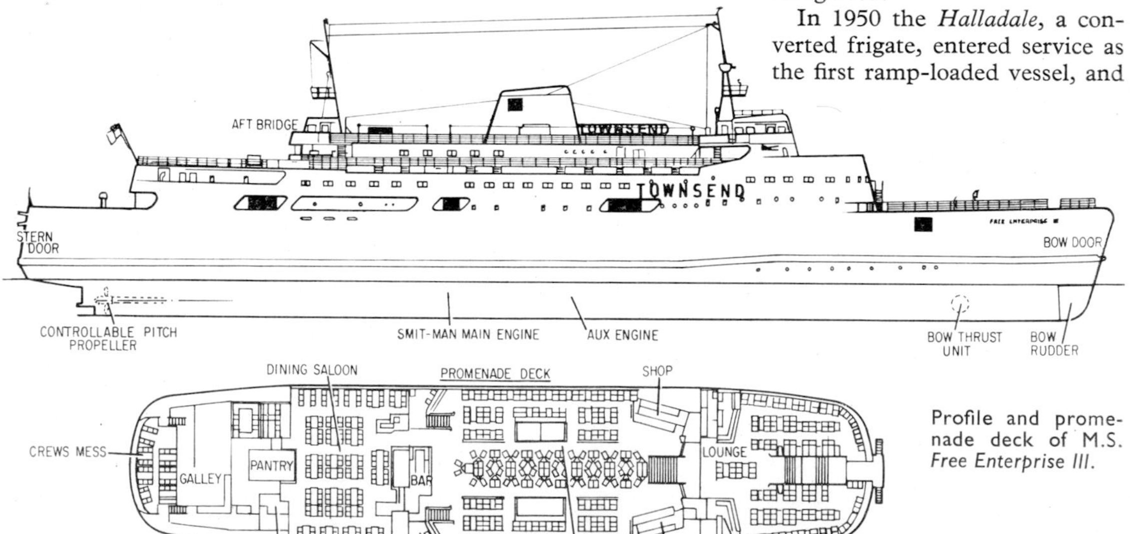

Profile and promenade deck of M.S. *Free Enterprise III.*

the ramp bridge installed at that time at Calais by Townsends is still in use.

Free Enterprise I was commissioned in 1962, *Free Enterprise II* in 1965, followed by *Free Enterprise III* in 1966. A further ship, the *Free Enterprise IV*, entered service in 1969. *Free Enterprise V* enters service in mid-1970.

Free Enterprise I carries 120 cars and 850 passengers, *Free Enterprise III* and *IV*, 250 and 1,200 respectively.

The following figures indicate the build-up of ferry operations between 1928 and 1967:

	Vehicles	*Passengers*
1928	2,261	7,831
1949	10,964	36,439
1955	19,179	64,728
1960	23,919	84,013
1965	129,328	427,319
1967	175,000	700,000
1968	200,000	800,000
1969	By mid-October, 1969, the figures for 1968 had been equalled.	

In 1966 2,687 commercial vehicles were carried, in 1967 17,250 (75% of these on Dover–Zeebrugge route). In 1968 35,000 carried.

Routes and Services

Dover–Calais. Up to 24 services a day. Passage time 1½ hours.

Dover–Zeebrugge. Up to four services a day. Passage time 4 hours (*Free Enterprise III*).

M.S. WINSTON CHURCHILL (1968)

Owners: THE UNITED STEAMSHIP CO. LTD. OF COPENHAGEN

Builders: CANTIERI NAVALI DEL TIRRENO E RIUNITI

Turbo-charged 10-cylinder B. & W. diesels, 15,500 i.h.p.

Twin screw

Over 23 knots at full engine output

Length overall 459 ft.

Beam 67 ft.

The design of the *Winston Churchill* incorporated the experience gained with the earlier M.S. *England.* She is the largest Danish passenger ship and, although fitted with bow and stern doors, looks very much like a conventional passenger liner.

The ship is divided into nine main watertight compartments, and 13 watertight sliding doors in the bulkheads can be closed electrically from the bridge. The ship is also subdivided into fire zones in accordance with the latest international recommendations; the 37 fireproof doors which separate the zones are also remotely controlled. In addition, an automatic sprinkler system is installed. Ventilation ducts incorporate built-in fire dampers and all ventilators can be closed from the bridge.

The *Winston Churchill* is fully air conditioned and passenger cabins have individual control of temperature. The system is balanced for an outside temperature down to −15°C., and simultaneously an inside temperature of 22°C. Change of air varies from eight to ten times an hour in the passenger and crew cabins to once a minute in the galley. "Cooling ceilings" in the First Class lounge and restaurant ensure a pleasant temperature without passengers noticing the source of the cooled air.

The car deck provides space for 180 vehicles. Hinged hanging decks enable private cars to be carried using special ship's trailers, whilst in the centre of the car deck there is sufficient headroom for lorries, including articulated units, trailers, coaches and the refrigerated semi-trailers now being used for the conveyance of Danish bacon to the U.K.

A 1,000-h.p. bow propeller and Sperry stabilisers are fitted which, together with the main engines, are controlled from the bridge.

Open plan passenger accommodation is in the modern Danish style and considerable use is made of largely glazed bulkheads between rooms.

The stern door of the *Winston Churchill.* The faired curved counter gives added protection to the stern door and adds enormously to the ship's appearance. At sea it is difficult to tell that the *Winston Churchill* is not a conventional passenger liner.

Photo courtesy: D.F.D.S.

First Class accommodation consists of lounge, bar, restaurant. A night club and bar are available to both classes. Other features include shops, bureaux and a children's playroom.

Second Class passengers have a separate lounge and restaurant and also share the facilities provided by the shops and bureaux.

First Class cabins, which are either one or two berth, have their own washbasins, showers and lavatories.

An export consignment of caravans. New caravans and tractors are regularly consigned by United Steamship Co. vessels. Also visible is a semi-trailer, insulated for the conveyance of bacon.

Photo courtesy: D.F.D.S.

The M.S. *Passat.* A small German short sea cargo liner which can be loaded either by derricks or by fork lift trucks through the doors at the after end of the hull.

Photo courtesy: D. W. A. Mercer

Second Class cabins are two or four berth and have their own washing facilities. Group accommodation is in four-berth cabins.

Total accommodation is for 462 passengers; 124 First Class, 274 Second Class and 64 in group accommodation.

The United Steamship Company was founded in 1866, and in 1867 the small *Anglo Dane* inaugurated a cargo service between Esbjerg and the U.K. Soon afterwards passengers began to be carried and the service developed steadily until special passenger ships were put into service, culminating in vessels such as the *Kronprinsesse Ingrid,* built in 1949 and with a capacity of 148 and 146 First and Second Class passengers respectively, and 1,700 tons of cargo.

The break with conventional ships came in 1964 with the entry into service of the *England,* a car/passenger ferry with vehicle access through side doors. The *Winston Churchill* commenced operations in 1967 after a special voyage to London to be officially named by Lady Churchill.

Between June and September these two ships maintain a daily service between Harwich and Esbjerg. During this period the needs of holiday makers are paramount and additional roll on/roll off cargo tonnage is brought in to cope with the commercial vehicles which are being carried in increasing numbers by the *Winston Churchill.* Between the end of September and the end of May the *Winston Churchill* provides three sailings a week. The *England,* which is not suitable for the carriage of commercial vehicles, is diverted to cruising, sailing as far afield as the West Indies.

The overnight open sea passage between Harwich and Esbjerg takes about 18 hours.

The triple-screw cross-channel packet S.S. *Newhaven.*

S.S. NEWHAVEN

Owners: FRENCH STATE RAILWAYS

The cross channel services between U.K., France and Belgium have changed out of all recognition in the last ten years. Fleets of passenger vessels have been put out of service and only on the routes between Dover and Ostend, Weymouth and the Channel Islands and Folkestone and Boulogne are they still employed. However, in the first 20 years or so of this century the cross channel packets were tremendously important ships and carried all passengers and mail going to the Continent. Even the mail for Australia and the Far East was taken via the channel and French railways to Marseilles when transit times could be saved as a result.

Advance in design and speed was remarkable. The change in propulsion was direct from paddles to steam turbines. Reciprocating engines were never used in cross-Channel steamers. Dennys of Dumbarton were famed for their vessels, but it is often forgotten that once the French State Railways started to provide ships for these routes they were able to build the equal of any British ship. Such a one was the *Newhaven* with speed of 24 knots which was built for the service between Newhaven and Dieppe. (The fastest ship on the route was the *Brighton* which could maintain 25 knots in suitable weather.) The *Newhaven* continued in service until 1939, although in the early '30s, the superstructure was plated-in and a single fat and not very beautiful funnel was substituted in order to bring her more in line with the *Worthing* and the *Brighton.*

Between the wars day and night services were run and it was a very rare occasion for one of these ships not to sail. The *Newhaven* could carry 1,000 First and Second Class passengers. First Class passengers had the use of a smoking room, dining saloon, ladies saloon (about 12 ft. square) and de luxe cabins and sleeping saloons for men and women. The Second Class passengers were provided with a small smoking room and sleeping saloons. All deck space was unprotected, although canvas screens were rigged on the promenade deck in bad weather.

The day service remains in operation as before although the ships involved are vehicle ferries. Apart from passengers, British Rail are carrying an increasing number of commercial vehicles which come to the U.K. from as far afield as Italy and Spain.

M.S. *Finnhansa.*
Photo courtesy: O/Y Finnlines Ltd.

M.S. FINNHANSA (1966)

Owners: O/Y FINNLINES LTD.
Builders: WARTSILA KON. SANDVIKENS SKEPPS, HELSINGFORS
Two Sulzer diesels, 14,000 b.h.p.
Twin screw
Service speed 20 knots
Length overall 441 ft.
Beam 66 ft.

The *Finnhansa* is employed on the ferry service between Lubck, Copenhagen, Karlskrona, Nynashamn and Helsinki. In summer an additional call is made at Slite. Passage time varies between 35–45 hours depending upon the route followed. Accommodation is provided for a maximum of 1,400 passengers. There are 106 First Class, 228 Tourist Class and 10 De Luxe cabins. Seats are also provided for over 1,000.

The car deck, which has bow and stern doors and four side-loading ports, can carry virtually any kind of freight which moves on wheels or caterpillar tracks, the heaviest of excavators and road levellers. Parts of the car deck are reinforced for heavy loads up to a maximum weight of 53 tons. Cargo holds can also carry a variety of cargoes, which are lowered and raised by lift. The total capacity of the ship is:

Holds—38 containers or flats with maximum weight of 20 tons each or dimensions 20 × 8 × 8 ft.

Car Deck—205 private cars, or alternatively 26 lorries and 44 private cars. Total capacity for private cars in the holds and on the car deck, 308.

Containers are loaded by a straddle carrier. Pallets and flats are loaded on to trailers and towed on board by tractors. Once in the hold flats, containers and pallets are moved to the point of stowage on rolling beams. Large consignments of chipboard and paper reels travel in the *Finnhansa*, and during the season large loads of fruit are carried.

First Class passengers have the use of a dining saloon, cafeteria, lounge and bar, verandah and swimming pool.

Tourist Class passengers also have similar facilities and a cinema is provided for use by both classes.

Drivers of commercial vehicles are provided with sauna baths.

The *Finnhansa*'s sister ship, the *Finnpartner*, was recently sold and O/Y Finnlines has now in service a new ferry, which will carry commercial vehicles only. In winter vessels entering Helsinki often need the assistance of icebreakers, many of which have been built by Wartsila.

M.S. *Spero.*
Photo courtesy: Ellerman's Wilson Line Ltd.

M.S. SPERO (1966)

Owners: ELLERMAN'S WILSON LINE LTD.
Builders: CAMMELL LAIRD (SHIPBUILDERS AND ENGINEERS) LTD.
Four Mirrlees diesels, 10,920 b.h.p.
Twin screw (controllable pitch)
Service speed 18 knots
Length overall 454 ft.
Beam 68 ft.

Gross tonnage 6,916
Deadweight tonnage 2,750

The *Spero* is a stern-loading vehicle ferry running on an all the year round service between Hull and Gothenburg. This ship has accommodation for 408 passengers in two- and four-berth cabins, there are also four double de luxe cabins. The majority of cabins have wash basins and many have showers and toilets in addition. All passengers have the use of a wide range of public rooms and spacious decks and the *Spero* is probably the only British ship equipped with sauna baths. Meals are served either in the cafeteria, or in the restaurant, where waiter service is provided. This system, together with the practice of selling accommodation exclusive of meals is becoming widespread.

The two vehicle decks can accommodate 100 cars and 100 trailers or containers—or a combination of each. A forward hold, served by two 10-ton cranes, is available for the conveyance of non-containerised cargo. In addition to the stern doors, there are three side ports for loading cars.

The *Spero* is stabilised and a bow thrust unit is fitted.

M.S. *Hawea*.

M.S. HAWEA (1967)

Owners: UNION STEAM SHIP CO. OF NEW ZEALAND LTD.
Builders: TAIKOO DOCKYARD AND ENGINEERING CO. OF HONG KONG LTD.

Two Polar diesels, 8,000 b.h.p.
Twin screw
Service speed 16·5 knots
Length overall 366 ft.
Beam 56 ft.
Deadweight tonnage 2,489

The *Hawea*, which was the first roll on/roll off vessel to enter service on the New Zealand coast, runs between Auckland, Littelton and Dunedin, taking 12 days on the round voyage.

Rising costs of conventional cargo handling methods led the U.S.S. Co. of N.Z. to consider new systems, and as long ago as 1959, 120-cu. ft. containers were introduced to effect economies. The need for further development was, however, recognised and the decision was made that a unit load system combined with a vehicle ferry would provide the solution. Before deciding on the type and size of the unit extensive research was carried out into the needs, equipment and facilities of shippers, consignees and transport operators in both Australia and New Zealand, and it was found that 12 tons was about the largest unit which could be conveniently handled. In addition it was considered that the smaller population concentrations existing in New Zealand and Australia when compared with Europe and North America, together with the smaller quantities of cargo moving, would make the use of standard ISO containers uneconomical. Planning was, therefore, centred around the introduction of a pallet similar to those which had been in use between Melbourne/Sydney and Hobart since 1964, and roll on/roll off ferries between Wellington and Littelton since 1965. The pallet, known as the "Seafreighter", is 14 ft. 5 in. long, 8 ft. wide, with 5 ft. high sides and end load retainers and canvas covers. It has a capacity of 12 tons and can be stacked two-high on the vehicle deck of the *Hawea*.

The *Hawea* can carry 2,250 tons of unitised cargo or a variety of combinations of vehicles and units. Loading is carried out over shore ramps and a link span through the ship's stern door. Upper deck cargo, which comprises vehicles and trailers, is loaded by ramp from the main vehicle deck, or by the ship's 15-ton crane. A container hold below the vehicle deck is used to carry the older 120-cu. ft. containers.

Units are loaded by fork lift trucks, each with a 15-ton capacity, and a fork lift truck, which can lift 8,000 lbs. stows containers in the hold. The hold is also loaded via hatches in the vehicle and upper decks. To ensure that there is no accumulation of exhaust in the vehicle deck, a ventilating system provides no less than 25 complete changes of air per hour. A Flume stabilising system is fitted and movements in the harbour are assisted by a bow thrust unit. The *Hawea* is also equipped—as are many other ships of this type—with self-tensioning winches which adjust mooring lines automatically to compensate for the movements of the vessel and for the rise and fall of tides.

In 1969, two new roll on/roll off ferries, the *Maheno* and the *Marama*, entered service between Auckland, Wellington and Melbourne or Sydney. Sailings, all fortnightly, are to the following schedules.

To Sydney
Auckland: Sail 10 p.m. Tuesday.
Wellington: Arrive 7 a.m. Thursday. Sail 1 p.m. Saturday.
Sydney: Arrive 3.30 p.m. Thursday. Sail noon Thursday.
Auckland: Arrive 5 p.m. Sunday.

To Melbourne
Auckland: Sail 10 p.m. Tuesday.
Wellington: Arrive 7 a.m. Thursday. Sail 5 p.m. Friday.
Melbourne: Arrive 6 a.m. Tuesday. Sail 5 p.m. Wednesday.
Auckland: Arrive 9 p.m. Sunday.

In this time the ships will be capable of handling up to 10,000 tons of cargo. The schedule of a round trip once a fortnight compares with the conventional vessels' timetable of one round trip approximately every 42 days.

This company also runs the following services:

Australian coastal ports.
Australian and Tasmanian ports.
Australian and New Zealand ports.
Passengers and cargo to Suva, Nukualofa, Vavau, Nive, Pago-Pago and Apia.
Unitised cargo service in conventional ships between Sydney and Hobart and Melbourne and Hobart.
In conjunction with the British India Steam Navigation Co. Ltd.: New Zealand to Singapore, Malaysian ports, Rangoon, Calcutta, Ceylon and Bombay.

M.S. PATRICIA (1966)

Owners: SWEDISH LLOYD
Builders: A/B LINDHOLMENS VARY, GOTHENBURG
Four Pielstick diesels, 10,000 b.h.p.
Twin screws
Service speed 18 knots
Length overall 463 ft.
Beam 85 ft.
Gross tonnage 7,900

The *Patricia* is a stern-loading vehicle and passenger ferry. Accommodation is provided for 740 one-class passengers. The vehicle deck has space for 100 cars and 100 containers or trailers. The *Patricia* runs between Southampton and Bilbao, and apart from the conveyance of passengers and cars, operates the MacAndrew Line's "Macpak" container service. Cargo is received at depots in Glasgow, Manchester, Birmingham and London and the *Patricia* leaves Southampton every four or five days. The crossing takes about 36 hours.

This photograph shows a "Macpack" container being loaded (stuffed) with miscellaneous packages (now known as break bulk cargo when carried in a cargo liner). Containerisation has simplified enormously the loading and stowage of general cargo. The immediate advantages are:

(*a*) In the holds of container ships the containers are secured by the vertical guide rails and there is little chance of their moving in a seaway. On deck the lashing of the container is a simple process although heavy seas are causing more damage than was at first expected.

M.S. *Patricia*.
Photo courtesy: D. W. A. Mercer.

A "Macpack" container being loaded on to the *Patricia* at Southampton. The tractor has been especially designed to operate within the restricted height of the vehicle deck.
Photo courtesy: MacAndrews & Co. Ltd.

(*b*) Dunnage, other than that used within the containers, is dispensed with, and the services of experienced stevedores and dockers are not required. In their place small teams of highly trained operators are used.

(*c*) The contents of one container will not generally damage the contents of another, e.g. in stowing a conventional cargo, care must be taken to see that one commodity is not spoilt by absorbing odour from another.

(*d*) Damage to units of cargo by the weight of others stored on top is avoided.

(*e*) The problem of stowing cargo for easy discharge at a range of ports, whilst at the same time maintaining trim and stability, is largely overcome.

The disadvantages of containers are not, however, to be overlooked. There is a limit to the types of cargo which can be carried and unless a flow of suitable cargo is available at either end, a considerable loss will arise from the carriage of empty containers.

The problems of insurance, which are complex, have not yet been really satisfactorily settled.

In addition, but this is not necessarily the fault of the ship as such, there is a possibility that too many ships of this type are being built and that competition will in time cut back profitability.

M.S. LEOPARD (1968)

Owners: NORMANDY FERRIES
Builders: ATELIERS ET CHANTIERS DE BRETAGNE
Two Pielstick diesels, 11,160 b.h.p.
Twin screws
Service speed 18 knots
Length overall 415 ft.
Beam 70 ft.
Gross tonnage 6,000

M.S. *Leopard*.
Photo courtesy: Normandy Ferries

Normandy Ferries is a company jointly set up and owned by the General Steam Navigation Co. Ltd. and the Société Anonyme de Gerance et d'Armement, Paris. The *Leopard* flies the French flag, the *Dragon*—an identical sister ship—the British flag. The General Steam Navigation Co. is itself a part of the P & O Group.

The two ferries, which are stabilised and fully air-conditioned, have accommodation for 850 passengers and 250 cars. A freight service is also provided and the main vehicle deck has a capacity of 65 large trailers (or containers, self-drive vehicles or palletised cargo). Cargo units up to 29 tons in weight can be handled at Southampton or Le Havre, whilst the Lisbon service is restricted to self-drive units not exceeding 15 tons all-up and with a wheelbase not exceeding 22 ft. In addition to the main vehicle deck, up to seven large units can be carried on the open after end of C deck, enabling vehicles carrying certain types of chemicals in bulk, hazardous, corrosive or inflammable cargo, to take advantage of the roll-on/roll-off facilities. Electrical and compressed air connections are provided for refrigerated and other special cargoes.

The developing operations of Normandy Ferries are an example of the efforts which are now made to keep ships of this type in full employment throughout the year. It is unfortunate that car ferries are subject to seasonal fluctuations and even the carriage of commercial vehicles will not always provide full cargoes. There is also a conflict of interest between private car owners and commercial vehicles, which is being solved by some companies in the construction of ferries which accept commercial vehicles only. Large companies such as the United Steamship Co. of Denmark bring in tonnage from other services to meet peak demand.

Normandy Ferries commenced operations between Southampton and Le Havre in June 1967, and so great has been the demand by passengers during the summer months that both ships are kept running full out.

To keep the vessels employed at other times further services have been developed, and in 1970 the following were in operation:

Southampton–Le Havre

Daily service throughout the year.

From May 16th to June 26th, additional weekend sailings—providing eight sailings per week in each direction.

From June 27th to September 12th, further additional sailings providing ten sailings per week in each direction.

Rosslare–Le Havre (Ireland's first regular and direct ferry sea link to the Continent, commenced in 1968.)

Between May 16th and October 4th a weekly service is provided, between June 27th and September 7th two sailings each way.

(During the 1968 season this new service operated at 80% capacity. On this service accommodation is restricted to 511.)

Southampton–Lisbon and Casablanca

Sailing every 11 days through the winter until May 1970.

From May 8th until June 5th (inclusive) and additional weekly sailing to Lisbon. The service is suspended during the summer and recommenced on September 14th.

The *Leopard* and *Dragon* provide de luxe cabins with shower, basin and toilet; standard two- and four-berth cabins with basin; four-berth couchettes and luxurious adjustable reclining seats with footrests.

Each ship offers a choice between cafeteria meal service or a first-class restaurant with waiter service and table d'hote meals. The two main saloons in each ship have their own bars. The upper saloons have dancing areas; the lower saloons ("Dragon's Den" and "Leopard's Lair") are furnished to provide a club atmosphere.

Other facilities on board these two ships include verandah decks with deck chairs, juke boxes for dancing, fruit machines (*Dragon* only), televisions and films, ship-to-shore telephone services and a nursery where mothers can attend to the needs of their children.

M.S. *Buffalo*.
Photo courtesy: Coast Lines Ltd.

M.S. BUFFALO (1961)

Owners: COAST LINES LTD.
Builders: ARDROSSAN DOCKYARD LTD.
Polar diesel, 2,800 b.h.p.
Single screw
Service speed 14 knots
Length overall 258 ft.
Beam 42 ft.
Deadweight tonnage 1,230

The M.S. *Buffalo*, with her sister ship the M.S. *Bison*, maintains a regular nightly unit load service between Liverpool and Belfast, each carrying approximately 60 unit loads. Ships of this type carry no cargo handling gear, the winches being used solely for opening and closing the hatches. Between the hatches the *Buffalo* is carrying a number of empty flats.

The S.S. *Normannia* is owned by British Rail and was originally a passenger vessel on the Southampton–Le Havre service. When British Rail withdrew from this service the *Normannia* was rebuilt as a vehicle ferry. Like the *Chantilly*, the *Normannia* now runs mainly between Dover and Boulogne, but she occasionally sails between Newhaven and Dieppe.

Unit load procedure, showing also use of slab hatch covers.
Photos courtesy: Coast Lines Ltd.

M.S. DORSET COAST

Coast Lines Ltd. maintains a network of unit load services on the Irish Sea, and the *Dorset Coast*, operating for Burns and Laird Lines Ltd. (part of the Coast Lines Group), provides a regular week-night sailing between Ardrossan and Larne. The capacity of this vessel is about 40 unit loads, stowed in the holds or on hatches.

This photograph clearly shows what is meant by unit loads. It can be a container, a tank or a flat loaded with a variety of commodities. From the draping of the tarpaulin covers it would appear that there are at least three different types of cargo loaded on to the flats. Also the method of lashing the units is variable; only a few men are needed to carry out this system. The lashings are, incidentally, similar to those used in L.S.Ts. and other wartime landing craft for securing tanks and other heavy equipment.

This illustration together with that adjoining it also shows how the slab hatch covers are moved by means of a single wire and neatly stacked in storage bays. The weather and 'tween deck hatch covers vary somewhat, but the method used is the same. This system should be compared with that on the *Sea Freightliner I.*

Other interesting points to be seen are the Sail Training Association's *Sir Winston Churchill* or *Malcolm Miller* about to leave with the assistance of Alexandra Towing Co. Ltd.'s tug. The vessel on the right has her tarpaulin hatch covers suspended by the cargo runners to act as "tents" over the hatches—it had presumably been raining. In the other photo the sail training ship has left and work has been resumed on the cargo ship.

Some Coast Line ships run under the colours of the Link Line, a group company which is concerned with unit load services between England, Scotland, Eire and Northern Ireland. British Rail and the British and Irish Steam Packet Co. Ltd. are also running unit load and container services on the Irish Sea.

The Belfast Steamship Co. Ltd. forms part of Coast Lines Ltd.

M.V. *Transcontainer I*
Photo courtesy: British Rail (Eastern Region)

M.V. TRANSCONTAINER 1 (1969)

For very many years the French National Railway have co-operated with the Southern Railway (now British Rail) in the provision of cargo and rail ferry services between France and the U.K. In recent years this co-operation has produced an extensive expansion of facilities and French Railways vessels are now calling at Harwich for the first time.

With the entry into service of a French rail ferry ship and the

The M.S. *Chantilly* was built in 1966 for service between Dover and Boulogne or Calais. On rare occasions this vessel is used on relief duties and this photograph was taken when she was on the Newhaven–Dieppe berth.

Transcontainer I, the following principal freight services are in operation.

(*a*) *Harwich–Dunkirk container service* carrying B.R. standard containers, privately owned containers, transcontainers, unit loads, flats, vehicles and "Kangaroo" trailers.

(*b*) *London–Dunkirk*. A thrice-weekly service carrying containers.

(*c*) *Newhaven–Dieppe*. This service, in addition to private cars, carries B.R. standard containers, small containers and roll on/roll off commercial vehicles which travel as far afield as Bordeaux and Spain.

(*d*) *Dover–Dunkirk Rail Ferry*. This service carries the overnight London (Stratford)–Paris Freightliner train. Facilities are available for B.R. containers, privately owned containers and transcontainers.

In addition, the ships employed carry large numbers of open and closed wagons for general purposes, privately owned tank wagons, Interfrigo refrigerated wagons and Transfesa wagons for service to Spain. The axles of these wagons are changed at the frontier to adapt to the gauge of the Spanish Railways. There is also an important and developing traffic in roll on/roll off vehicles.

(*e*) *Harwich–Dunkirk Rail Ferry*. This service performs a similar function to (*d*) above. During the season enormous tonnages of fresh fruit are brought to the U.K. from the South of France, Italy and Spain.

At Harwich and Dunkirk there are extensive co-ordinated rail services which ensure prompt delivery of containers to consignees and depots. French Railways are now building a new fleet of wagons for the traffic and already there are 22 depots in France with gantry cranes, either completed or in the process of completion, which are capable of handling 40-ft. containers. Since June 1969, special block container trains have been operating from Paris to Bordeaux, Marseilles and Toulouse.

Also being developed is the "Kangaroo" system by which modified semi-trailers are carried by rail to all parts of the Continent.

The *Transcontainer I* is typical of several ships in operation on the short sea trades. With a length of 342 ft. and a beam of 62 ft., this vessel has a stern door through which containers are loaded on slave trailers. In the garage deck two gantry cranes place the containers in position and achieve a loading factor similar to that of hatch loaded container ships. Containers stowed on the upper deck remain on slave trailers throughout the voyage. Openings in the upper deck also allow the ship to be loaded by shore container cranes.

The *Transcontainer I* also carries road vehicles, lorries, semi-trailers, etc., as well as freight of any kind on wheels including flats and unit loads. Total container capacity is 192 of 20 ft. in length, 125 of 30 ft. in length, or any combination of 20-ft., 30-ft. or 40-ft. transcontainers up to a total corresponding to the above limits.

Accommodation is provided for 36 passengers (mainly lorry drivers) in six four-berth and six two-berth cabins.

Two diesel engines with a total output of 4,400 b.h.p. give a service speed of 15 knots and enable the *Transcontainer I* to carry out a complete round voyage between Harwich and Dunkirk every 24 hours, although for the time being the service is operated from each port every other day.

M.S. *Rynstroom*.

M.S. RYNSTROOM (1966)

Owners: HOLLAND STEAMSHIP COMPANY.

Builders: ARNHEMSCHE SCHEEPSBOUW MIJ. N.V., ARNHEM

M.A.N. diesel, 1,800 b.h.p.
Single screw
Service speed 14 knots
Length overall 243 ft. (approx.)
Beam 36 ft. (approx.)
Deadweight tonnage 804

An unusual small cargo liner in which hatch loading has been dispensed with. All cargo is handled by fork lift trucks and entry is via side ramp on to a space the level of which is half way between the two main decks. Ramps lead to the appropriate decks and access to the holds is via lifts. During sea voyages one of the ramps is secured in rubber seatings thus ensuring that the entry to the cargo spaces is watertight.

The Holland Steamship Co. maintains a twice-weekly service between Amsterdam and Shoreham. The open sea passage is about 15 hours in duration and a full cargo can be loaded or unloaded in seven to eight hours. The *Rynstroom* is able to complete a round voyage in two days less than conventional ships on the same route.

The S.S. *St. George* approaching the link span at Harwich. The *St. George* is the largest ship in the British Rail fleet and one of the largest ferries operating between Great Britain and the Continent. Until recently the day and night services between Harwich and the Hook of Holland were operated by different ships. The *St. George* can, however, function equally well on both and at the same time carry a large number of vehicles. This is a good example of the way in which shipowners obtain more intensive running from their ships.

Photo courtesy: British Rail (Eastern Region)

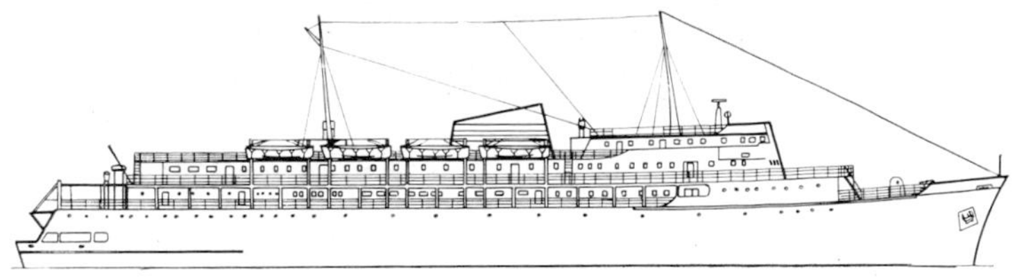

M.S. PRINCESS OF TASMANIA (1959)

Owners: Australian National Line
Builders: Australian Shipbuilding Board
Two Polar diesels, 17,200 b.h.p.
Twin screw
Service speed 17¾ knots
Length overall 370 ft.
Beam 58 ft.
Gross tonnage 3,963

In 1959 the Australian National Line introduced a car ferry service between Melbourne and Devonport (Tasmania). A nightly service is maintained by the *Princess of Tasmania*, which covers the 235 miles in 14½ hours.

This vessel, which is stern loading and discharging, has a turntable at the forward end of the vehicle deck. With the use of portable car decks and a lift-loaded orlop deck about 110 cars can be embarked. The stern door is large enough to admit the largest commercial vehicles.

Accommodation is provided for 334 passengers. Cabins are available for 178 in single-, double- and four-berth cabins; the rest have the use of aircraft-type seats in the lounges.

A Voith-Schneider bow propulsion unit and Denny Brown stabilisers are fitted and the wheelhouse has an extensive range of navigational aids.

The longer service between Sydney, Hobart, Bell Bay and Burnie is maintained by the larger *Empress of Australia* and sailings are provided about three times a fortnight in both directions.

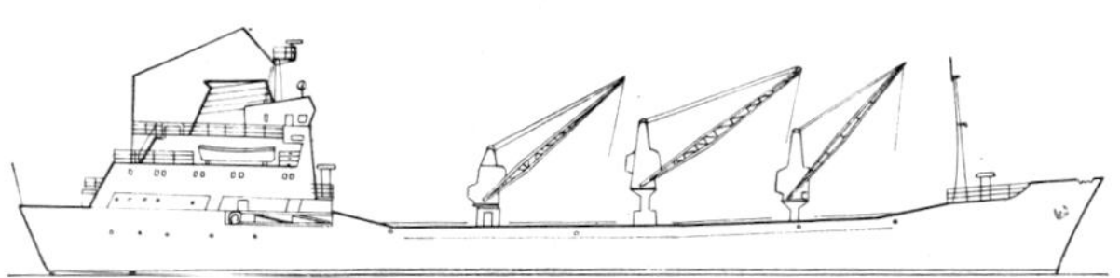

M.S. CLIO (1965)

Owners: Finland Steamship Co. Ltd., Helsinki
Builders: Wartsila Crichton-Vulcan, Turku
Sulzer diesel, 3,400 b.h.p.
Single screw
Service speed 14·5 knots
Length overall 300 ft.
Beam 46 ft.

The *Clio* and her sister ship the *Fennia* are employed between Finland and London. Cargo to London includes paper, cellulose and other timber products. Three hundred cars can be carried on the return journey. The cargo space is divided into three decks and the hatches stretch almost the full width of the ship. Cars can be loaded by cranes, two of which can handle up to 8 tons, or through side doors into the upper 'tween decks. From this deck hydraulic lifts take the cars to lower decks. All 'tween deck hatches are flush and general cargo can be handled by fork lift trucks.

M.S. PASTEUR (1966)

Built at Dunkirk for the Cie. Messageries Maritimes, the *Pasteur* is typical of the smaller cargo-passenger liners which have been built in recent years. She is 570·9 ft. long overall with a beam of 80 ft. Sulzer diesels of 24,000 b.h.p. produce a service speed of 20 knots through twin screws. Stabilisers are fitted. Accommodation is provided for 163 First Class passengers and 266 Second Class passengers. Both classes have separate public rooms and swimming pools, but share the theatre, beauty parlour and barber shop. The voyage from Le Havre to Buenos Aires takes about 12 days, including calls at Southampton, Vigo, Lisbon, Las Palmas, Rio de Janeiro and Montevideo.

The call at Southampton was initiated in 1968, and the *Pasteur* now constitutes the only passenger link between Southampton and South America.

Photo courtesy: Messageries Maritimes

CHAPTER 5

Passenger Liners

FOR something over a decade the passenger liner section of the shipping industry has been undergoing a slow and increasingly painful transition. Immediately after V.J. Day shipping companies laid on skeleton services, and, as more ships returned from requisitioning and replacement tonnage was delivered, things began to return to normal. The demand for passages was enormous and many people found themselves forced to wait for months before they could set out on their journeys. This was indeed paradise for the shipping companies, but during this period of abnormal profitability the airlines were literally spreading their wings and providing a means of travel which immediately attracted patronage from the business section of the community.

From this time on the shipping companies were faced with one crisis after another. The granting of independence to India had serious effects on the demand for passenger shipping, and the granting of independence to colony after colony led to a progressive deterioration in the general situation.

As the airlines steadily continued their penetration of the shipping market, the leading shipping companies promoted expensive and concentrated advertising campaigns. But company after company found that they were falling more and more below the break-even line and one by one services were reduced or withdrawn altogether.

The following list, which is by no means exhaustive, indicates the severity of the times through which the ships had passed:

Anchor Line: Services to India and Canada withdrawn.

B.I. to East Africa: Service withdrawn.

U.C. to East Africa: Service withdrawn.

Cunard to U.S.A. and Canada: Summer services only to U.S.A.

Bullard King to East Africa: Service withdrawn.

New Zealand Shipping Co.: Services phased out, mainly because of shortage of cargoes and the introduction of new tonnage which made the passenger ships surplus to requirements.

Furness Withy to Newfoundland: Services withdrawn.

Furness Withy, New York to Bermuda: Service withdrawn.

Elder Dempster to West Africa: One ship remaining in service.

Royal Mail to South America: Services withdrawn and ships transferred to associated Shaw Savill Line.

P.S.N.C. to Central America and West Coast of South America: Services withdrawn.

Foreign companies suffered to a similar extent. Passenger services by the Royal Rotterdam Lloyd Line and the Nederland Line ceased. For a time the three ships involved, the *Oranje*, *Johan Van Oldenbarnevelt* and *Willem Ruys*, were placed on a new round-the-world service; this failed to establish itself and the vessels were disposed of. The French Line is now represented on the North Atlantic by the *France* alone. The Cie. Messageries Maritimes services to the Far East and liberated colonies have been severely curtailed.

In an effort to find new employment for the ships which were not sold or scrapped, owners turned to holiday voyages or cruising. At the moment their efforts are meeting with a measure of success and there is no reason why they should not substantially increase their share of the holiday travel potential which has still to be fully exploited. However, it is one thing to operate profitable cruises with ships whose depreciation charges are based on 1950–55 building costs, it is quite another to produce the same results with new ships costing £10,000,000 or more each. Furthermore, the airline operators are now deeply involved in the holiday business and they will do their utmost from an undeniable position of advantage to see that the expansion of their own interests continues unabated.

At the present time the building of passenger liners is more or less at a standstill, but some confidence in the future can be detected. Both the Norwegian America Line and the Swedish American Line have built liners of moderate tonnage in which they have attempted to meet the needs of both regular service voyages and cruising. Italian Lines have built new ships for the Far East and Atlantic trades and other Continental shipowners have also built new ships for the South America run. In each case these ships are equally capable of the dual function. Several ships of modest dimensions have also been ordered for cruising, and these will be employed almost exclusively between the U.S.A., the Bahamas and the West Indies. In one case a ship has been ordered by an American airline corporation, others have been ordered by shipping companies which have had no previous experience of operating passenger ships.

The M.S. *Kungsholm* entering Gothenburg.
Photo courtesy: Swedish American Line

M.S. KUNGSHOLM (1965)

Owners: SWEDISH AMERICAN LINE
Builders: JOHN BROWN & CO. (CLYDEBANK) LTD.
Two 760/1500 VG-9U Götaverken diesels, 25,200 b.h.p.
Twin screw
Service speed 21 knots
Length overall 660 ft.
Beam 87 ft.
Gross tonnage 25,700
750 passengers (108 first class, 37 interchangeable, 605 tourist), on transatlantic voyages, 450 cruising.

The *Kungsholm* was designed as a dual purpose ship and spends a considerable part of each year cruising from the U.S.A.

On the Atlantic run the cost of a passage depends upon the location of the cabin, public rooms being available to all passengers.

The *Kungsholm* has ten decks, and a feature of the accommodation is the allocation of one and a half decks to the crew. Petty officers have single cabins and seamen, stewards, etc., have double cabins with full facilities.

There are 304 passenger cabins, of which 252 are outside. The great majority have baths and lavatories. The accompanying photograph shows the layout of a typical two-berth cabin. During the day the beds convert into settees.

Public rooms are decorated in modern Swedish style with clean lines and clever use of colour. The dining room, with seating for 504, allows meals to be taken at one sitting during cruises. In addition there is a main lounge with a domed ceiling covered with gold leaf. Carpeting is in dark blue and the furniture and curtains shades of gold and light beige. The forward lounge, flanked on each side by verandahs, is screened with large windows and serves as an excellent observation point. Other public rooms include cocktail bars and shopping area, writing rooms and sports room. The entire accommodation is air conditioned.

Passengers have the use of extensive deck areas, and the whole of the boat deck is screened with tall windows. Above the

A First Class two-berth cabin on the *Kungsholm*. The beds have been turned into settees for day use and the cabin gives the impression of being one large sitting room. The windows are set in from the side of the ship and natural light is provided by portholes behind them.
Photo courtesy: Swedish American Line

The Tourist Class lounge on the *Rotterdam* is one of the finest rooms of this class ever built into a ship.
Photo courtesy: Holland America Line Ltd.

A spacious First Class cabin on the *Rotterdam*. (Opposite)
Photo courtesy: Holland America Line Ltd.

boat deck is a partly screened sun deck. The open air swimming pool is thoroughly protected from the elements, whilst a second indoor pool is also provided.

Fire protection complies with the latest international recommendations. Sprinkler systems are installed throughout the accommodation, and automatic fire alarms and smoke detectors are located in the wheelhouse. There are 125 fire-resisting doors as well as a comprehensive outfit of hydrants, hoses and extinguishers.

The ship is divided into 11 watertight compartments, the bulkheads of which have 44 watertight doors. These and also the fire-resisting doors are remotely controlled from the bridge.

The *Kungsholm* is equipped with eight lifeboats with a total capacity of nearly 1,000. Four tenders, mainly for use during cruises, have a capacity of 240. In addition there are inflatable life rafts for more than 600 persons.

No cargo is carried, but two derricks are fitted to handle baggage and stores.

During the summer months the *Kungsholm* operates between Gothenburg, Copenhagen and New York, the voyage taking eight days. In winter the ship sails from New York on cruises, one of which encircles the world and calls at such places as the Galapagos Islands, Cook and Society Islands, Honolulu and Los Angeles.

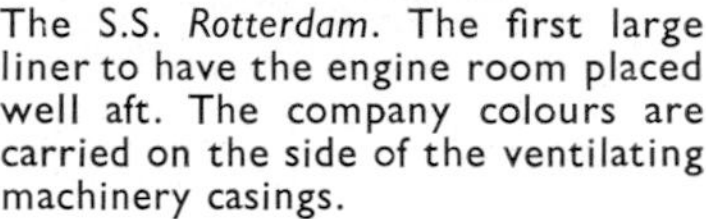

The S.S. *Rotterdam*. The first large liner to have the engine room placed well aft. The company colours are carried on the side of the ventilating machinery casings.

Photo courtesy: D. W. A. Mercer

S.S. ROTTERDAM (1959)

Owners: HOLLAND-AMERICA LINE
Builders: ROTTERDAM DRY DOCK CO.
Steam double reduction geared turbines
Twin screw
Service speed 20·5 knots
Length overall 748 ft.
Beam 94 ft.
Gross tonnage 38,645
Passengers: 580 First Class (some cabins interchangeable to Tourist Class), 789 Tourist Class. About 700 one class for cruises.

The *Rotterdam* is the largest Dutch passenger ship. In 1959, when she entered service, the *Rotterdam* introduced a new concept in travel. The placing of the engines aft allowed the whole of the midship section of the ship to be used for passenger accommodation and every advantage has been taken of this. A special feature is the space allocated to the Tourist Class.

Decks throughout the length of the ship are devoted alternately to First and Tourist Classes, and some of the Tourist public rooms are some of the finest to be found in any ship. Both dining rooms are more than one deck high and the staircase leading to them is modelled on the famous double staircase at Chambord in which two separate staircases are built

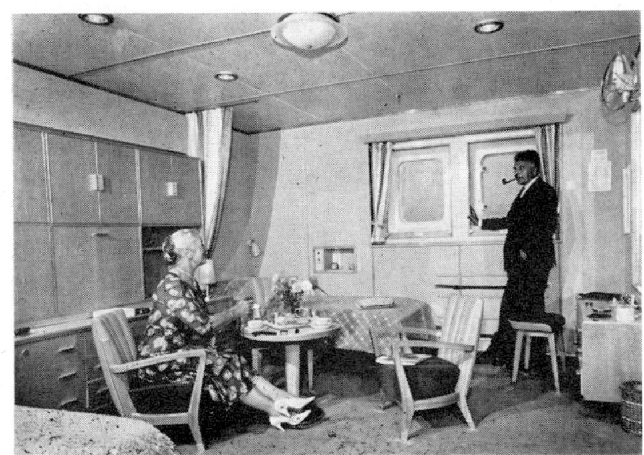

The children's playroom on the *Rotterdam*.

Trained staff are carried to look after children during specified hours and most liners also have a separate children's dining room.

Photo courtesy: Holland America Line Ltd.

The decorated door to the First Class smoking room.
Photo courtesy: Holland America Line Ltd.

within the same overall area so that people can mount or descend without meeting each other.

The cinema, two decks high and one of the largest afloat, seats an audience of over 600, and because of the layout of the decks, Tourist Class passengers enter the stalls, while First Class passengers enter the circle from their own foyer.

Cabins are large and beautifully furnished and in both classes one-, two-, three- and four-berth cabins are available. The majority of them have showers and lavatory en suite.

In the Tourist Class the following public rooms have been provided: verandah, sun room, "Cafe de la Paix" with dance floor, foyer, club room, shops, Ocean Bar, library, lounge (which spans the whole width of the ship and has deck to ceiling windows), cinema, La Fontaine Dining Room, indoor swimming pool with gymnasium and Turkish baths, outside swimming pool and extensive open and covered deck space with observation deck above the boat deck.

The *Rotterdam* is now permanently employed on cruises from New York. A typical itinerary is Bermuda, St. Maarten, Martinique, Barbados, St. Lucia, St. Thomas, San Juan, St. Croix or Freeport, Nassau, Bermuda. Once a year the *Rotterdam* carries out a round-the-world cruise, calling at 21 ports. The 1969 cruise cost a minimum of $3,365 per person.

S.S. *Empress of Canada.*
Photo courtesy: Canadian Pacific Steamships Ltd.

S.S. EMPRESS OF CANADA (1961)

Owners: CANADIAN PACIFIC STEAMSHIPS LTD.
Builders: VICKERS ARMSTRONGS (SHIPBUILDERS) LTD.
Double reduction geared turbines, Pametrada design, 30,000 s.h.p. (maximum)
Twin screw
Service speed 21 knots
Length overall 650 ft.
Beam 86 ft.
Gross tonnage 27,300
Deadweight tonnage 9,000
Strengthened for navigation in ice
Passengers: First Class 192, Tourist 856. Limited to 750 when cruising.

The First Class accommodation of the *Empress of Canada* is confined mainly to the forward end of the promenade deck and the Empress deck below. Public rooms at these levels comprise the forward lounge (St. Lawrence Club) and a circular lounge called the Mayfair Room. Both of these rooms are flanked on both sides and in front by an enclosed promenade deck with large triple windows. The study on the Empress deck is ideal for quiet occupations such as reading and writing. The dining saloon (Salle Frontenac) is three decks down. All decks, including the lower deck and the swimming pool, are served by lifts.

Tourist Class accommodation occupies the whole of the main deck, the after end of the upper deck and a considerable length of the Empress deck and promenade deck. The Carleton Restaurant is on a level with the Salle Frontenac. Both saloons are served from central kitchens.

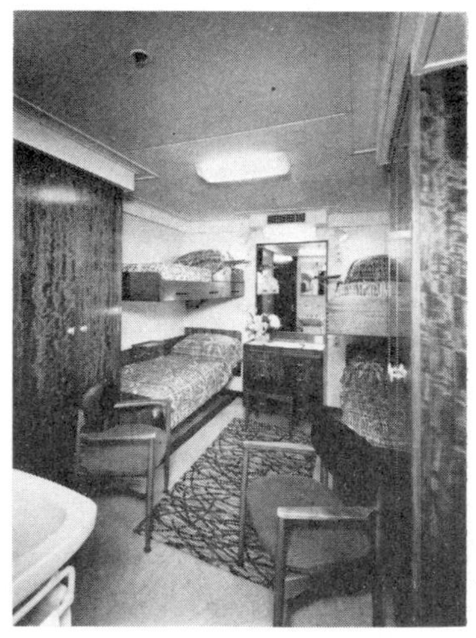

The "Mayfair" room, the principal First Class lounge.
Photo courtesy: Canadian Pacific Steamships Ltd.

The Coral Pool.
Photo courtesy: Canadian Pacific Steamships Ltd.

The Canada Room is a large lounge with a central dancing space and is shared by both First and Tourist Class. The Windsor Lounge is a smaller room exclusively for Tourist Class. At the after end of the Empress deck the Banff Club opens up on to a promenade. Children are catered for in the "Den" on the promenade deck. Glassed-in promenades flank the main public rooms and a large area of open promenade is provided on the promenade deck.

Both the cinema and the swimming pool have common use as have the shop, barber shop and beauty salon.

In the First Class there are four blocks of suite rooms and six verandah suite rooms. Most of the other cabins are single or doubles, all with private baths and lavatories.

Tourist Class cabins are also of a very high standard. Over 70% of them have private facilities and are arranged for two to four people. During the day the upper berths stow away into the bulkheads.

All passenger and crew accommodation is fully air conditioned and this has been extended to the enclosed promenades where, to the maximum extent possible in glazed spaces, a comfortable temperature is maintained.

When cruising the full range of accommodation is available to all passengers, and a pastel blue glass fibre swimming pool is fitted into No. 5 hatchway at the after end of the Empress deck. Four launches, carrying 70 passengers, are embarked and specially built accommodation ladders and landing platforms are provided. The children's room is converted into the Verandah Cafe containing a bar.

Crew accommodation is on the restaurant deck and lower deck in two-, four- and six-berth cabins. A recreation room is provided on the upper deck and a promenade deck (known as an

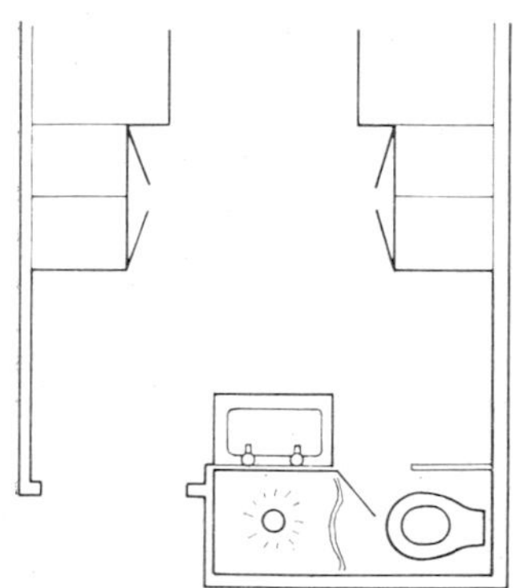

A four-berth Tourist Class cabin on the *Empress of Canada*.
Photo courtesy: Canadian Pacific Steamships Ltd.

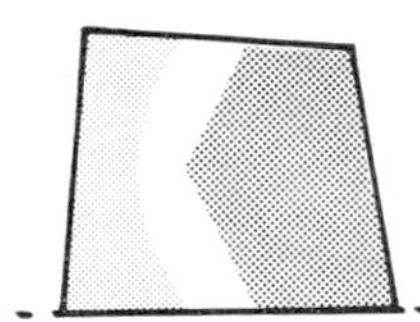

Since the photograph opposite was taken, a new motif has been designed for the funnels of Canadian Pacific ships. The inscription has also been added to the hulls of all this company's ships.

The kitchens which cater for both First and Tourist Class. In many older liners each class had its own kitchens and much unnecessary duplication of equipment resulted.
Photo courtesy: Canadian Pacific Steamships Ltd.

The profile of the *Empress of Canada*. As in most modern ships complete decks are allocated to each class. Air conditioning has also made it possible for more inside cabins to be provided.

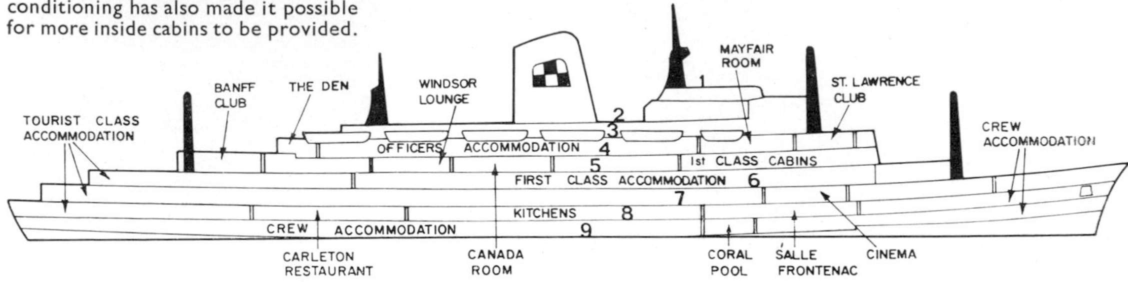

airing space) on the Empress deck forward.

Officers are all accommodated on the sports deck forward and the promenade deck aft. The Captain, Staff Commander, Chief Engineer, Purser and Chief Steward are provided with suites. Other officers have single-berth cabins. Each department has its own wardroom.

In addition to the laundrette service for passengers, a full-scale laundry, capable of handling passengers' requirements as well as the ship's linen, is installed.

A hospital with four general wards, three isolation wards and ancillary rooms meets the full needs of passengers and crew.

The passenger accommodation is fitted with a sprinkler system and the cargo holds have CO_2 fire extinguishing installations. A smoke detecting cabinet is located on the bridge.

There are five cargo holds, four of which are fitted with 'tween decks. Insulated cargo can be carried and Nos. 2 and 5 holds are fitted with permanent grain divisions. All holds are served by trunked hatchways, those for No. 4 hold passing through five decks.

The *Empress of Canada* is employed between June and November on the run from Liverpool to Quebec and Montreal (St. John, N.B., in winter). During the winter she cruises from the U.S.A.

Cruising . . .

It is difficult to say just when cruising became an accepted form of holiday, but in 1891 the Hamburg American Line sent their *Augusta Victoria* on an experimental cruise to the Mediterranean. It was a success and in 1901 the *Prinzessin Victoria Louisa* of the same line was the first ship to be built specifically for cruising. In 1904 the P and O Line converted one of their ageing mail ships—the *Rome*—for cruising purposes. This ship was renamed *Vectis*. The attitude towards cruising in those days was summed up by a writer on the subject who said, "In the winter time cruises set in the direction of the Mediterranean; in the summer the yachtsman becomes bolder and is carried to wilder and more inhospitable climes. The Baltic is not adventurous enough for him; he searches out the recesses of the Norwegian Fjords, and looks on the dreary scenery of the North Cape with the sun shining at midnight."

The First World War interrupted progress, but several ships built after 1920 were designed to undertake cruises in addition to their more usual duties. Several lines, including the Cunard and Canadian Pacific, sent ships cruising each year, and the White Star Liner *Homeric* carried out at least one 11-week luxury cruise each year from New York to the Mediterranean. These cruises and others from New York ceased with the Wall Street crash in 1929, and as the "slump" moved to Europe more and more liners which were running unprofitably on regular runs were sent cruising. It was at this time that cruising became "popular" and £1 per day was the cost of the cheapest cruise. At the other end of the scale a five-months cruise, covering 37,500 miles and going right round the world, cost from 305 guineas. In one fortnight in the summer of 1934, when the *Olympic* arrived at Southampton from New York with about 90 First Class passengers, at least six ships left the former port on cruises to the Mediterranean and the Atlantic Isles. These included the *City of Nagpur*, *Orontes*, *Strathaird* and *Atlantis*. Other cruises also left during the same period from London and Liverpool. By this time, too, the *Atlantis*, *Arandora Star*, *Vandyck*, *Homeric*, *Voltaire*, *Stella Polaris* (built for cruising in 1927 and still in service) and other vessels were permanently cruising. The *Mauretania* carried out a series of cruises as did the *Aquitania*. Others of the world's largest ships involved were the *Belgenland*, *Empress of Britain* and the Italian *Augustus*. This activity carried on

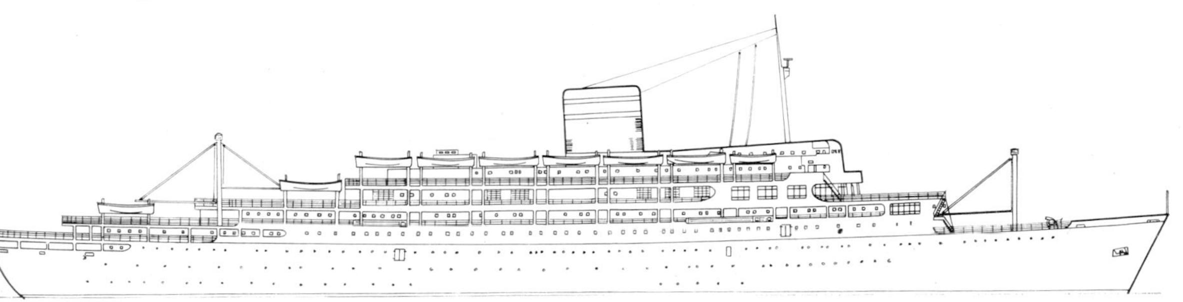

S.S. SANTA MARIA (1953)

Owners: Companhia Colonial de Navegacao
Builders: J. Cockerill-Ougree S.A.
Two D.R. geared turbines
Twin screw
Service speed 20 knots
Length overall 610 ft.
Beam 76 ft.
Gross tonnage 20,906
Deadweight tonnage about 7,600

A Belgian-built passenger liner for Portuguese owners. Accommodation is provided for 156 First Class, 226 Cabin Class and 696 Tourist Class passengers. Much of the superstructure of this vessel is of aluminium alloy.

The *Santa Maria* runs between Lisbon and Vigo and Funchal, Teneriffe, La Guaira, Willemstad and Port Everglades.

This company is the last operating a strictly colonial route. This is between Lisbon and East Africa and the vessels on this service—the *Imperio*, *Patria* and *Infante Dom Henrique*—still regularly carry troops to Portuguese East and West Africa. Another feature of this particular service is the widely spaced territories at which calls are made en route. They are: Funchal (Madeira), Sao Tome (Portuguese Island to the West of Libreville), Luanda, Lobito and Mossamedes (Portuguese West Africa), Cape Town, Lourenco Marques, Beira, Mocambique (Portuguese East Africa).

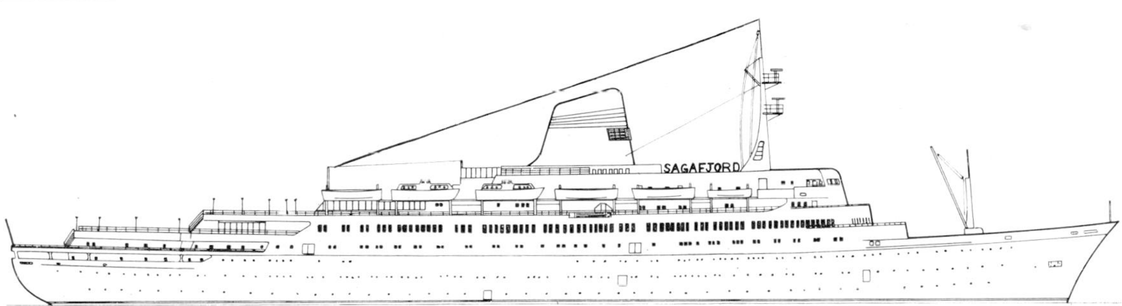

M.S. SAGAFJORD (1965)

Owners: Norwegian America Line
Builders: Societe des Forges et Chantiers de la Méditerranée, La Seyne
Two Sulzer diesels, 24,000 b.h.p.
Twin screw
Service speed 20 knots
Length overall 620 ft.
Beam 82 ft.
Gross tonnage 24,000

The Norwegian America Line operate three medium-sized passenger liers of which the *Sagafjord* is the most recent. This ship has been designed specifically to undertake scheduled North Atlantic sailings and extensive cruise schedules. On regular voyages 800 First and Tourist Class passengers are carried. The cost of passage depends on the type of cabin occupied and with certain exceptions the public rooms are available to both classes. On cruises the passenger list is restricted to 450. Public rooms include a ballroom, clubroom, dining room, rising through two decks, a garden lounge, library and theatre. In addition there are two swimming pools, one indoor, a beauty parlour, barber shop and shopping centre.

The cabins are mainly single and doubles, 90% of them have tub baths with showers; the rest have private showers. 90% of all cabins are outside. The ship is completely air conditioned with individual temperature control in the cabins.

During the summer between May and September, the *Sagafjord* runs with the *Bergensfjord* between Oslo, Copenhagen, Kristiansand, Stavanger, Bergen and New York.

For the rest of the year both vessels are employed on cruises from New York. The 1968/9 programme for the *Sagafjord* included cruises to the West Indies, around South America, 52 days; to 24 ports in the Pacific, including the Galapagos Islands, Papeete, Sydney, Guam, Yokohama, Honolulu and Acapulco, 86 days; and to Northern Europe and the North Cape, 45 days.

The third ship in the fleet—the *Oslofjord*—is permanently employed on cruising from Southampton.

until 1939, but in the meantime a steady procession of liners, some of them no more than 12 years old, went to the shipbreakers.

After 1945, the demand for passages on scheduled sailings left few ships available for cruising, but in 1949 the Cunard *Caronia* was built for relief work on the North Atlantic and luxury cruising out of New York. In 1960 the Royal Mail Line's *Andes* was converted for permanent cruising, and, as the airlines began to eat into shipping revenues, the pattern of the '30s was repeated, but with one difference—economic prosperity gave people the opportunity of spending money on holidays, and cruising prospered. Some owners solved their problems by selling. A Union Castle liner became a full-time cruising liner of the Incres Line. The old P and O liner *Mongolia* was purchased and sent cruising in the Caribbean. As cross-channel steamers became redundant they were bought by Greek and Italian companies, who used them either for cruising or on scheduled holiday services. Even the P. and A. Campbell ship *Empress Queen*, which had been built for South Coast excursion and cross-channel work, was refitted by new owners and placed on service in the Mediterranean and Aegean. A Canadian coastal passenger ship now operates in the same area and a German vessel built for service between the mainland and Heligoland is now cruising out of Vancouver.

Throughout 1968 cruise liners of several nationalities left British ports on a wide variety of cruises, and during the months of July and August departures averaged nearly one a day. In addition, cruises left regularly from Venice and other Mediterranean ports, their passengers having been airlifted from the U.K. and centres on the Continent.

New York is another centre of activity throughout the year, whence ships leave regularly on Caribbean and world cruises. Some cruises now actually start from Nassau and San Juan. The P and O Line operates cruises from Sydney, and the Spanish Ybarra Line runs a series of cruises from Buenos Aires to other South American ports, the Caribbean and the Mediterranean.

The S.S. *France*.
Photo courtesy: French Line

S.S. FRANCE (1961)

Owners: FRENCH LINE (CIE. GENERALE TRANSATLANTIQUE)
Builders: CHANTIER DE L'ATLANTIQUE, PENHOET YARD, ST. NAZAIRE
Four high-pressure steam turbines, 160,000 b.h.p.
Quadruple screws
Service speed 30 knots
Length overall 1,035 ft.
Beam 110 ft.
Gross tonnage 66,300
Passengers: 500 First and 1,500 Tourist on N. Atlantic. 1,250 First Class cruising.
Crew: 1,000

Built at a cost of nearly £30,000,000, the *France*, although continuing the tradition of absolute luxury on the North Atlantic, was also designed to operate as a cruise liner during the winter months. The *France* also reflects the trend which developed in the early '50s, to allocate a far greater area of the ship to Tourist Class, and to do away with Cabin Class, which in many respects was the equivalent of the pre-war Second Class.

The *France* is as perfect as it is possible to make a ship, and she complies with the 1960 international safety standards and the 1966 international fire safety requirements. Non-combustible materials have been used exclusively in her construction and furnishing, and sprinkler systems have been fitted throughout the accommodation.

The design and furnishings of the public rooms and cabins are of the highest standards, and in addition to being the largest ship in the world, she also has the longest promenade deck (341 ft. along each side), the largest area devoted to children (6,181 sq. ft.),

The First Class dining saloon.  *Photo courtesy: French Line*

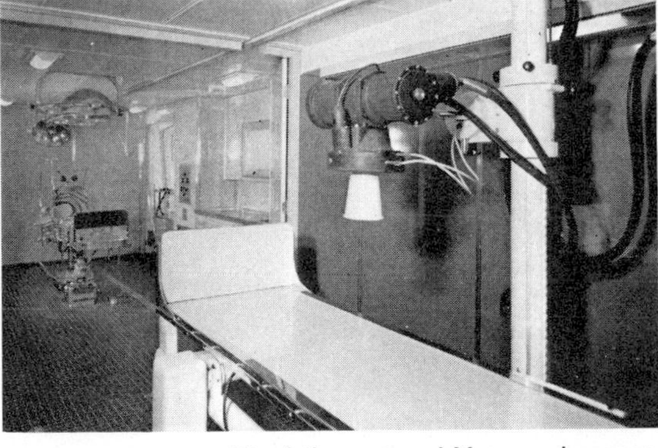

The fully equipped X-ray and operating room. *Photo courtesy: French Line*

wall-to-wall carpeting throughout the accommodation, the greatest numbers of bars in any ship, including the longest in the maritime world (69 ft.) and the largest theatre afloat, with seating for 664.

Passenger accommodation, which is fully air conditioned, is located on nine of the ship's 11 decks. First Class and Tourist Class occupy alternate decks throughout the length of the ship.

First Class accommodation includes a main lounge with a dance floor area of 1,000 sq. ft., a dining room seating over 400 persons, a smoking room with a marble dance floor, a library with 6,000 books in several languages. There is also a card room, terrace, a 33 ft. swimming pool, gymnasium and sports arena.

Tourist Class passengers have almost identical public rooms, and the main lounge is the largest room in the ship with an area of nearly 12,000 sq. ft. The dining room seats 828 and 100 children can be served in their own room.

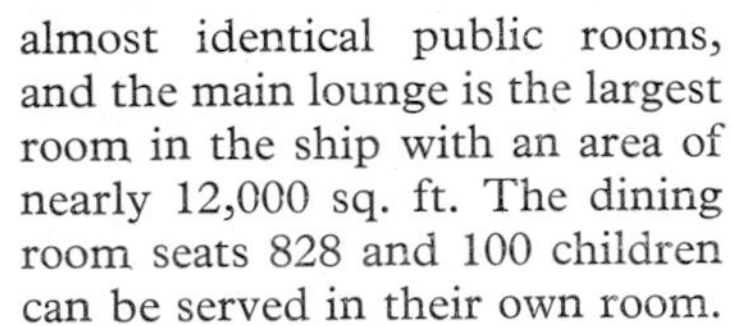

Communal facilities include the chapel, the theatre and the hospital, which has full X-ray and operating equipment. Cardiograph readings can be sent to Europe or the U.S. via Belino apparatus or Early Bird satellite.

Kennels have been provided for 20 dogs—each kennel has a carpet—and the exercise spaces boast such refinements as Parisian milestones, English lamp posts and New York fire hydrants.

Between May and the beginning of October, the *France* maintains a fortnightly service from Le Havre to Southampton and New York, sailing on a

A two-berth outside cabin on the *France*. *Photo courtesy: French Line*

The First Class smoking room. *Photo courtesy: French Line*

The bedroom of the *Ile de France* suite.

There are several similar suites on board, some of which have separate day rooms and connecting bedrooms.
Photo courtesy: French Line

Friday and arriving on the following Wednesday. The return voyage commences on Thursday and arrives at Le Havre on Tuesday.

Cruising commences in late October, and until the middle of March the *France* undertakes cruises from New York. These last from 6½ to 33 days. From the end of March until the return to N. Atlantic service the *France* carries out a further series of cruises from Cannes. The duration of these cruises varies between 4 and 15½ days.

The success of the *France* is evident from the fact that cruise accommodation has been 95% taken up. An average of 85% take-up has been achieved on N. Atlantic service.

The N. Atlantic service is run in co-operation with the *Queen Elizabeth 2*, each ship taking alternate sailings. The *Q.E.2* now calls at Le Havre instead of Cherbourg and the interests of the Cunard Line in France are looked after by the French Line.

The running of a ship like the *France* is a complex matter and involves a large number of staff ashore as well as afloat. The following items are a few of those carried on board:

Pieces of linen	364,000
Silverware	47,500
Plates	23,700
Glasses	44,000

Stores for one round trip include:

Meat 15 tons, poultry 4 tons, fish 5 tons, eggs 68,000, milk 4,000 quarts, cream 1,000 quarts, fresh fruit 13 tons, vegetables 30 tons. The wine cellar carries: champagne 50,000 bottles, fine wines, whisky, gin, liquuers, table wines beer and mineral waters.

Ashore, a full-time laundry is occupied with soiled linen from the *France* and the French Line's other passenger ships. A large staff is employed negotiating contracts for supplies. French polishers, upholsterers and painters are always available to repair damage to furnishing and decorations, and a small army of cleaners board the ship immediately on arrival at Le Havre and carry out a spring clean from stem to stern.

S.S. *Oriana*.
Photo courtesy: D. W. A. Mercer

S.S. ORIANA (1960)

The *Oriana* was built for the Orient Line by Vickers-Armstrongs (Shipbuilders) Ltd. before the interests of the P & O and Orient Lines were merged. The *Oriana* is a twin screw geared-turbine ship. The engines deliver 65,000 s.b.p. and the service speed of the ship is 27·5 knots. 688 First Class passengers and 1,496 Tourist Class passengers are carried.

Although the P & O Line still maintains its services to Australia throughout the year, the present schedules bear little relation to the pre-war pattern of services, when ships sailed via the Suez Canal to Sydney, returning by the same route. As with most other lines, regular passengers and immigrants are insufficient to keep the ships profitably employed, and great emphasis is now laid on holiday voyages. The routes have been extended to New Zealand and across the Pacific to Canada and the U.S.A. Vessels may sail either by the Cape or the Panama Canal and make a triple crossing of the Pacific or occasionally completely encircle the world before returning to the U.K. The following examples of routes indicate the range of ports now visited by P & O ships.

The other ships of the fleet are employed on similarly varied itineraries. For example, the *Iberia* leaves Southampton on 27th August 1970 and arrives at Sydney, via Capetown, on 2nd October. The ship then cruises until 3rd January 1971, and sails for Southampton, via Port Elizabeth and Dakar, arriving on 6th February.

Cargo liners—now with the new names *Pando Cove*, *Pando Head* and *Pando Strait*—on the Far East route also carry 12 passengers.

S.S. CANBERRA (1961)
The largest liner built in the U.K. until the *Queen Elizabeth 2*, the *Canberra* was built by Harland & Wolff Ltd. for the P & O Line, and has a gross tonnage of 45,270 with a length overall of 818·5 ft. and a beam of 102·4 ft. Turbo-electric machinery driving twin screws produces 68,000 s.h.p. The service speed of the ship is 27·5 knots. Accommodation is provided for 548 First Class and 1,690 Tourist Class passengers.
Photo courtesy: D. W. A. Mercer

S.S. CANBERRA. Voyage schedule for 1970

London	12th January
Southampton	
Rotterdam	
Lisbon	
Casablanca	
Las Palmas	15th January
Dakar	
Freetown	
Cape Town	23rd January
Durban	25th January
Mombasa	
Bombay	
Colombo	
Penang	
Port Swettenham	
Singapore	
Fremantle	3rd February
Adelaide	
Melbourne	6th February
Sydney	8–10th February
Darwin	
Auckland	13th February
Suva	
Pago Pago	
Nuku'alofa	16th February
Hong Kong	
Kobe	
Yokohama	
Honolulu	20th February
Vancouver	25th February
Seattle	
San Francisco	27–28th February
Los Angeles	1st March
San Francisco	
Vancouver	
Honolulu	5th March
Yokohama	12–13th March
Kobe	14–15th March
Nagasaki	17th March
Hong Kong	19–21st March
Manila	
Suva	19–21st March
Nuku'alofa	
Auckland	
Wellington	
Sydney	29th March

Sydney	1st April
Melbourne	2nd April
Darwin	
Auckland	6th April
Suva	
Pago Pago	
Nuku'alofa	9th April
Hong Kong	
Kobe	
Yokohama	
Honolulu	13th April
Vancouver	18th April
Seattle	
San Francisco	20–21st April
Los Angeles	22nd April
Acapulco	25th April
Balboa/Cristobal	28–29th April
Willemstad	
Caracas Bay	
Port of Spain	
Bridgetown	
Kingston	
Nassau	3rd May
Port Everglades	4th May
Hamilton	
Funchal	
Lisbon	11th May
Cherbourg	13th May
Southampton	14th May

Between 24th May and 23rd August, vessel carries out a series of cruises from Southampton.

London	6th September
Southampton	7th September
Rotterdam	
Lisbon	
Casablanca	
Las Palmas	14th September
Dakar	15th September
Freetown	
Cape Town	
Durban	
Mombasa	18th September
Bombay	21st September
Colombo	24th September
Penang	25–26th Sept.
Port Swettenham	28th September
Singapore	3rd October
Fremantle	
Adelaide	
Melbourne	
Sydney	
Darwin	
Auckland	
Suva	
Pago Pago	11th October
Nuku'alofa	
Hong Kong	14th October

Vessel cruising from Australian ports.

Sydney	17th November
Melbourne	18–19th Nov.
Adelaide	
Fremantle	22nd November
Darwin	
Singapore	
Port Swettenham	
Penang	
Colombo	
Durban	29–30th Nov.
Port Elizabeth	
Cape Town	2nd December
Dakar	
Funchal	10th December
Las Palmas	
Teneriffe	
Casablanca	
Gibraltar	
Lisbon	12th December
Le Havre	
Rotterdam	
Southampton	15th December

Followed by Christmas cruise.

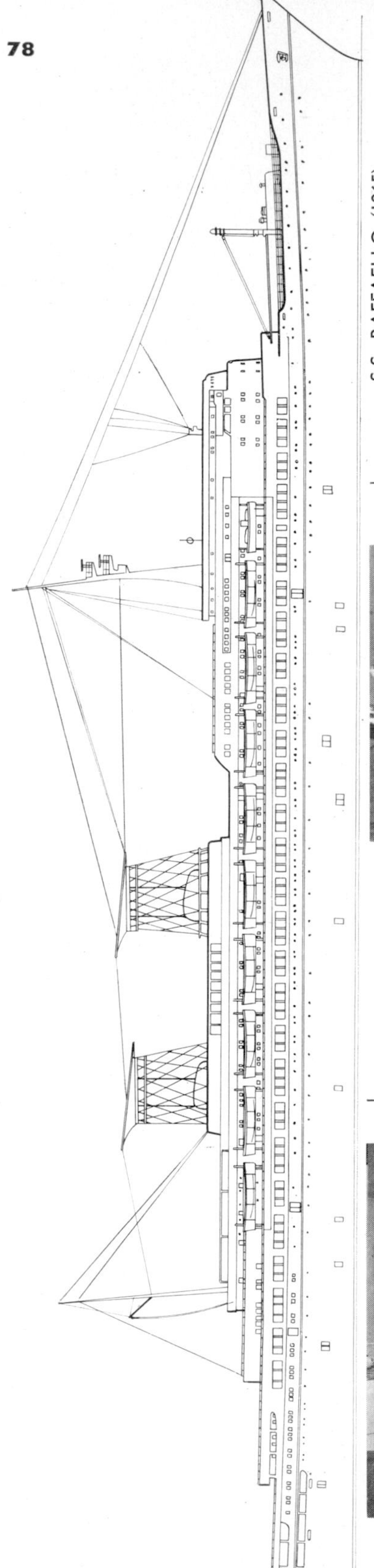

S.S. RAFFAELLO (1965)

Owners: Italia
Steam turbines
Twin screw
Service speed 26·5 knots
Length overall 902 ft.
Beam 102 ft.
Gross tonnage 46,000
Denny Brown stabilisers

The *Raffaello* and her sister ship, the *Michelangelo*, are the two largest Italian liners. Each ship has 30 public rooms and 741 cabins with accommodation for 1,773 passengers. There are three classes, First, Cabin and Tourist, space being allocated in the traditional manner.

The Italia Line passenger fleet is one of the largest in the world and transatlantic services are maintained by four large vessels, the other two being the *Leonardo Da Vinci* (33,340 gross tons) and the *Christofo Colombo* (29,430 gross tons). Three routes are operated between Italy and the U.S.A. At the moment the *Raffaello* runs as follows:

Outwards: Palermo or Genoa, Cannes, Naples, Barcelona, Algeciras, Lisbon, Halifax, New York. (Ports of call vary from time to time.)

Homewards: New York, Lisbon, Algeciras, Naples, Cannes, Genoa. (Ports of call vary from time to time.)

The Russian liner *Alexandr Pushkin* is operated by the Baltic Steamship Company. In winter this ship cruises to the Atlantic Isles and the West coast of Africa. In summer she is employed on a regular service between Europe and Canada.
Photo courtesy: D. W. A. Mercer

A first-class cabin in the S.S. *Santa Magdalena*.
Photo courtesy: Grace Line Inc.

S.S. *Santa Magdalena*.
Photo courtesy: Grace Line Inc.

S.S. SANTA MAGDALENA (1963)

Owners: GRACE LINE INCORPORATED
Builders: BETHLEHEM STEEL COMPANY, SHIPBUILDING DIVISION
Geared turbine, 1,800 s.h.p.
Single screw
Service speed 20 knots
Length overall 547 ft.
Beam 79 ft.
Gross tonnage 14,300
Deadweight tonnage 9,200
Fitted with stabilisers
Fully air conditioned
Passengers: 125
Sister ships: *Santa Mariana, Santa Maria, Santa Mercedes*

The Grace Line service from New York to the West Coast of South America serves four countries, Colombia, Ecuador, Panama and Peru, and the decor of each ship is related to one of these countries. The *Santa Magdalena* is devoted to Colombia and the decorative motifs take the form of murals, carving, ceramics and paintings based on ancient Colombian Indian arts and crafts, landscapes, animals, birds and fishes.

Throughout the passenger accommodation, fireproof and fire-resistant materials have been extensively used. All bulkheads are faced with "Micarta" plastics with a backing of marinite.

Public rooms consist of a dining room with floor to ceiling windows, a main lounge and a second lounge facing aft and overlooking the swimming pool. There is also a children's playroom. Adequate deck space is provided and the observation deck above the bridge is used as an open-air cinema.

There are 49 staterooms, all First Class, and each has a private bathroom. Bulkheads and the facings of beds and built-in furniture are in "Micarta", and the ceilings are soundproofed with acoustic blocks. Three basic colour schemes have been used, bright print curtains and bedspreads contrasting with plain wall surfaces.

The cargo handling gear in the *Santa Magdalena* is unusual. Outward cargoes consist of industrial and consumer goods and refrigerated food. Homeward the principal cargo is bananas, oils, coffee and other agricultural produce.

Most of the outward cargo can be containerised or palletised and provision is made for the stowage of 175 20-ft. containers on or below deck. These are handled by four gantry cranes with a lifting capacity of 20 tons each. Occasionally 40-ft. containers are shipped and these are lifted by two gantries married together and giving a total lifting capacity of 40 tons. Special spreaders can be used to load uncrated vehicles.

With the exception of hold No. 1, all pallet cargo is handled automatically. Access to the holds is through side doors. Under-deck cranes with an outreach of 15 ft. and a working capacity of about six tons lift pallets and cars from the quay. Once on board they are moved automatically to any point in the holds by a system of built-in horizontal conveyors and vertical lifts. Final stowage is by fork lift trucks.

For handling bananas a second similar system is installed. The *Santa Magdalena* has ten tanks for the conveyance of 1,000 tons of bulk liquid cargo.

The route followed by this vessel is: Port Newark, Port au Prince, Kingston, Santo Domingo, Cartagena, Cristobal, Balboa, Buenaventura, Guayaquil, Calloa. Returning via Guayaquil, Buenaventura, Balboa, Cristobal, Port Newark. The service is maintained throughout the year with weekly sailings from Port Newark.

THE QUEEN ELIZABETH 2

Photos courtesy: Cunard Line

1. The *Queen Elizabeth 2.*

5. Grill Room.

3. Theatre Bar.

2. Queen's Room.

4. The Look Out.

S.S. S.A. VAAL (1961)

Owners: South African Marine Corporation Ltd.
Builders: John Brown & Co. (Clydebank) Ltd.
Four geared turbines, 40,000 s.h.p.
Twin screw
Service speed 23 knots
Length overall 762 ft.
Beam 90 ft.
Gross tonnage 32,697

The *S.A. Vaal* was purchased from the Union Castle Line in 1966 when the South African Government decided to set up its own shipping organisation. This vessel's previous name was *Transvaal Castle*. The *Pretoria Castle* was bought at the same time and renamed *S.A. Oranje*. Both vessels sail in the main mail service and take their turn with the Union Castle ships. Clan Line cargo liners were also transferred, and several ships purchased from other lines produced quite a large fleet in a very short time. "Safmarine", as it is called, is now operating vessels built to its own particular requirements, and henceforth an increasing proportion of South African imports and exports will be carried in ships flying the Republic's ensign and carrying the national colours on the funnels.

The *S.A. Vaal* is a one-class ship, the fare depending upon the accommodation occupied. Unlike practically any other of the large liners remaining in regular service, cargo carrying still represents an important feature of the Union Castle and South African Marine Corporation ships. The *S.A. Vaal* can carry about 14,000 tons of cargo and is also equipped to carry wine in bulk.

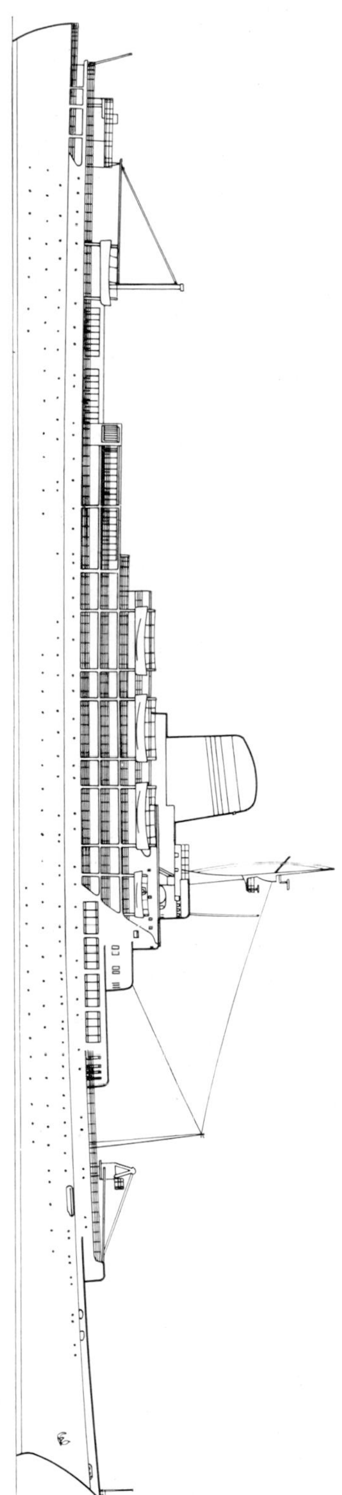

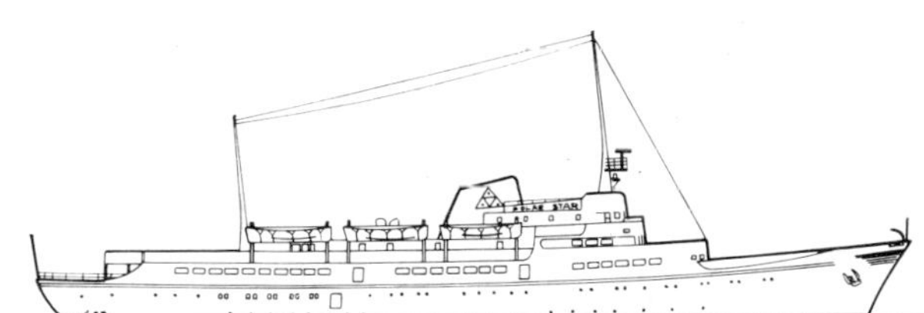

M.S. POLAR STAR (1955)

Owners: Alaska Cruise Lines Ltd.
Builders: Blohm and Voss
Five Maybach diesels driving A.E.G. Electric Motors, 1,200 b.h.p.
Twin screw
Service speed 17 knots

The *Polar Star* was built as the *Wappen Von Hamburg* for the day excursion service between Hamburg, Cuxhaven and Heligoland. The ship was licensed to carry about 1,600 passengers and they had the use of two saloons, one with a dance floor, a lounge, smoke room and verandahs. In 1961, presumably because of a failing public interest in this sort of activity, the *Wappen Van Hamburg* was sold to Nomikos Lines of Piraeus, who refitted her and installed cabin accommodation for about 190 passengers. Renamed *Delos*, this vessel was employed cruising and on scheduled voyages in the Aegean Sea and through the Greek islands. After some years the *Delos* was used as a hospital ship in Vietnam. In 1967 the *Delos* was purchased by the Alaska Cruise Lines Ltd., and received yet a third name—*Polar Star*. The *Polar Star* is now used for regular cruises from Vancouver up the inside passage to Alaska.

Externally the *Polar Star* remains substantially unaltered and is one of the few ships bought by Greek cruise operators not to have been completely changed both internally and externally. This is no doubt because the *Wappen Von Hamburg* was one of the most modern ships to have been purchased for this purpose.

S.S. BREMEN (1938)

The Norddeutscher Lloyd Line's *Bremen* was built in 1938 for the Compagnie-Sud. Atlantique as the *Pasteur*. The war started before she entered service and when she returned to French hands afterwards she was employed on trooping voyages. By 1958 conditions were beginning to deteriorate on the South American passenger services and she was sold to the Norddeutscher Lloyd. Her first real passenger sailing was carried out for this company and she has since been regularly employed between Bremerhaven, Southampton, Cherbourg and New York during the summer season, and cruises during the winter. Accommodation is provided for 216 First Class and 906 Tourist Class passengers. The *Bremen*'s gross tonnage is 32,336 on dimensions of 697 ft. overall and 90 ft. beam.

Photo courtesy: D. W. A. Mercer.

M.S. ANGELINA LAURO

During the past 15 years many passenger liners have been sold by their original owners and refitted for other routes. The United States Line's *America*, four Cunard liners, a C.P.R. liner and others from similarly well known companies are plying waters far from their original haunts.

The *Oranje* of the Nederland Line once ran to the Dutch East Indies. When this colony became independent, passenger business declined and the ship was put on a round-the-world service. In 1966 she was sold to the Lauro Line, refitted at a cost of about £8,000,000 and placed on that company's service to Australia via Genoa, Naples, Messina and the Cape. From the accommodation point of view the *Angelina Lauro* is virtually a new ship, although the outline of the old *Oranje* is still discernible.

The length of this ship has been increased to 672·4 ft.; the beam is 83·6 ft. The three original Sulzer diesels have a total power of 38,000 h.p. and have had a degree of automation fitted. Triple screws drive the ship at about 23 knots which is faster than the speed at which she originally operated. Passenger capacity is over 1,600 in First and Tourist Class.

Photo courtesy: D. W. A. Mercer

The M.S. *Oranje* before conversion.

Photo courtesy: D. W. A. Mercer.

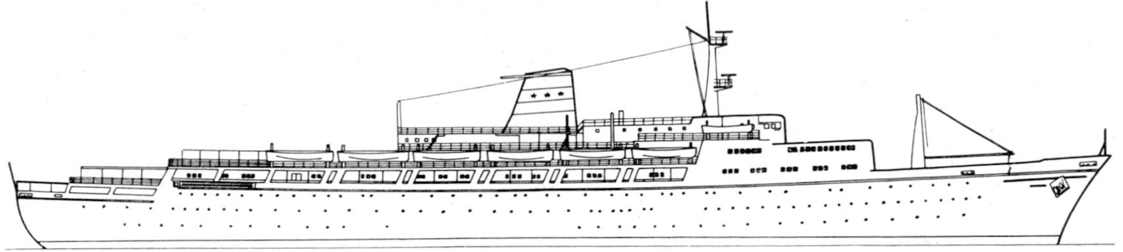

S.S. FLAVIA (1961)
Owners: Cogedar Line
Length overall 558 ft
Beam 70 ft
Gross Tonnage 15,465
Service speed 18 knots

Built in 1961 as the *Media* of the Cunard Line this vessel was sold to the Cogedar Line when the Liverpool–New York passenger service became uneconomic. An extensive refit was carried out in Italy and only the hull—which was altered at bow and stern—and the engines were retained. The *Flavia* is quite unrecognisable as the old *Media* and is one of the most successful of modifications—visually at least—which has been undertaken.

The *Flavia* is a one-class ship with accommodation for 1,224 passengers and 85% of the cabins have private facilities. All of the accommodation is air conditioned and passengers have the use of a wide range of public rooms, screened promenades and two swimming pools. At present the *Flavia* is sailing under Costa Line colours and maintains a twice weekly service between Miami and Nassau.

Photo courtesy: D. W. A. Mercer

M.V. PRINS DER NEDERLANDEN (1957)

Owners: ROYAL NETHERLANDS STEAMSHIP CO. LTD.
Builders: MACHINEFABRIEK EN SCHEEPSWERF, VAN P. SMIT JR., ROTTERDAM
B. & W. diesel, 4,500 b.h.p.
Single screw
Service speed 15 knots
Length overall 432 ft.
Beam 57 ft.
Deadweight tonnage 5,200
Gross tonnage 7,220

The *Prins der Nederlanden* has accommodation for 116 passengers in one class. In addition there are berths for 68 passengers in group accommodation.

With her sister ship the *Oranje Nassau* the *Prins der Nederlanden* is employed in the company's West Indian and Caribbean services. Calls are made at Southampton, Port of Spain, Willemstad (Curaçao), Oranyistad (Aruba), Kingston (Jamaica) and Porta Delgada. The round voyage takes about 28 days.

The S.S. *Atlantis* cruising in the Norwegian fjords.

Holiday Voyages

Holiday voyages date back much further than cruises, for in the 1840's intrepid, and they really were intrepid, tourists began to visit various Eastern Mediterranean ports by travelling on scheduled liner services. As ships became larger and more comfortable so the number of passengers who travelled for pleasure increased. By 1914 passenger lines advertised widely the attractions of holiday voyages and a sea trip had become the doctor's prescription for many ills. Voyages into the Mediterranean and to the Atlantic Isles had become popular, and several companies operating passenger-cargo liners, provided a wide variety of scheduled sailings between ports in the United Kingdom. Accommodation varied from 12 to over 400, for example on ships sailing between London and Leith.

The introduction of Tourist Class following the general fall-off in emigrant trade after the First World War led to an increasing business in holiday travel. Travel agencies co-operated by providing better hotels and facilities at a number of ports, and Alexandria, for instance, received a continuous and increasing number of Europeans who wished to visit Cairo and the Nile Valley. It is an interesting fact that by 1906 Thomas Cook and Son had a fleet of eleven river steamers and several sailing vessels known as Dahabeahs, for private hire

In 1936 a single Tourist Class ticket to Tangier by the Union Castle Line cost about £3 10s.—and party rates and student fares had opened up the possibility of holiday voyages to the States to thousands of people.

After the Second World War, holiday travellers found it difficult to book passages on the principal routes, but the situation eased and once again shipping companies started to advertise the attractions of holiday voyages. In 1955 the *Southern Cross* was built by the Shaw Savill Line and inaugurated a new round-the-world service. The success of this ship led to the construction of the *Northern Star*, and these two ships have been joined by the three Royal Mail Line's ships

The *Fairstar* of the Fairstar Shipping Corporation (a unit of the Sitmar Group) is employed in the company's service between Southampton, Las Palmas, Capetown, Fremantle, Adelaide, Melbourne and Sydney.

The single voyage takes about five weeks and one class accommodation is provided for over 1,900 passengers.

The *Fairstar* was built in 1957 as the Bibby troopship *Oxfordshire*. She was sold to Sitmar when the government decided to carry all troops by air. As the *Oxfordshire* provision was made for 220 First Class, 100 Second Class and 180 Third Class passengers in addition to 1,000 troops.

Photo courtesy: D. W. A. Mercer.

FRITZ HECKERT (1961)

Built by VEB Mathias-Thesen Werft, the *Fritz Heckert* is owned by the Free German Trade Union Movement (F.D.G.B.). She is a one-class ship with air conditioned accommodation for 400 passengers. The *Fritz Heckert* is employed exclusively on cruising, to Baltic and Norwegian ports in summer and to the Mediterranean and Black Sea in winter. She is 459 ft. overall in length with a beam of 57 ft. An unusual combination of free-piston gas turbines and geared diesels of 9,600 b.h.p. give a service speed of 15 knots.

Photo courtesy: D. W. A. Mercer.

The M.S. *Istra* was built in 1964 for the Jadranska Linijska Plovidba. She has a gross tonnage of 5,200, and can accommodate about 270 passengers.

The *Istra* and her sister ship the *Dalmatija* were placed on service between Yugoslavia and Egypt and Israel. After the hostilities between Israel and Egypt both ships were withdrawn. The Dalmatija has since been employed on voyages between Venice, Athens and the Greek islands. The *Istra* has been employed on various charters and in 1969 she commenced a series of cruises from Wilhelmshaven and Norway. This particular charter lasted until the autumn when passengers cruised from Germany to Genoa. En route a call was made at Newhaven, whence the passengers made a short visit to London. A similar call was made at Newhaven in June and it is believed that the *Istra* was the largest ship to have entered that harbour prior to the *Golfito*.

which were withdrawn from the South American Service.

The Union Castle Line, which is, incidentally, one of the few passenger lines never to have sent a mail liner on cruises or to have extended the traditional itinerary to attract holiday voyagers, is nevertheless reputed for the facilities provided. The fine weather route, the 11-day schedule and the tremendous attractions of the South African ports visited, constitute the ideal ingredients for a holiday.

The P & O Line has expanded its operations enormously in the last 15 years and the account of the *Oriana* on page 76 sets out the variety and interest of voyages which are available to the people of at least four nations.

There are now no passenger coastal ships of the sort which used to run between London and Scotland and 12-passenger ships

S.S. PRESIDENT ROOSEVELT (1944)

The *President Roosevelt* was built in 1944 as a standard type troopship. She was refitted by the American President Lines and now with two other similar ships, the *President Wilson* and *President Cleveland*, maintains the luxury passenger service between San Francisco and Manila, with calls at Los Angeles, Honolulu, Yokohama, Keelung and Hong Kong. Occasional calls are also made at Papeete, Pago Pago, Suva, Auckland, Sydney, Port Moresby, Bali and Singapore.

The *President Roosevelt* is a twin screw ship with a service speed of 20 knots. She is propelled by double-reduction geared turbines.

Photo courtesy: Collection of Eric Johnson, New Orleans.

are few and far between. The demise of the excursion steamer has been adequately chronicled and the last stronghold of holiday voyages is centred in Scotland where the ships of the David MacBrayne fleet maintain regular communications with the Western Isles and the Hebrides, and the North of Scotland, Orkney and Shetland Shipping Co. Ltd. still provide attractive holidays by regular service vessels.

M.S. ILLIRIA (1962)

Owned by "Adriatica" Soc. Per Azioni Di Nav., the *Illiria* is a twin screw motor ship with a service speed of 18.75 knots. She runs from Trieste to Yugoslavia, Greece and Crete, calling at Dubrovnik, Katakolon, Nauplion, Delos, Mykonos, Rhodes, Iraklion, Santorini, Piraeus, Itea and Kotor.

Accommodation is provided for 120 First Class passengers and includes a verandah lounge, dining room, sun deck and swimming pool. *Adriatica* organise 11-day holiday cruises in this ship, flying passengers to and from Venice by B.E.A.

Photo courtesy: C. G. Trimboli.

The German Atlantic Line's *Hamburg* entered service in June 1969 when her maiden voyage took her to New York. Originally designed for the North Atlantic Service and cruising, the *Hamburg* will probably be employed mainly in the latter role. With a gross tonnage of 25,000 tons she is the largest liner to be built for several years. All the space in the ship is devoted to passenger requirements (600 cruising, 800 on North Atlantic service) and includes 316 staterooms, two ballrooms, a swimming pool and three restaurants. Other features include several large public rooms, a theatre, beauty parlour, children's playroom and sauna and massage rooms.

The Holland-America Line are planning to build a liner for cruising, but the *Hamburg* may prove to be the last liner built with a view to sailing on regular scheduled services.

Photo courtesy: German Atlantic Line.

S.S. *Carmania*.

Photo courtesy: D. W. A. Mercer.

S.S. CARMANIA (1954)

Owners: CUNARD STEAMSHIP CO. LTD.
Builders: JOHN BROWN & CO. LTD.
Geared turbines, 21,500 b.h.p.
Twin screw
Service speed 20 knots
Length overall 608 ft.
Beam 80 ft.
Gross tonnage 21,637
Deadweight tonnage 9,500
Passengers: restricted one class on cruises.

Built in 1954 as the *Saxonia*, this ship was the first of four similar vessels for the intermediate New York service and the St. Lawrence (Quebec and Montreal) service. As a First and Tourist Class ship the *Saxonia* broke Cunard tradition by having a far greater proportion of tourist passengers than any previous ship.

In 1962 the ship was refitted at a cost of about £2,000,000 to bring her accommodation up to the standards by then expected by the Americans and Canadians, who made up the majority of passengers, and also to adapt the accommodation to the needs of cruising. Side screens were fitted on the after deck and a lido area formed by extending these decks and installing a swimming pool. Lavatories and showers (or baths) were incorporated into the majority of cabins, this in itself being a major task requiring extensive replanning. At the same time all of the accommodation was air conditioned. On recommissioning the ship was renamed *Carmania*.

Following the decision of the Cunard Line to pull out of unremunerative services and reduce the passenger fleet to three ships (*Queen Elizabeth*, *Franconia* and *Carmania*) the *Carmania* was turned over to full time cruising. In this new role she is a one-class ship and the public rooms are more than adequate to meet the needs of the most discerning. These rooms are noted for their comfort and are outstanding examples of skilful use of colour and good design.

Between January and March, 1970, the *Carmania* carries out five West Indian cruises from Nassau. Between May and August there are six cruises from Southampton. Then follows a series of cruises in the Mediterranean based on Palma or Naples. Passengers join and/or leave the ship by air.

The previous *Carmania* was built in 1905 and ran in the Liverpool–Boston–New York service. She was equipped with turbines and the success of these engines in comparison with the quadruple expansion engines installed in her otherwise identical sister, the *Caronia*, led to the adoption of turbines for all subsequent big ships in the fleet.

In 1914 the *Carmania* was converted into an armed merchant cruiser and on September 14th of that year sank the German armed merchant cruiser *Cap Trafalgar* after a bitter two-hour engagement. The *Carmania* herself received 79 direct hits.

In 1932, after six years on the London–New York service and in the middle of the great economic recession, she went to the breaker's yard.

The M.S. *Starward* was built in 1968 by A.G. "Weser" for Kloster's Rederi who operate a regular passenger service between Miami and Nassau. The *Starward*, which is of 13,100 tons, can carry 750 passengers and about 250 cars, trailers and containers at a service speed of 21 knots.

Also in 1968, Freeport Cruise Lines Ltd., of Grand Bahamas, put into service a vessel carrying 1,500 passengers and 150 cars. The *Freeport*, which has a speed of 22 knots and a gross tonnage of 10,488, will be employed on a service between Miami and Freeport.

Another large ship—the *Boheme*—entered service in the same year. This vessel, which is owned by O. Wallennius, is designed to carry 500 passengers and has a gross tonnage of 9,870 tons and a service speed of about 21 knots. The *Boheme* is to carry out cruises of one week's duration from Miami, visiting various Caribbean ports.

The last conventional passenger liner to enter service was the *Hamburg* (23,000 gross tons), of the Deutsche-Atlantic Line, and it would seem that the smaller ship with higher passenger density and the capacity to carry vehicles is the ship of the future. Developed from the ferries which opened up new services in European and Mediterranean waters, they are flexible and able to be employed on a wide variety of routes and between ports which the larger liners cannot use. Many of the ships in service can be described either as car ferries or passenger liners and are a quite logical development of the ships built between 1950 and about 1960.

At the moment the West Indies appears to offer unlimited opportunities to passengers and ferry ship operators. Such was the situation some years ago in the Mediterranean, but recent development has been limited. It will be interesting to see when the U.S.–West Indies trade reaches saturation point. That time is some years ahead, but whatever happens, the modern ships at present working there will have no difficulty in adapting themselves to service in the next part of the world to be developed for holiday travel.

An impression of the M.S. *Starward*

Some Details of Earlier Accomodation

S.S. IVERNIA

The S.S. *Ivernia* was built in 1900 and carried 164 First, 200 Second and 1,600 Third Class passengers.

The plan shows a section of the Third Class accommodation which extended throughout the length of the ship, with the exception of about 30 ft. at the bow and 30 ft. at the stern. There were two types of provision: cabins with up to six bunks for families, and tables and benches along the centre line of the ship, and the open type of berthing illustrated. Bunks were arranged in two tiers, which was better than the arrangements in many other ships where they were in tiers of three.

By the time the *Ivernia* entered service, the carriage of emigrants to the States was a well-controlled business and government regulations laid down not only the amount of space to be allocated to each passenger, but also the amount and type of food which was to be supplied.

Food was served on the mess system from four pantries, having been first carried from the galley two decks up. Sanitary arrangements consisted of three washrooms for men and three for women. There was a total of six baths, about 24 w.c.'s and a similarly restricted number of washbasins.

On the deck above the accommodation, Third Class passengers had their promenade deck (then called the "airing space" in many ships). It was totally enclosed, being in fact the upper 'tween deck, and the major source of air was through two large deck openings. In good weather the emigrants were allowed out on the shelter deck. The accommodation below decks was ventilated by forced air and extractor fans, but in bad weather with people sick, portholes closed and deck openings covered, the conditions must have been unpleasant in the extreme.

Two communal rooms completed the accommodation—a smoking room and a ladies room, both with a seating capacity of about 50.

All of the bunks and cabins were portable and were often dismantled and stowed away on the return voyage to provide additional cargo space.

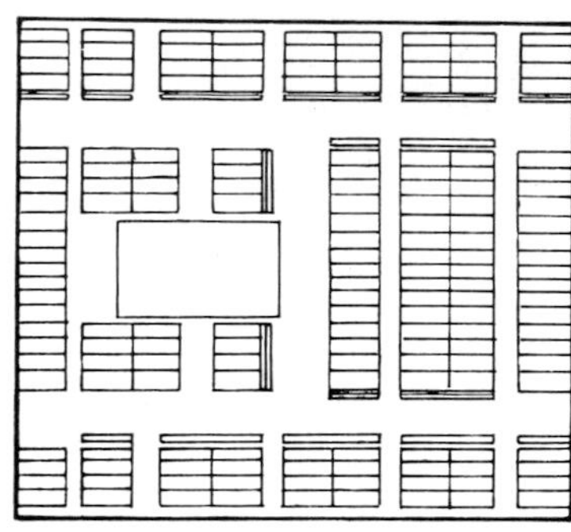

0 6 12 18 24

The S.S. *Tintagel Castle* of 1896. This Union Castle liner provided accommodation very similar to that of the *Tantallon Castle*. When built the *Tintagel Castle* was fitted with square sails on the foremast, jibs and fore and aft sails on the other masts. By this time, however, engines and propeller shafts were performing with amazing reliability and few liners after this period were rigged with yards. Jibs and fore and aft sails continued for some time after, but their value, even in an emergency, was questionable.

First Class passengers in the *Tantallon Castle* of 1894 were accommodated at the after end of the vessel in sailing ship fashion. They were provided with a drawing room, dining saloon—also used as a lounge—and a smoking room which was the exclusive domain of the men.

The smoking room was small and natural lighting was through portholes and a skylight. The decks were planked and partially covered with runners. The dècor faithfully reflected the St. James' club atmosphere, and consisted of heavily-panelled mahogany walls almost to the deckhead. The ceiling was panelled in Georgian style, painted white with gold embossed decorations. The mast, too, was encased in an octagonal shape and panelled to match the walls. Heavy damask curtains framed the portholes and kept out the draught from the single doors. Shelves were provided to hold pots of ferns and other plants. The bench seats were heavily stuffed and covered in leather as were the revolving chairs which were securely fixed to the deck.

The adjacent bar was equipped with adequate shelving and storage space for the wines and spirits which were consumed in no mean quantities. Service was through a hatch to the duty stewards.

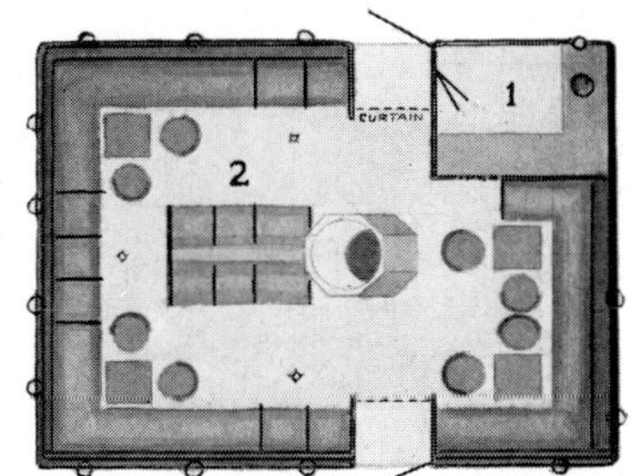

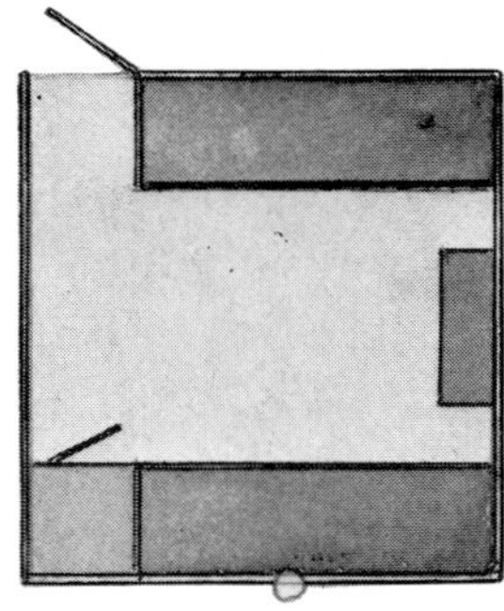

First Class passengers were accommodated in two- or four-berth cabins, and the four berth illustrated is typical. Decks were also planked as were the alleyways, and a runner was laid between the bunks. Additonal furniture consisted of a single wardrobe and drawer space under the lower bunks. Bulkheads were lined with white painted deal boards and the ceiling was also painted white, but not covered in any way. Washing facilities, where provided, consisted of a china wash bowl in a wooden frame which hinged down from a substantially constructed wooden cabinet. Water was supplied in cans by the steward and was disposed of into a metal slop container by raising the bowl into the vertical position.

Such a cabin might have been occupied by four ladies, and bearing in mind the voluminous clothing of the age it is very difficult to imagine how they managed in such a restricted area and with so little storage space.

Emigrant ships to South Africa, Australia and New Zealand were never as large as those to Canada and the United States, and in general the conditions on board were much better. Even in the '80s all Third Class passengers were berthed in cabins and the communal rooms were far superior. The accompanying plans illustrate the Third Class smoke room and music room of the Union Castle liner *Gloucester Castle* built in 1911. This ship was one of the "intermediate" class of liners, which were slower than the mail ships and had a greater cargo capacity.

Accommodation was provided for 75 First, 110 Second and 200 Third Class passengers. In addition to the two rooms illustrated, a dining saloon was also provided.

The decoration of these rooms would have been of the simplest and it is doubtful whether the bulkheads were anything but bare painted steel. The ceilings would certainly not have been panelled. Decks were lino covered. Heating in the winter was by steam. In summer large deckhead fans, probably two in each room, assisted the circulation of air entering through the portholes.

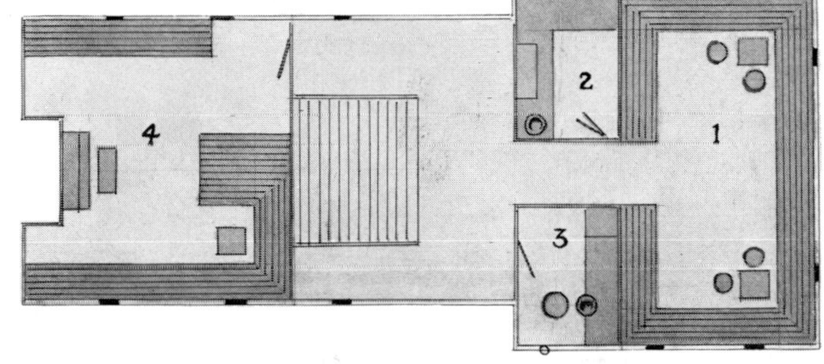

Key to Plan
1. Smoking room.
2. Bar.
3. Barber shop.
4. Music room.

0 5 10

M.S. S.A. VAN DER STEL (1967)

The *S.A. Van Der Stel* was built by Verolme Schpsw. for the South African Marine Corporation Ltd. This vessel is powered by a M.A.N. diesel producing 13,800 b.h.p. and has a service speed of 21 knots. Deadweight tonnage is 12,075 and dimensions are 542 ft. long overall and 75 ft. beam. The *S.A. Van Der Stel* is equipped with two Stulcken derricks, each capable of lifting 125 tons. When used together 250 tons can be lifted. This ship is at present employed on the company's service between South Africa and U.K./Continent.

Photo courtesy: South African Marine Corporation (U.K.) Ltd.

CHAPTER 6

Cargo Liners, Meat and Fruit Ships

CARGO liners provide a regular transport service for a wide range of goods. Outward bound these usually consist of manufactured articles ranging from heavy machinery to pins. Homeward, cargoes can include manufactured goods, such as those imported from Hong Kong and Japan, semi-processed raw materials such as logs and rubber, and a wide variety of basic foodstuffs, of which rice, cocoa beans, coffee and ground nuts are examples. In addition, liquid cargoes are carried and these include latex and other vegetable oils.

It would seem that with such an abundance of products it should not be difficult to ensure that ships always have full cargoes. Unfortunately this is not the case. The problems besetting the cargo liner trades are too complex to deal with in a book of this nature, but the following list gives some indication of the economic and political events which can upset the most carefully worked out schedules and lead to part cargoes and sometimes no cargo at all.

(*a*) The imposition of import quotas. A well-known move for balancing exports and imports. Such action can mean the withdrawal of large blocks of cargo.

(*b*) The industrialisation of countries whose economic structure has hitherto been agricultural. In the short term this can lead to heavier exports. In the long term the effect can be a reduction in trade.

(*c*) Wars and civil disturbances. The recent hostilities between Israel and Egypt caused the re-routing of ships around the Cape. Dislocation of services and an immediate surcharge on cargo rates followed. The civil war in Nigeria also led to a drastic reduction in the tonnage offered for export.

(*d*) Drought, in fact any periods of prolonged abnormal weather, can affect the output of agricultural countries. Plant diseases have had similar effects.

(*e*) Dock labour stoppages leading to immobilisation of ships and the accumulation of vast backlogs of goods. The inability of ships to sail distrupts schedules and homeward cargoes suffer in consequence.

(*f*) Out of date dock facilities and transport systems which cannot efficiently handle the cargoes passing through.

(*g*) The seasonal nature of many of the products carried and the resultant peaks and troughs in the demand for cargo space.

The modern cargo liner probably represents the ultimate of this type of ship. Basically the design has not changed for many years, but each unit of the whole has been improved to such a degree that a cargo liner is now infinitely superior to its counterparts built as recently as ten years ago. It reflects a slow but steady increase in world trade in its increased tonnage and is fitted out with the sophisticated cargo-handling appliances described in Chapter 10. Semi automation and automatic data logging appliances have led to the reduction in the size of engine room staffs. Cargo ventilating systems have been improved out of recognition. Above all the most significant advance has been in speed. The Moore McCormack *Mormacdraco* has completed passages at average speeds in excess of 24 knots, and the Union Castle cargo liner

The flush fitting hatch cover and wing compartment in the *Taupo*. The sills have been removed and a fork lift truck has free access to stow a pallet of general cargo. In earlier ships all cargo is manhandled into wing compartments.
Photo courtesy: New Zealand Shipping Co. Ltd.

Southampton Castle is also required to maintain a similar rate of progress, with something in reserve for emergencies. The new generation of ships, however, have speeds more in the region of 20 knots with the ability to make up delays on passage.

All this is required to get the goods to the destination on time and in good shape—the two factors which more than anything else determine the ability of the cargo liner to stay afloat in one of the world's most competitive trades.

M.S. *River Niger*.
Photo courtesy: Nigerian National Shipping Co. Ltd.

M.S. RIVER NIGER (1968)

Owners: NIGERIAN NATIONAL SHIPPING LINE LTD.
Builders: RHEINSTAHL NORDSEEWERKE G.M.B.H., EMDEN
B. & W. diesel, 7,200 b.h.p.
Single screw
Service speed 16·5 knots
Length overall 447 ft.
Beam 62 ft.

The Nigerian National Line was formed in 1958/9 with a nominal capital of £2,000,000, half of which was subscribed by the Nigerian Government. The second half was subscribed by the Elder Dempster/Palm Line Group, which has also provided advice, services and technical skill.

Two secondhand ships were purchased. Conference admission was gained and Nigerian participation in the carriage of freight was established. After three years of experience the financial interest of the Elder Dempster/Palm Line Group was bought out, and the company became entirely Nigerian-owned.

Additions to the fleet were made and with the acquisition of the four River Class ships the total now stands at 12.

The success of the line is of real value to Nigeria both from the prestige point of view and also the earning of foreign currency and the retention of freight money within the country.

A comprehensive training scheme is in force for sea-going personnel. Three Nigerian officers have passed for Master; 12 for Chief Officer and more than 20 for Second Officer. 80% of the engine room staffs are Nigerian, while new officer cadets train in British schools and technical colleges. Nigerian management trainees are seconded to U.K. offices with the intention of taking over all aspects of the company's activities.

The vessels of the Nigerian National Line do not follow a strict pattern of sailings. Ships from the U.K. load at London or Liverpool and run a fast service to a variety of West African ports. Others call at up to ten ports, having either loaded at a single port in the U.K. or at various North European ports.

The following are two schedules for vessels arriving in Europe to discharge and load:

River Niger			
	arrived	Glasgow	12th October
sailed		Glasgow	19th October
	arrived	Greenock	19th October
sailed		Greenock	22nd October
	arrived	Liverpool (discharge completed 29/10)	23rd October
sailed		Liverpool	? November (delayed by dock strike)
El Kanemi			
	arrived	Dublin	6th October
sailed		Dublin	9th October
	arrived	Belfast (discharge completed 18/10)	10th October
sailed		Belfast (in ballast)	18th October
	arrived	Bremen	21st October
Dry-docked			22nd–29th October
Commenced loading			29th October
sailed		Bremen	31st October
	arrived	Hamburg	1st November
sailed		Hamburg	2nd November
	arrived	Antwerp	4th November
sailed		Antwerp	4th November
	arrived	Rotterdam	5th November
sailed		Rotterdam	6th November
	arrived	Dunkirk	7th November

sailed		Dunkirk	8th November
	arrived	Rouen	9th November
sailed		Rouen	11th November

for Dakar, Monrovia, Abidjan, Takoradi, Tema, Lagos/Apapa and Douala. Arrival in Douala was scheduled for 4th December.

On homeward voyages the company's ships carry a wide variety of industrial and consumer goods. During a voyage from Amsterdam (and other N. European ports), the *River Benue* discharged at several ports, including Lagos. Here the following items were unloaded:

Full-cream unsweetened condensed milk	8,680 cartons
Full-cream sweetened condensed milk	700 cartons
Full-cream unsweetened milk powder	304 cartons
Sterilised milk	17 cartons
Active dry yeast	250 cartons (24 lb. each)
Steel files	12 cases
Agricultural implements	1 case
Posterbooks	2 cartons
Colovinyl tiles	303 cartons
Tile cement (deck cargo)	70 drums
Linoglass	2 cartons
Flamingo irons (Danish product)	2 cases
Personal effects	2 cases
Electric lamp bulbs (Philips, Holland)	29 cartons
Electric "lampware" (Philips, Holland)	84 cartons
Printed matter (Philips, Holland)	1 carton
Aluminium silicate	600 bags
Advertising material	1 case
Electrical fittings	1 case
Paint (deck cargo)	10 drums
Rubber washers	4 bags
Anhydrous ammonia (deck cargo)	50 cylinders
Butanox (deck cargo)	2 containers
Used cars	2
Calcium carbide	250 drums
Synthetic resin	23 drums
Isolating lacquer (deck cargo)	10 drums
Removal goods	3 containers
Canned fish (Danish product)	60 cartons

At previous ports cargo unloaded included: stockfish, beer, medical plaster, used musical organ for mission work, printing ink, wrapping paper, aluminium rods, jute twine, cotton wool, printed fabrics, remnants, bitumen, duplicating ink, wine, butter, gin, port, rayon and cotton cloth, onions, poultry feed, cigars, medicine (patent), preserved vegetables, preserves, olive oil, laboratory instruments, shoe polish, etc.

Outward cargoes consist of timber and agricultural products. The cocoa season extends between November and April, and during that time 250,000 tons are exported from Nigeria. Ghana and Sierra Leone. The Spanish territories and the ex-French territories account for a further 575,000 tons. Other commodities exported from Nigeria include ground nuts 140,000 tons, palm kernels 400,000 tons, palm oil 130–140,000 tons. Cotton lint and cotton seed 45–50,000 tons. Both of these products have a high stowage factor and need a considerable amount of space.

The following are actual examples of export cargoes loaded:

1 *Tema*
72 tons old coins (high copper content) for U.K.
Sapele
30 tons logs, 30 tons sawn timber, 25 tons rubber for Amsterdam, 208 tons logs, 45 tons sawn timber, 190 tons rubber and 200 tons cocoa for London.
Warri
3,400 tons of logs for London, 100 tons of logs for Amsterdam.
Apapa
1,730 tons cocoa, 300 tons cocoacake for Amsterdam.
Freetown
500 tons palm kernels for Amsterdam.

2 *Apapa*
1,800 tons groundnut cake, 50 tons logs, 13 tons sawn timber, 60 tons plywood, 41 tons skins for Belfast. 500 tons groundnut cake, 60 tons logs, 97 tons sawn timber for Dublin.
Abidjan
538 tons sawn timber, 26 tons veneers, 93 tons logs for Belfast. 96 tons logs, 31 tons veneers, 461 tons sawn timber for Dublin.
Takoradi
433 tons cocoa liquor, 190 tons sawn timber, 5 tons cocoa butter for Belfast. 647 tons sawn timber, 17 tons logs, 58 tons plywood, 2 tons sundries for Dublin.
Freetown
300 tons bagged offal for Belfast. 550 tons bagged offal, 3 tons piassava for Dublin.

During the cocoa season, ships of the Nigerian National Shipping Line have visited ports on the South East coast of the U.S.A. West African oil and oilseeds have been carried to Detroit and Chicago, returning to Lagos with bulk cargoes of grain.

M.S. *Clan Grant.*
Photo courtesy: Cayzer, Irvine & Co. Ltd.

M.S. CLAN GRANT (1962)

Owners: THE CLAN LINE STEAMERS LTD.
Builders: GREENOCK DOCKYARD CO. LTD.
Barclay, Curle Sulzer diesel, 7,700 b.h.p.
Service speed 16 knots
Length overall 497 ft.
Beam 63 ft.
Deadweight tonnage 11,780

The *Clan Grant* is one of a series of cargo liners built for service on either the South and East Africa or Ceylon, India and Pakistan runs of the Clan Line. These vessels are equipped to carry a wide variety of general cargo and 16 derricks serve five holds. In addition a heavy lift derrick is fitted at No. 3 hold.

Later vessels in the company's fleet are highly automated and the engine rooms are designed so that one engineer officer and an assistant can maintain watch. A detailed analysis of a voyage by the *Clan Alpine*, built in 1967, follows:

Clan Alpine Voyage (Southbound)

(1) *Ports and time spent loading*

Loading port	*Arrived*		*Sailed*	
Birkenhead	11.55	14th April	00.12	30th April
Discharging ports				
Teneriffe	07.00	4th May	14.30	4th May
Durban	10.11	18th May	13.22	26th May
L. Marques	07.40	27th May	07.00	29th May
Beira	11.35	30th May	06.30	3rd June

(2) *Type of cargo carried*

Cargo consisted in part of unpacked motor cars, C.K.D. motor vehicles, heavy tractors 10–13 tons each, machinery—including lifts of 74 tons, 35 tons, 32 tons, 23 tons and various others ranging up to 20 tons, steel work, steel sheet in coils, soda ash, peat in bales, lubricating oil in drums, sheet glass, whisky, cycles, chemicals, also 100 tons weight various chemicals on deck and general cargo.

(3) *Distance and time to discharge port*

Liverpool–Teneriffe	1,650 miles	4 days
Teneriffe–Durban	5,250 miles	14 days
Durban–L. Marques	304 miles	18 hours
L. Marques–Beira	484 miles	28 hours

Clan Alpine Voyage (Northbound)

This vessel loaded at ports in Portuguese East Africa and the Republic of South Africa for West Coast U.K. She called at Las Palmas for fuel replenishment only. (*continued at top of page*)

M.S. GLENFALLOCH (1963)

Owners: GLEN LINE LTD.
Builders: FAIRFIELD SHIPBUILDING & ENGINEERING CO. LTD.
9-cylinder Sulzer diesels, 18,000 s.h.p. 21,000 s.h.p. on full output.
Single screw
Service speed 20 knots
Length overall 544 ft.
Beam 74 ft. 6 in.
Deadweight tonnage 13,000

The *Glenfalloch* is one of four identical sister ships and has an all-welded hull, with part of the superstructure built of aluminium. The bulbous bow was incorporated following tests by the National Physical Laboratory in their experimental tank at Teddington.

The *Glenfalloch* is equipped with 26 derricks with capacities varying between 5 and 15 tons. In addition there is one derrick with a safe working load of 40 tons. There are two 'tween decks which run throughout the cargo spaces. 800,000 cu. ft. of refrigerated space is available and cargoes can be carried in special deep-freeze chambers at temperatures down to −15°F. There are also eight tanks with a capacity of 1,682 liquid tons for bulk liquids. The cargo spaces are equipped with Cargocaire equipment which dehumidifies and ventilates. Air can be controlled to suit different types of cargo through 11 separate units. Recorders are located on the bridge where a continuous watch can be kept and adjustments made to take account of the outside atmosphere.

Contrary to general belief, ships travelling to the Far East encounter a wide range of temperatures, varying from the extreme heat of the Red Sea in summer to the bitter cold of North China and North Japan in the winter. The air conditioning of the passenger and crew accommodation is therefore very comprehensive and a comfortable

(1) *Ports and time spent loading/discharging*

	Arrived		Sailed	
Loading ports				
Beira	11.35	30th May	06.30	3rd June
L. Marques	15.00	4th June	07.45	8th June
Durban	08.05	9th June	17.54	14th June
East London	16.00	15th June	12.00	16th June
Port Elizabeth	00.30	17th June	20.12	18th June
Cape Town	00.10	20th June	07.05	22nd June
Bunkering port				
Las Palmas	19.30	3rd July	02.05	4th July
Discharge ports				
Belfast	19.55	8th July	20.50	10th July
Liverpool	10.01	11th July	17.50	19th July
Ellesmere Port	22.30	19th July	12.00	24th July
Manchester	20.55	24th July	07.35	5th August (entered dry-dock)

(2) *Type of cargo carried*

Cargo comprised mainly of copper, wood pulp and canned goods, together with smaller quantities of tobacco, asbestos, cotton, ferro manganese, hardboard, maize starch, bark extract, zinc, mica, aluminium, granite, tea, pollards and sundry items of general cargo.

(3) *Distance and time between ports*

Beira–L. Marques	484 miles	32½ hours
L. Marques–Durban	304 miles	1 day
Durban–East London	290 miles	22 hours
East London–Port Elizabeth	140 miles	12 hours
Port Elizabeth–Cape Town	435 miles	28 hours
Cape Town–Las Palmas	4,475 miles	11½ days
Las Palmas–Belfast	1,674 miles	4½ days
Belfast–Liverpool	150 miles	13 hours
Liverpool–Ellesmere Port	14 miles	5 hours
Ellesmere Port–Manchester	36 miles	9 hours

---

temperature can be maintained under any conditions. The crew numbers 70 officers and men, and 12 passengers can be carried in very comfortable accommodation.

The Glen Line runs three separate services to the Far East, each sailing once a month and giving a service about once a fortnight to the principal ports.

The three services call at the following ports:

'A'—Hull, Middlesbrough, Hamburg, London to Singapore, Port Swettenham, Hong Kong, Yokohama, Nagoya and Kobe.

'B'—Hamburg, Rotterdam, London to Singapore, Port Swettenham, Penang, Bangkok, Tsingtao, Hsinkang.

'C'—*Glenfalloch*, *Glenlyon*, *Glenogle* and *Flintshire* of the associated Shire Line:

M.S. Glenfalloch.
Photo courtesy: Glen Line Ltd.

Manila: dep. 28 Oct.
Shanghai: arr. 1 Nov., dep. 4 Nov.
Yokohama: arr. 7 Nov., dep. 11 Nov.
Shimizu: arr./dep. 12 Nov.
Nagoya: arr./dep. 13 Nov.
Kobe: dep. 15 Nov.
Hong Kong: arr. 19 Nov., dep. 22 Nov.
Singapore: dep. 28 Nov.
Port Swettenham: dep. 1 Dec.
Penang: dep. 2 Dec.
London: arr. Dec. 25
Hamburg: arr. 7 Jan., dep. 8 Jan.
Rotterdam: arr. 10 Jan., dep. 11 Jan.
Antwerp: arr. 12 Jan., dep. 13 Jan.
London: arr. 14 Jan., dep. 23 Jan.
Singapore: arr. 16 Feb.
Hong Kong: arr. 22 Feb.
Manila: arr. 26 Feb.
Yokohama: arr. 7 Mar.
Kobe: arr. 11 Mar.
Shanghai: arr. 1 Mar.

Cargoes carried on the three services are as follows:

Japan—Homeward

Motor cars, motor cycles, optical goods, cameras, canned food, textiles, timber, radios, electrical accessories, toys, frozen foods, salmon, hardware, fancy goods, etc.

Hong Kong—Homeward

Textiles, made-up garments, toys, electrical goods, foodstuffs, hardware, etc.

Singapore—Homeward

Rubber, canned pineapple timber, latex, bulk vegetable oils, etc.

Japan—Outwards
Machine parts, motor cars, car spares, books, paper, essences, lubricating oil, agricultural machinery, etc.
Hong Kong—Outwards
Whisky, electrical equipment, Horlicks, cosmetics, engine parts, footwear, clothing, plastics, woollen garments, beer, etc.
Singapore—Outwards
Quick-frozen foods, bacon, butter, medicines, auto rolls, cars, scrap metal axles, Nescafé, chill rooms, frozen products, etc.

M.S. *Hammonia*.
Photo courtesy: D. W. A. Mercer.

M.S. HAMMONIA (1965)

Owners: HAMBURG-AMERICA LINE
Builders: BLOHM & VOSS
9-cylinder diesel, 18,900 b.h.p.
Single screw
Service speed 21 knots
Length overall 539 ft.
Beam 73 ft.
Deadweight tonnage 12,644
12 passengers

The M.S. *Hammonia* is one of five identical sister ships built for the Far East trade, and competes with ships of the P & O Line, Ben Line, Blue Funnel and Glen Line.

This ship can carry mixed, bulk and refrigerated cargoes and there are also tanks for the conveyance of chemicals, latex and edible oils. Cargo is handled by 23 derricks with a safe working load of up to 10 tons and a Stulcken derrick with a capacity of 80 tons.

Hamburg–America services to the Far East are conducted jointly with the North German Lloyd. Sailings are frequent and ports of call on the outward run are as follows:

Hamburg, Bremerhaven, Antwerp, Rotterdam, George Town (Penang), Port Swettenham Singapore, Manila, Hong Kong Keelung, Pusan, Kobe and Yokohama.

Similar calls are made on the return voyage, but in both cases they can vary according to cargo requirements. When the Suez Canal is open calls are also made at Colombo, Djibouti and Port Said.

The *Hammonia* upon entering service became the 55th ship in the fleet. The Hamburg–America Line also runs services to the coasts of North America, Mexico, the West coasts of Central and South America as well as to Indonesia and Australia. The maintenance of this extensive pattern of cargo liner services requires the co-operation of almost 400 freight and passenger agencies in five continents.

The wheelhouse of the *Shahristan*.
Photo courtesy: Frank C. Strick & Co. Ltd.

M.S. SHAHRISTAN (1965)

Owners: FRANK C. STRICK & CO. LTD.
Builders: J. READHEAD & SONS LTD.
6-cylinder Doxford diesel 10,000 b.h.p.
Single screw
Service speed 19·5 knots
Length overall 503 ft.
Beam 67·5 ft.
Deadweight tonnage 12,100

The *Shahristan* has two sister ships, the *Registan* and *Serbistan*. These ships can carry all types of general and bulk cargo and edible oils. The main engine can be controlled from the bridge or from an insulated control room in the engine room. Cargo gear on the *Shahristan* (the others have different equipment) consists of a 180-ton Stulcken derrick, two 7-ton cranes, three 3-ton cranes and four 10-ton derricks. Flush hatch covers are fitted in the 'tween decks to permit the use of fork lift trucks. The accommodation is fully air conditioned and all open deck spaces on the bridge and in way of the accommodation are covered with permanent awnings to provide relief from the extreme heat of the Persian Gulf and the Red Sea.

Strick Line vessels load at a combination of two or three ports out of Grangemouth, Glasgow, Middlesbrough, Liverpool, Manchester, Cardiff, London and Antwerp. Discharge ports are between Muscat and Basrah and include a varied number of the following:

Muscat, Mina Al Fahal, Bandar Abbas, Ras El Khaimah, Sharjah, Dubai, Abu Dhabi, Jebel

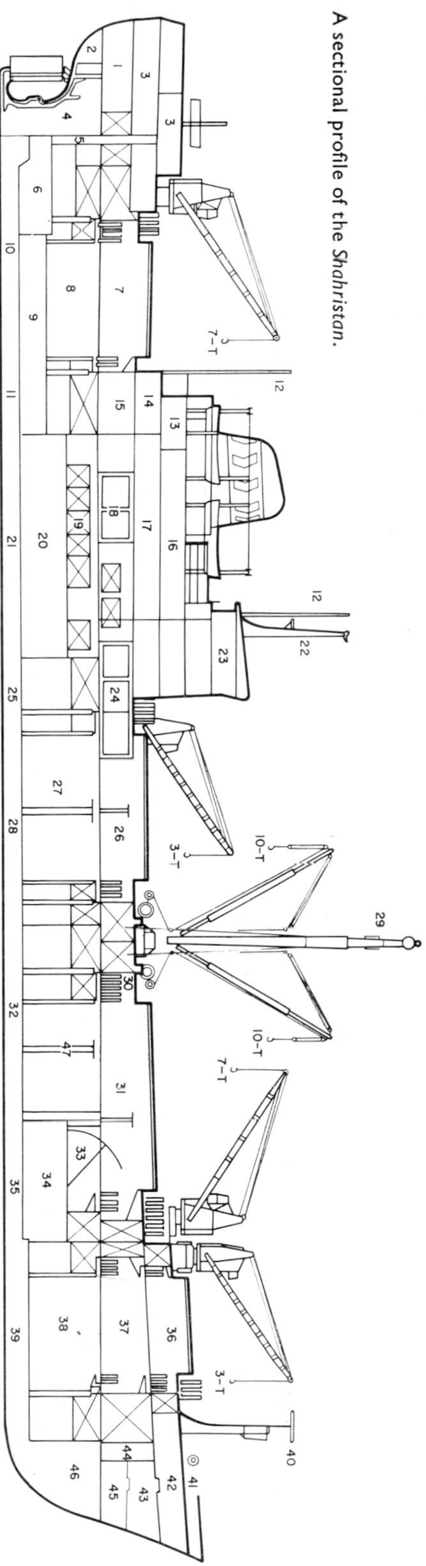

A sectional profile of the *Shahristan.*

1. Steering Gear Compartment
2. Store
3. Crew Accommodation
4. Aft Peak WB Tank
5. Tunnel Escape
6. Tunnel Recess
7. No. 5 'Tweendecks
8. No. 5 Hold
9. Shaft Tunnel
10. No. 9 DB Tank OF/WB
11. No. 8 DB Tank OF/WB
12. Aerial Mast
13. Lounge
14. Galley
15. Dry Stores
16. Officers' Accommodation
17. Accommodation
18. Domestic Refrigeration
19. Oil Storage Tanks
20. Machinery Space
21. Feed water, Lub. Oil, Domestic Fresh Water Tanks
22. Signal Mast
23. Chart Room and Wheelhouse
24. Cargo Refrigeration Rooms
25. No 5 DB Tan OP/WB
26. No. 4 'Tweendecks
27. No. 4 Hold
28. No. 4 DB Tank OP/WB
29. 180-ton Derrick
30. Winch Motor Room
31. No. 2 and 3 'Tweendecks
32. No. 3 DB Tank OF/WB
33. No. 2 Lower 'Tweendecks
34. No. 2 Hold or Deep Tank. Cargo or WB
35. No. 2 DB Tank WB
36. Forecastle 'Tweendecks
37. Forecastle Lower 'Tween decks
38. No. 1 Hold
39. No. 1 DB Tank WB
40. Radar
41. Electric Windlass
42. Store
43. Upper Fore Peak Store
44. Chain Locker
45. Lower Fore Peak Store
46. Fore Peak Tank F.W.
47. No. 3 Hold

Dhanna, Das Island, Doha/ Umm Said, Bahrain, Damman, Ras Tanura, Bushire, Kharg Island, Ras El Khafji, Khor El Mufatta, Khor El Ami, Mina Al Ahmadi, Kuwait, Ganoweh, Aban, Bandar Sharpour, Khorramshahr and Basrah.

The services are operated in conjunction with Ellerman Lines. No hard and fast schedules are maintained, instead a pattern of five sailings eastbound each month is planned to meet the varied needs of exporters. Time in port is entirely dependent on the amount of cargo to be handled.

During the closure of the Suez Canal, steaming distance per round voyage is 22,200 miles, taking about 150 days. When operating via Suez, a round voyage takes about 120 days.

Cargo Eastbound

Mixed general, including foodstuffs, consumer goods, oil company equipment, pipeline construction gear, commercial vehicles and cars, tugs and launches (deck cargo), all types of machinery and chemicals.

Cargo Westbound

Mainly homogenous, such as full cargoes of maize, oats, wheat, sugar and ores from various sources in the Indian Ocean and African scaboard.

M.S. *Shahristan.*
Photo courtesy: Frank C. Strick & Co. Ltd.

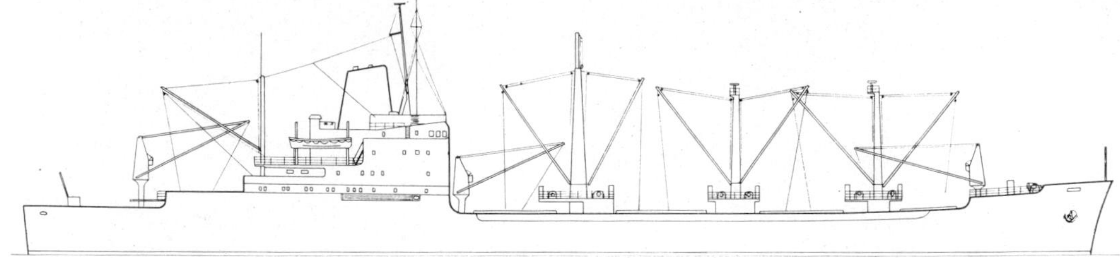

M.S. FRIESENSTEIN (1968)
Owners: Norddeutscher Lloyd
Builders: Lubecker Flenderwerke
M.A.N. diesel, 18,400 b.h.p.
Single screw
Service speed 21½ knots
Length overall 530 ft.
Beam 74 ft.
Deadweight tonnage (open/closed) 9,768/12,787.

Cargo liner built for express service between North Continental ports–Taiwan, Japan and Korea. Triple hatches (aft of 80-ton Stulcken derrick). Extensive tank accommodation for oils and other liquid cargoes. Twelve passengers carried.

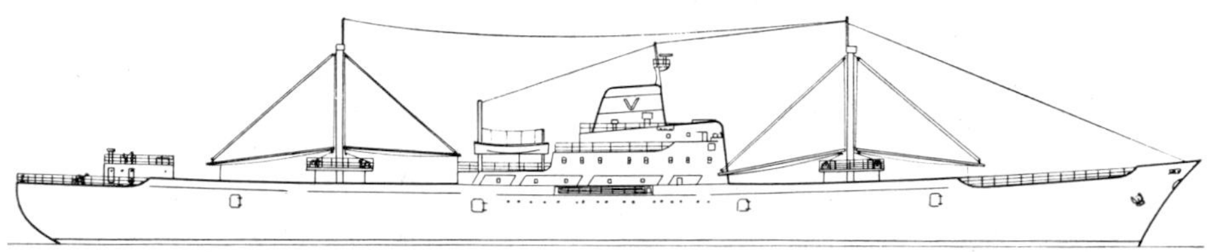

M.S. ONDINE (1960)
Owners: Caribbean-Atlantic Cargo Inc., Panama
Builders: Chantiers Navals des Flandres, Bruges
M.A.N. diesel, 7,200 b.h.p.
Single screw
Service speed 19 knots
Length overall 456 ft.
Beam 55 ft.
Deadweight tonnage 4,433

This vessel is an example of tramp fruitships built in the early '60s. Not so large as some more modern vessels, the limited dimensions allow the ship to operate between a wide range of ports. At the moment the *Ondine* is on long-term charter to the Standard Fruit Steamship Co. of New Orleans, and works between the West Indies, Central America and U.S. East Coast ports.

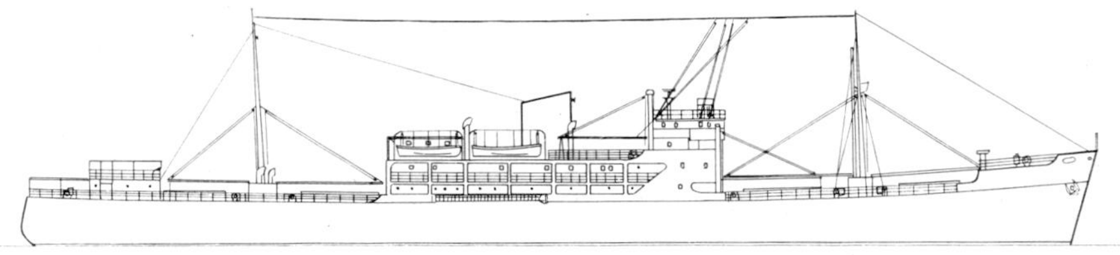

M.S. EBRO (1952)
Owners: Royal Mail Lines Ltd.
Builders: Harland and Wolff
B. & W. diesel, 4,500 b.h.p.
Single screw
Service speed 14 knots
Length overall 427·5 ft.
Beam 58·5 ft.
Deadweight tonnage 8,101
Sister ship *Essequibo*

The *Ebro* was built for the Royal Mail Line service between London, Bermuda and the West Indies. Although smaller than many cargo liners she is typical of many vessels trading to the West Indies, where ports can accept ships of only limited size. Accommodation is provided for 12 passengers.

The Royal Mail Line now forms part of the Furness Group and the *Ebro* will be placed on service as required, probably on the Bermuda, Bahamas and West Indies run or to Colombia, Cristobal, Central America and Mexico.

Outward cargoes may include industrial machinery, agricultural implements, electrical goods, fertilisers, paper, detergents, etc.

Homeward Furness Group ships bring cotton, coffee, lumber, cottonseed, sugar, rum, phosphates and sulphur.

S.S. DEL RIO

The *Del Rio* was built in 1961 by the Avondale Shipyards Incorporated for the Delta Line of New Orleans. She has an overall length of 516 ft. and a beam of 70·25 ft. and a deadweight tonnage of 10,930.

At the time of her building the *Del Rio* was a revolutionary ship, being one of the first to be equipped with triple hatches on the weather deck. This arrangement permits up to 90% of the cargo to be stowed without lateral manual operations. The *Del Rio* was also fitted with one of the first Stulcken derricks which, at the time, looked heavy and ungainly. The developments which have occurred, however, in this type of derrick can be judged by comparing this photo with those of the *Hammonia* (page 96) and *Uhenfels* (page 142).

The *Del Rio* has a speed of 18 knots and is propelled by two geared Westinghouse turbines with a combined output of 10,600 s.h.p.

Photo courtesy: Collection of Eric Johnson, New Orleans

M.S. *France Maru* from Shipbuilding & Marine Engineering in Japan.

M.S. FRANCE MARU (1967)

Owners: KAWASAKI KISEN KAISHA LTD.
Builders: KAWASAKI DOCKYARD CO. LTD.
M.A.N. diesel, 13,200 b.h.p.
Single screw
Service speed 19·8 knots
Length overall 550 ft. (approx.)
Beam 74 ft. (approx.)
Deadweight tonnage 14,196

The *France Maru* is built to carry general cargo and refrigerated cargo. In addition the design is such to allow the loading of standard ISO containers. Side ports are provided at both sides of the second deck and fork lift trucks can transfer cargo on the flaps of the doors which lower to the horizontal position. The *France Maru* has an extensively automated engine room.

The Ellerman Hall cargo liner S.S. *City of Pekin* of 1921. The vessel was one of a large fleet of similar ships all propelled by turbines. The majority of tramp steamers were driven by steam reciprocating engines, but by the late '30s the diesel was being eased extensively in all classes of cargo ships and tankers.

M.S. *Straat Holland*.

M.S. STRAAT HOLLAND (1967)

Owners: ROYAL INTEROCEAN LINES
Builders: NIPPON KOKAN KABUSHIKI KAISHA
B. & W. diesel, 13,500 b.h.p.
Single screw
Service speed 20 knots
Length overall 530 ft. (approx.)
Beam 71 ft. (approx.)
Deadweight tonnage 12,500

The *Straat Holland* is the first of four sister ships delivered by this yard. In addition to general cargo this vessel can carry refrigerated cargo, liquid products and, unusually, iron ore. No. 1 lower hold is also specially equipped for the stowage of ferro-silicon.

The hatches to No. 4 hold are triple and palletised cargo or containers can be loaded directly into the position of stowage. Six cranes and six derricks with capacities ranging from 2–10 tons are provided.

The main engines are controlled from a control room at 'tween deck level and extensive use is made of automatic gear for both data logging and control of the main and auxiliary engines and the refrigeration machinery.

The *Straat Holland* is equipped with a new anti-rolling system developed by NKK, utilising wing tanks fitted across the width of the ship's beam. A central water flow valve regulates gravity transfer of water between the tanks to counteract rolling. This particular system requires no power to move the water and is in continual operation even when the ship is in harbour.

Royal Interocean Lines maintain a wide network of cargo liner services including (*a*) Australia, Japan, Hong Kong, Australia (passenger). (*b*) India, Ceylon, Malaysia to E. and S. Australia. (*c*) China (Shanghai) to Japan and S. and W. Africa. (*d*) Japan, Hong Kong, Singapore, Malaysia, South Africa (Durban and Cape Town) and South America (Rio de Janeiro, Santos, Montevideo and Buenos Aires).

M.S. *Athenian*.
Photo courtesy: A. G. Ingram Ltd.

M.S. ATHENIAN (1966)

Owners: ELLERMAN AND PAPAYANNI LINE
Builders: H. ROBB & CO. LTD., LEITH.
6-cylinder Mirrlees-National diesel, 2,580 b.h.p.
Single screw
Service speed 13 knots
Length overall 308 ft.
Beam 45·66 ft.
Deadweight tonnage: 2,300 as open shelter decker, 3,900 as closed shelter decker

The *Athenian* is primarily designed to carry general and palletised cargo, but one of her features is that she is readily adaptable as an all-container ship, including a number of refrigerated cargo containers. Facilities for accelerated cargo handling include clear holds with extra-large hatches (62 ft. 10 in. × 24 ft.; 62 ft. 10 in. × 34 ft. 6 in.). The hatch covers on the upper deck are of the latest single-pull type, and those on the second deck flush steel-hingeing, hydraulically-operated, and strengthened to take 4-ton fork lift trucks. There are also extended tonnage openings to enable fork lift trucks to be driven the full length of the 'tween decks. Cargo is handled by three electro-hydraulic 5-ton deck cranes and one 5-ton derrick crane capable of lifting up to 25 tons.

This vessel is also fitted with an extremely comprehensive range of communications and navigational equipment. Officers and crew, other than cadets, are accommodated in single-berth cabins.

The holds and 'tween decks, which are equipped with a CO_2 fire-extinguishing system, have independent mechanical supply and exhaust ventilation at 30 air changes per hour (empty holds) for the carriage of fruit. The Thompson ship derrick/crane is designed for one-man operation and the rig can be quickly changed from 5 to 25 ton working.

Much research has recently been carried out to formulate paints with greater resistance to corrosion, and with, at the same time, a longer life than those which have been more or less standard for many years.

The paint systems for the *Athenian* have been developed by the marine division of the Storry Smithson Group of paint companies and "Storrishield" epoxy resin has been used on underwater surfaces and top sides. Chlorinated rubber paints have been applied to the decks and polyurethane gloss paints used for internal surfaces. In addition, the engine room has been extensively treated with special oil-resistant coatings.

Sincer her maiden voyage in August 1966, the *Athenian* has been regularly employed on service to the Mediterranean.

A recent round voyage to Malta, Cyprus and Israel occupied 39 days, the itinerary being as follows:

Sailed London 4th October.
Arrived Malta 11th October.
Sailed Malta 16th October.
Arrived Limassol 19th October.
Sailed Limassol 20th October.
Arrived Famagusta 21st October.
Sailed Famagusta 22nd October.
Arrived Ashdod 23rd October.
Sailed Ashdod 24th October.
Arrived Haifa 25th October.
Sailed Haifa 30th October.
Arrived London 12th November.
Distance run 6,922 miles.

Loaded London for:

Malta. Carpets, timber, paint, confectionery, preserves, cigarettes.

Famagusta. Biscuits, animal feeding stuffs, confectionery, flour, electrical machinery, steelwork, secondhand motor tyres, rusks, tractors.

Haifa. Electric light bulbs, paper, synthetic resin and tractor parts.

Limassol. Empty wine containers, preserves.

Ashod. Electric light bulbs, confectionery, steel pipes, coils of steel strips, plastic sheets and paper.

Loaded Ashdod for:

London. Fruit juices in tins and cartons.

Loaded Haifa for:

London. Fruit juices in tins in refrigerated containers. Fresh citrus fruit and plywood.

S.S. *Chuscal.*
Photo courtesy: Elders & Fyffes Ltd.

S.S. CHUSCAL (1961)

Owners: ELDERS AND FYFFES LTD.
Builders: ALEXANDER STEPHEN & SONS LTD.
Pametrada design turbines
Single screw
Service speed 18 knots
Length overall 411 ft.
Beam 56·5 ft.
Gross tonnage 6,282

The S.S. *Chuscal* is one of four similar ships designed for the carriage of bananas between the West Indies and the United Kingdom. Bananas, one stem to a cardboard carton, are stowed in 14 insulated cargo spaces. The cartons are perforated and stowage must ensure that the circulation of air is unimpeded. Fans keep the cargo temperature between 50°F. and 60°F. depending upon the variety of bananas carried, and the range of temperature must be kept within one degree in order to prevent chilling or premature ripening. Constant change of air is required as the bananas, which are warm when loaded, also give out a good deal of heat on passage.

Up to 135,000 cartons of bananas can be carried.

Accommodation is provided for 12 passengers and the passage time is about ten days.

Regular services are maintained throughout the year as bananas are a non-seasonal fruit and full shipments are always available. The company's trade to West Cameroon was terminated in 1961.

Discharging frozen lambs from the M.S. *Tekoa.* A sling of cargo is being lifted from the hatch and it should be noted that carcasses are always laid nose to tail.
Photo courtesy: New Zealand Shipping Co. Ltd.

The M.S. *Mataura*
The "Taupo" Class of ships from which the *Mataura* was developed, were equipped with a full set of Hallen derricks.
Photo courtesy: New Zealand Shipping Co. Ltd.

M.S. MATAURA (1968)

Owners: THE NEW ZEALAND SHIPPING CO. LTD.
Builders: MITSUI SHIPBUILDING AND ENGINEERING CO. LTD.
Mitsui B. & W. diesel, 20,700 b.h.p.
Single screw
Service speed 20 knots
Length overall 540 ft.
Beam 74 ft. 6 in.

The *Mataura* and her sister ship *Manapouri* are much improved versions of the four highly successful *Taupo* Class ships which entered service in 1966/67.

The *Mataura* has five main cargo compartments, four forward of the superstructure and one aft, with twin hatches fitted at Nos. 3 and 4 holds and 'tween decks, providing 624,560 cu. ft. of space, 546,319 cu. ft. of which is for refrigerated cargoes. The minimum overal carriage temperature is 0°F. (—18°C.) and temperatures are automatically controlled to predetermined values and continuously scanned and recorded by automatic data logging.

Externally heated stainless steel lined tanks, with a capacity of 7,283 cu. ft., are provided for the carriage of liquid cargo. Also provided are lock-up spaces, one for general cargo and six for refrigerated cargo.

The *Mataura*'s cargo lifting gear consists of Universal Hallen swinging derricks at Nos. 1, 2, 3 and 4 hatches and 5-ton Asea electric cranes at Nos. 2, 3, 4 and 5 hatches. The derricks at Nos. 2, 3 and 4 hatches are designed to handle lifts up to 25 tons; both derricks and cranes are operated by one man, as against two in earlier ships using union purchase gear.

In the holds, 'tween decks and lockers, where there is no sheer or camber and the hydraulically-operated steel hatch covers fit flush with the decks, double-wheeled fork lift trucks with an all-up weight of 8 tons can be freely operated within each hatch. The installation of portable sills and widened doors to the wing compartments further extends the area of operation of the fork lift trucks.

As a result of continuous work study and the installation of more sophisticated equipment, the *Mataura*'s complement of 43 officers, petty officers and ratings compares with 47 in the *Taupo* Class and 56 in earlier motor ships of similar tonnage.

A number of containers can be carried, if required, on Nos. 2, 3 and 4 weather deck hatches and underdeck on the same hatch square.

On her maiden voyage the *Mataura* loaded in the meat service from the South Island, N.Z., using the all-weather mechanical meat loaders installed at Timaru and Bluff. The cargo, which was loaded in 11½ working days amounted to 5,674 tons of refrigerated cargo and 1,204 tons of general cargo. The total number of items loaded was 383,038 and included in this were 313,631 carcases of lamb. Before the introduction, in January 1968, of the South Island meat service which uses two ports only, the ship would probably have taken more than three weeks to load and might well have loaded at three or more ports.

The following summary of a recent voyage of the M.S. *Hertford* must not be taken as typical since the loading schedules of the ships of both the New Zealand Shipping Co. and the Federal Steam Navigation Co. Ltd. are kept under continual scrutiny and alterations are made dependent upon the time of year and the availability and type of cargo offering:

L = Load D = Discharge
B = Bunkers

NOTES: (1) Loaded 16,500 Tons Wt. and Mt. general cargo in U.K. (full ship). (2) Loaded 6,750 Tons Wt. and Mt. refrigerated and general cargo in N.Z. (nearly full ship).

At Napier and Port Chalmers ship loaded for ½ day and 3 days respectively, concurrently with discharge.

Tons Wt. = Actual weight of cargo.

Tons Mt. = Measurement tons. Measurement tons are used as a basis for calculating freight rates and are applied when the stowage factor is above 40 cu. ft. to one actual ton. Measurement tonnage is not standard and varies from trade to trade.

Hertford Voyage 37—1968

		Arrived	*Sailed*	*Miles*
Swansea	(L)	Voyage comm. 23/4	a.m. 24/4	
Newport	(L)	a.m. 24/4	p.m. 26/4	40
Liverpool	(L)	p.m. 27/4	a.m. 18/5	250
Curaçao	(B)	p.m. 28/5	a.m. 29/5	4,065
Colon		a.m. 31/5	—	693
Balboa		—	p.m. 31/5	50
Auckland	(D)	a.m. 19/6	p.m. 6/7	6,600
Napier	(D & L)	p.m. 7/7	p.m. 10/7	370
Lyttelton	(D)	p.m. 11/7	p.m. 18/7	330
Port Chalmers	(D & L)	a.m. 19/7	a.m. 23/7	177
Timaru	(L)	p.m. 23/7	p.m. 27/7	80
Bluff	(L)	a.m. 28/7	p.m. 3/8	223
Balboa		p.m. 20/8	—	6,763
Colon		—	p.m. 21/8	50
Curaçao	(B)	Noon 23/8	Midnight 23/8	693
London	(D)	p.m. 3/9	a.m. 12/9	4,256
Liverpool	(D)	a.m. 14/9	Complete discharge Voyage ended 1/10	617
				25,257

London to Wellington

Comparative time in days for *Mataura* and earlier slower motorships

	Miles	*At 15·5 knots*	*At 20·0 knots*
London–Curacao	4,256	11·4	8:9
Curaçao (for bunkers)	—	0·5	0:5
Curaçao–Colon	693	1·9	1:4
Panama Canal transit	50	1·0	1:0
Balboa–Wellington	6,585	17·7	13:7
	11,584	32:5	25:5

NOTE: When calculating the time required for a voyage to New Zealand, half a day for bunkering at Curaçao and a whole day (24 hours) for transitting the Panama Canal is allowed. The actual time required depends on traffic conditions. The International Date Line should also be taken into account.

M.S. PORT CHALMERS (1968)

Owners: PORT LINE LTD.
Builders: UPPER CLYDE SHIPBUILDERS LTD., LINTHOUSE DIVISION.
Two Clark-Sulzer diesels, 26,000 b.h.p.
Twin screw
Length overall 612 ft.
Beam 81 ft.
Deadweight tonnage 19,710

The *Port Chalmers* is the largest refrigerated ship in the world, and the deadweight tonnage of 19,710 far outstrips that of any other refrigerated cargo liner afloat or building. The cargo capacity has probably only been topped by few conventional ships. (The Atlantic Transport Line's *Minnewaska,* which was built in 1923 carried just over 19,800 tons. The *Minnesota* of the same line had a deadweight tonnage of about 28,000 and also carried 3,000 passengers).

Cargo is carried in seven main holds, of which five are fully refrigerated. In addition there is extensive tank capacity for the carriage of liquid cargo. The refrigerating equipment holds temperatures between 0°F. to —10°F. Cargo equipment consists of four 10-ton derricks and two 15-ton derricks, all of which are operated by independent topping and slewing winches. There are three 5-ton travelling cranes and one fixed crane of similar capacity. In addition there is a 25-ton Thomson swinging derrick.

In order to stow palletised and unitised cargo most economically,

Stainless steel wine containers and empty port barrels awaiting shipment. Shoreham is now the largest wine importing port in the country and has gained this business mainly at the expense of the Port of London. Bulk shipments are pumped into shore storage tanks for onward conveyance by tanker lorries. Containers are carried on semi-trailers as shown in this illustration.

Mobile shore cranes unloading granulated cork from the *Fauna*. The majority of products unloaded at outports are usually transported by road to London or other central markets.

The M.S. *Port Chalmers*
Photo courtesy: Port Line Ltd.

A refrigerated 'tween deck on the *Port Chalmers*. When cargo is stowed it is usually laid on wooden planks and timber. This is called "dunnage" and a ship uses enormous quantities of it on every voyage. The *Port Chalmers* has experimental aluminium strips which are permanently secured to the deck and should be able to function indefinitely.

Photo courtesy: Shipping World & Shipbuilder.

the ship is without sheer for the greater part of its length. There is no camber and 'tween deck hatches are flush with the deck. All of this type of cargo can be handled by fork lift trucks. The *Port Chalmers* is also designed to carry two tiers of containers on the bridge deck.

Control of the main engine is either from the bridge or from the engine room.

Twelve passengers are carried in single- and double-berth cabins. There is a lounge, smoke room and a dining room which is shared with the ship's officers. Officers also have their own lounge and recreation room.

The Port Line runs services from the U.K. to Australia via the Cape, to New Zealand via Panama and from Canada and the U.S. to New Zealand and Australia via Panama.

M.S. TUGELALAND (1966)

Owners: CLOBUS-REEDEREI G.M.B.H., HAMBURG
Builders: DEUTSCHE WERFT, HAMBURG
M.A.N. diesel, 9,600 b.h.p.
Single screw
Service speed 19 knots
Length overall 511·3 ft.
Beam 30 ft.
Deadweight tonnage 13,400

A fast German cargo liner employed between Germany and South and East Africa.

M.S. *Tugelaland.*
Photo courtesy: D. W. A. Mercer.

M.S. SAMARIA (1965)

Owners: CUNARD STEAMSHIP CO. LTD.
Builders: CAMMELL, LAIRD & CO. LTD.
Sulzer diesel, 9,600 b.h.p.
Single screw
Service speed 17·5 knots
Length overall 457 ft.
Beam 60 ft.
Deadweight tonnage 7,500

The *Samaria* is one of a series of ships built for the various services run by the Cunard Line between the U.K., U.S.A. and Canada. Although somewhat slower than other cargo liners on the Atlantic, schedules have been arranged to avoid dead days in

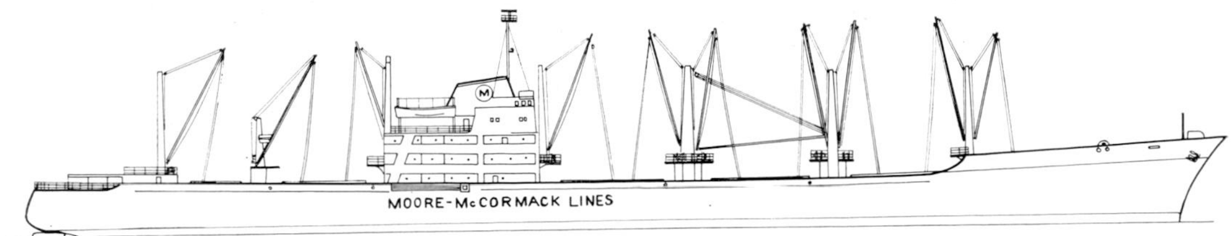

S.S. MORMACVEGA (1964)

Owners: Moore-McCormack Lines Inc.
Builders: Ingalls Ship Building Corporation
Geared turbines, 19,000 s.h.p.
Single screw
Service speed 21 knots
Length overall 550·75 ft.
Beam 75·17 ft.
Deadweight tonnage 12,055

The *Mormacvega* is one of six fast cargo liners built in 1964 and 1965 for the Moore-McCormack Lines. Triple hatches are provided at Nos. 3, 4 and 5 holds and these holds are also fitted with upper and lower 'tween decks. Refrigerated cargo is carried in No. 6 hold and there are deep tanks for liquid cargo in No. 1 hold.

Moore-McCormack Lines operate world-wide services from East and West Coast U.S. ports and Great Lakes ports. Much consideration was given to the cargo handling equipment of these vessels and it was decided that apart from one crane serving No. 5 hatch the use of conventional derricks would provide the fastest and most economical method.

Although the service speed of these ships is quoted as 21 knots they frequently complete passages at average speeds in exceeds of 24 knots.

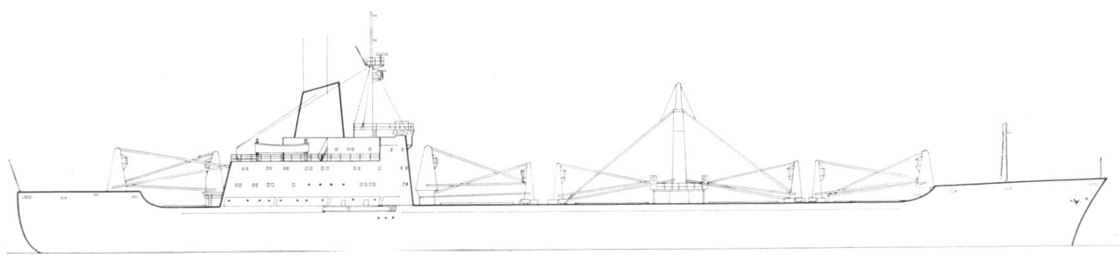

M.S. STRATHARDLE (1967)

Owners: P & O
Builders: Mitsui Shipbuilding and Engineering Co. Ltd.
B. & W. diesel, 20,700 b.h.p.
Single screw
Service speed 21 knots
Length overall 563 ft.
Beam 79 ft. 6 in.
Deadweight tonnage 12,552

The first of three cargo liners built to operate an accelerated service from the U.K. to the Far East. Scheduled sailing time to Singapore is 20 days, to Hong Kong 25 days, and to Yokohama 30 days. The *Strathardle*, which has bridge control of the main engines, can carry a wide variety of general cargoes, including 500 tons of liquid cargo and 27,500 cu. ft. of refrigerated cargo. Twin hatches in three holds enable containers to be stowed and temporary 'tween decks can be erected for the conveyance of cars.

Cargo is handled by eight Hauglund electro-hydraulic cranes, seven of which have a 5-ton capacity, the eighth can lift 15 tons. In addition two Hallen crane derricks with capacities of 30 and 15 tons respectively have been fitted.

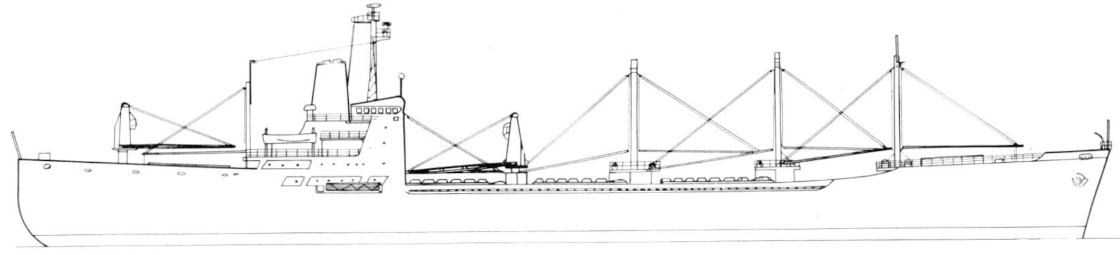

M.S. BREMEN MARU (1966)

Owners: Mitsui O.S.K. Lines
Builders: Mitsui Shipbuilding and Engineering Co. Ltd.
B. & W. diesel, 18,400 b.h.p.
Single screw
Service speed 20 knots
Length overall 537 ft. approx.
Beam 76 ft.
Deadweight tonnage 12,551

In order to meet the increasing competition on the Europe–Far East service, the Mitsui O.S.K. Lines have built four fast cargo liners. In general terms they are very similar to the ships built by Blue Funnel, Ben, and Glen Lines. Service times have been reduced to 28 days from Japan to Europe and 25 days in the reverse direction.

Cargo is handled by cranes and derricks with capacities between 6 and 30 tons.

On trials the *Bremen Maru* achieved a speed of over 24 knots. Such reserves of speed are necessary to make up delays and maintain the very strict sailing schedules.

M.S. Samaria *Photo courtesy: D. W. A. Mercer.*

A remarkable view into No. 3 hold. The hydraulic hatches are open on the right hand side of Nos. 1 and 2 'tween decks and No. 3 'tween deck is visible. There is still one more lower hold which cannot be seen. The whole of the insulated hold is sheathed in aluminium and the battens which protect the insulation from damage can be seen lining the ship's side. Also visible are the ventilation ducts in the folded hatch covers.
Photo courtesy: Shipping World & Shipbuilder.

port, both here and in America. The ship is designed for handling palletised cargo and containers can be carried in limited numbers.

At the moment the *Samaria* operates between Liverpool and New York and six days are spent loading general cargo at Liverpool.

The M.S. *San Joaquin Valley*
Photo courtesy: Johnson Line, Stockholm.

M.S. SAN JOAQUIN VALLEY (1968)

Owners: JOHNSON LINE, STOCKHOLM
Builders: WÄRTSILÄ KON. SANDVIKENS SKEPPS, HELSINGFORS
Two Wärtsilä S.E.M.T. Pielstick diesels, 14,880 s.h.p.
Single screw
Service speed 22 knots
Length overall 505 ft.
Beam 68 ft.
Deadweight tonnage 7,900

The *San Joaquin Valley* is one of the largest vessels afloat able to carry meat, fish or fruit. There are six holds and all except one have twin hatches. Holds 2, 3, 4 and 5 are subdivided into four 'tween decks, whilst Nos. 1 and 6 have two decks each, the remaining space being used for water ballast. Temperature of the holds can be varied between −25°C. and −12°C., and the cooled-air refrigerating system provides the equivalent of 75 changes of air per hour. Air is pumped into the 'tween decks through ducts in the deckhead. Axial fans ensure complete circulation during the vertical passage of the air, whilst air is also exhausted to the atmosphere to clear gasses produced by the cargo.

All refrigerating programmes are computerised and push-button selection automatically controls hold temperatures for different types of cargo.

The engine control room is fitted with data logging equipment which provides extensive information about the performance of the main engines. A separate but similar system is provided for the refrigeration plant.

The *San Joaquin Valley* has a Kamewa adjustable pitch propeller. Control of engine revolutions and propeller pitch is controlled from the bridge, which is also fitted with an engine room alarm system. This is put into operation during the periods—of up to 16 hours—when the engine room is unattended.

Cargo gear comprises a complete outfit of eight cranes.

The *San Joaquin Valley* was first employed on the company's service to the River Plate. At the end of the meat season she was transferred to the North Pacific service. She will carry general cargo outwards and bring home fruit, vegetables and fish.

Loading ports vary but the itinerary usually includes the same North Pacific ports. A typical outward voyage is as follows:

Loading Dates:
Stockholm, 26th–29th Oct.
Finland, 30th Oct.–1st Nov.
Copenhagen, 3rd–4th Nov.
Aarhus, 5th Nov.
Gothenburg, 6th–9th Nov.
Bremen, 11th Nov.
Antwerp, 13th Nov.
London, 14th–15th Nov.

Arrival Dates:
Los Angeles, 4th Dec.
San Francisco, 7th Dec.
Oakland, 8th Dec.
Vancouver, 10th Dec.
Seattle, 13th Dec.
Portland, 16th Dec.

Approximately once a month a ship omits Vancouver, Seattle and Portland and terminates the voyage at Honolulu.

The other North European loading port not called at on this particular voyage is Hamburg.

The total round voyage time is approximately 84 days. The Johnson Line also maintains a co-ordinated fully containerised service on the same route. Six cellular vessels are now in service or being built, and each vessel can carry the equivalent of 672 20 ft. and 40 ft. ISO containers. Earlier cargo liners of the fleet have been refitted to carry a limited number of containers in addition to break bulk cargo. Calls are made at Los Angeles, San Francisco and Vancouver, and the round trip from Sweden via Germany and Tilbury takes approximately 56 days.

M.S. *Good Hope Castle.*
Photo courtesy: Cayzer, Irvine & Co. Ltd.

M.S. GOOD HOPE CASTLE (1966)

Owners: UNION CASTLE MAIL S.S. CO. LTD.
Builders: SWAN HUNTER AND WIGHAM RICHARDSON LTD.
Two Wallsend Sulzer diesels, 34,720 b.h.p.
Twin screw
Service speed 22·5 knots
Length overall 592 ft.
Beam 77 ft.
Deadweight tonnage 11,200

Post-war changes in the pattern of passenger travel led the Union Castle Line to reconsider the need for a weekly passenger ship from Southampton to Capetown and vice versa. With the speeding up of the schedule to 11½ days sailing time between these two ports, it became possible to meet passenger commitments with five liners, although seven ships would be required to maintain the important mail and cargo services. The *Good Hope Castle* and the *Southampton Castle* were built in 1965 to fill the two sailings in a seven-week rota and they are the first purely cargo liners to be employed in this way.

Both vessels have a considerable reserve of speed and they are required to remain in continuous service throughout the year with the exception of a period of two or three days for dry docking. To permit such intensive running the engine room is planned so that repairs and maintenance may be carried out during periods in harbour, and the staff is augmented by mechanics.

The *Good Hope Castle* has extensive refrigerated holds, but because the ports of Southampton, Cape Town, East London and Durban have extensive shore facilities, ship's gear has been limited to seven 15-ton derricks and one 40-ton Hallen derrick.

Steel hatch covers are provided on both the weather and 'tween decks, of which there are three, and a full range of navigational instruments is carried.

In planning the engine room, the experience gained with earlier Clan Line automated ships was incorporated, and one Senior Engineer officer and one Junior Engineer officer comprise a watch. All engine and refrigeration controls are located in a soundproof control room and an extensive system of recording devices enables a close and continuous watch to be maintained from the same room.

On the outward voyage a wide variety of general cargo can be carried and there is ample space for cargoes of chilled, frozen and deep-frozen meat. Fruit is carried under controlled temperatures

M.S. *Fauna*

The M.S. *Tinnum* is an example of a smaller vessel which can be used either on a cargo liner berth or tramping. She is owned by K. G. Zerssen & Co. and was built in 1956 by Werft Nobiskrug at Rendsburg. The *Tinnum* has a speed of 15 knots, an overall length of 373 ft. and a beam of 49 ft. 6,400 tons of cargo can be carried and special provision is made for the carriage of hides and wine in bulk.

Photo courtesy: D. W. A. Mercer.

and deep tanks are provided for the bulk transport of wine.

Additional accommodation for 12 passengers has now been built into these ships.

M.S. FAUNA (1966)

Owners: D/G NEPTUN, BREMEN
Builders: SCHIFFT. UNTERWESER, BREMERHAVEN
8-cylinder Deutz diesel, 1,500 b.h.p.
Single screw
Service speed 12 knots
Length overall 240·6 ft.
Beam 37·8 ft.
Deadweight tonnage 2,348

The *Fauna* is typical of many German and Dutch-built vessels. They are built with 'tween decks and are equally suitable for cargo liner or tramp operations. They are to be seen as far afield as the Mediterranean and the Baltic.

The *Fauna* trades between Spain, Portugal and North European ports and on a recent voyage from Lisbon and Leixoes she called at Shoreham and discharged 450 tons of cargo made up of: granulated cork, wine in casks and metal containers, dried vegetables, sardines, liqueurs, granite for kerbstones, pine timber (packaged) for fencing, and boxwood (pine). Similar commodities were unloaded at Dover and Antwerp and the passage took about nine days.

Chartered Tramp Ships . . .

As has been mentioned before, cargo liner companies have for many years chartered ships during peak trading periods. To meet this demand other companies build either ships for full-time employment of this type or vessels which can operate mainly in the tramp (bulk) trades with occasional periods of charter. This method of ship operation has been increasing of late and several cross-channel and Baltic container services are run entirely with ships on long term charter agreements.

Two ships suitable for liner or tramp trading are the *Fidentia*, owned by the Metcalfe Shipping Co. Ltd. and the *Trebartha* of Hain Nourse Ltd. Hain Nourse is an amalgamation of the Hain Steamship Co. Ltd. and the Nourse Line, both of which companies are part of the P & O Group.

Originally the Hain Line was engaged entirely in the tramping trade, its ships being registered at, and managed from, St. Ives in Cornwall. The company was acquired by the P & O Line in 1917. The Nourse Line was founded in 1861 and in its early days was well known for its fleet of fine sailing ships. As part of the P & O Group it continued independent operations between Calcutta and Rangoon to Cuba and the West Indies, and between Calcutta and the U.K. After 1945, Nourse Line ships were often on charter to the P & O and the British India Line (also a part of the P & O Group), but now there are only two ships in service carrying traditional Nourse names.

The extent of chartering by cargo lines is shown by the following information, which was extracted from a single issue of *Lloyd's List and Shipping Gazette* by permission of the Editor of that journal.

Clan Line Service to South and East Africa—M.S. *Amberton*, 11,000 tons deadweight, service speed 12 knots. Owned by Chapman and Willan Ltd.

P & O Services to Fremantle, Adelaide and Sydney—M.S. *Trevaylor*, 10,300 tons deadweight, service speed 13½ knots owned by Hain Nourse Ltd.

Strick and Ellerman Joint Service to Arabian and Iranian Ports—S.S. *Fidentia*, 6,500 tons deadweight service speed 10 knots. Owned by Metcalfe Shipping Co. Ltd.

Liners Maritimas Argentinas, Lamport & Holt Line Ltd. and Houlder Brothers & Co.'s Joint Service to the River Plate—M.S. *Glenmoor*, 9,540 tons deadweight, service speed 13 knots. Owned by the Moore Line Ltd.

Cunard Line Service to Halifax (N.S.) and St. John (N.B.)—M.S. *Lundefjell*, approx. 6,750 tons deadweight, service speed 14½ knots. Owned by Olsen and Ugelstad (Norway).

Safmarine Service to South and East Africa—*Irish Rowan*, 14,950 tons deadweight, service speed 15 knots. Owned by Irish Shipping Ltd.

Clan Line, Hall Line and Harrison Line Joint Service to East Africa—M.S. *Aegean Dolphin*, 12,730 tons deadweight, service speed 15 knots. Owned by Pacific Trading Corporation (Panamanium).

Canadian Pacific Service to Montreal—M.S. *Inishowen Head*, approx. 12,000 tons deadweight, service speed 15 knots. Owned by G. Heyn & Sons Ltd.

In addition the M.S. *Springbank* and the M.S. *Taybank*, both owned by The Bank Ltd., were on charter to Strick and Ellerman Lines. The *Rathlin Head* and *Torr Head* were also employed on Canadian Pacific service. Cunard had the *Prins Philips Willm* and the *John Schroder* sailing to Montreal and the central Mediterranean respectively. There were also more than a dozen other chartered ships advertised to sail on regular cargo services. The periods covered by the advertised schedules varied from about a week to six weeks. In addition, several British companies advertised, but did not give details of sailings or names of the ships due to sail.

M.S. *Fidentia*.
Photo courtesy: D. W. A. Mercer.

M.S. *Trebartha*.
Photo courtesy: D. W. A. Mercer.

The M.S. *Magician*.
Photo courtesy: Harrison Line.

M.S. MAGICIAN (1968)

Owners: HARRISON LINE
Builders: THE DOXFORD & SUNDERLAND SHIPBUILDING AND ENGINEERING CO. LTD.
Sulzer diesel, 12,800 b.h.p.
Single screw
Service speed 18 knots
Length overall 494 ft.
Beam 63 ft.
Deadweight tonnage 11,100

The *Magician*, and an identical sister ship the *Historian*, were handed over to the Harrison Line in 1968. These two ships will operate mainly on the company's African trades and many factors were taken into account before the ships were designed.

The type of cargo carried on this service varies considerably and can be summed up as general, refrigerated, ventilated, liquid, heavy lift, lock up (items which must be segregated from the main cargo for safety reasons or because of their high value) and commodities, often in large quantities, which do not require 'tween deck stowage. In addition it was necessary to construct a ship, which would load and discharge simultaneously and maintain adequate stability. Because of the number of ports visited, efficient and economical cargo handling gear is essential.

In designing these ships the company could call on experience gained with a vessel which had been in service for four years, and it was decided to use the best features of this ship and incorporate improvements.

In investigating cargo handling gear it was found that whilst conventional derricks required less initial capital outlay and had a higher hook speed than cranes, derricks in union purchase could only pick up from one point and land it in one position in the hatch. In addition, rigging and re-rigging derricks, both on going to sea and entering port was a time-consuming operation. The investigation also established a third and very important point in that the loading cycle was controlled, not by the hook speed of the gear, but by the time taken to position the cargo in its final stow. It was, therefore, decided to use cranes, and, in order to take full advantage of their ability to spot load, the hatches at Nos. 2 and 3 holds were extended to almost the full width of the ship. No. 4 hatch is also wider than had previously been the practice. The flat-topped steel hatch covers are designed to load up to 300 lb. per sq. ft. and are able to carry locomotives weighing 80 tons. The hatch cover sections can also be split at any section, so that deck cargo for later ports can be left stowed on part of the covers while other cargo is discharged from the 'tween decks and hold.

In the 'tween decks, flush hatch covers are divided with four sections, so that when the need is for hold space the forward section stows forward, the aft

The M.S. *Suffren* of the French Line. This cargo liner was built in 1967. She has a speed of 18 knots and a gross tonnage of 6,772. The weather deck hatches at holds Nos. 2, 3 and 4 are fitted flush with the deck for the stowage of containers.
Photo courtesy: French Line.

section—aft and the centre section—in two sections—stows to the respective sides of the ship. This arrangement allows an extremely flexible arrangement of "open" or 'tween deck spaces.

Locker requirements vary considerably on outward and homeward voyages. The doors of the lockers have, therefore, been arranged to swing through 180 degrees so that they can be secured flush with the ship's side or a divisional bulkhead. This allows the space, when not required for lock-up cargo to be used as a normal 'tween deck.

Consideration was given to a ship with engines aft, but it was decided that such an arrangement would not easily maintain a satisfactory longitudinal trim in ballast or loaded conditions without the provision of exceedingly large deep tanks or trimming tanks. It was, therefore, decided to place one hatch aft of the engine room and sacrifice a certain amount of the square section of the hull.

The problem of lateral stability was solved by dividing four double-bottom tanks longitudinally as well as at the centre line, thus forming 16 separate tanks and reducing the free flow of ballast to a point where the heaviest lifts could be embarked in safety.

Further cargo facilities provided include deep tanks for the carriage of dry cargo or unheated edible oils. These tanks can also be used for water ballast.

Forced ventilation is supplied to all cargo spaces giving five air changes per hour. No. 4 'tween deck is suitable for the carriage of citrus fruit with reversible fans giving 15 air changes per hour. Gas extractors are fitted throughout No. 1 hatch to ensure the safety of paints, chemicals, etc. Extensive refrigerated space, totalling 7,000 cu. ft., can carry a variety of commodities. It consists of four chambers, which can be operated independently with temperature ranges of 60°F. to −10°F.

To handle heavy lifts each ship is equipped with a 150-ton Stulcken derrick to serve Nos. 3 and 4 hatches. Of the latest design, this derrick can be operated by two men, and, by simple use of a special pendulum block, lighter loads can be lifted at increased hook speed. In earlier ships, a split superstructure was adopted, so that navigation could be carried out from a point ahead of the Stulcken posts. In the *Magician*

The S.S. *Historian* of 1924. A typical unit of the pre-war Harrison fleet. The *Historian* had a deadweight tonnage of about 9,200 on dimensions of 420 × 42 ft. She was fitted with coal-fired boilers and triple expansion reciprocating engines and had a service speed of approximately 12 knots.

The 1924 *Historian* was sunk in the war, and a standard war-time cargo ship built in 1943 took the name.

the derrick controls have been resited on deck and it was decided that the ship could be safely conned from aft, with a considerable saving in capital cost in the construction of a single superstructure.

The Harrison Line operates a fleet of about 30 ships and provides the following services:

M.S. *Finnforest*.
Photo courtesy: D. W. A. Mercer.

M.S. FINNFOREST (1963)

Owners: O/Y FINNLINES LTD.
Builders: RHEINSTAHL NORDSEEWERKE
B. & W. diesel, 6,500 b.h.p.
Single screw
Service speed 16 knots
Length overall 454 ft.
Beam 61 ft. 6 in.
Deadweight tonnage 9,829

In addition to car ferries O/Y Finnlines operate a fleet of over 23 cargo liners. General cargo services are operated to ports in the U.S. from the Baltic and N. Europe, but calls are not made at any British ports. Loading and discharging ports vary, the following being examples:

Finnforest

Outwards: Oulu 27–28/9, Kemi 29–30/8, Hamina 2–5/9, then to New York 17/9, Harbour Side 18/9, Newark 19/9, Providence 20/9, Philadelphia 23/9, Camden 24/9, Baltimore 25/9, and Hampton Roads 26/9. (Loading at Philadelphia, Baltimore and Hamptons Roads (tobacco).)

Homeward: Rotterdam 11/10, Hamburg 14/10, Helsinki 16/10.

Services are also in operation to Gulf ports, loading and discharging at New Orleans, Houston and Mobile.

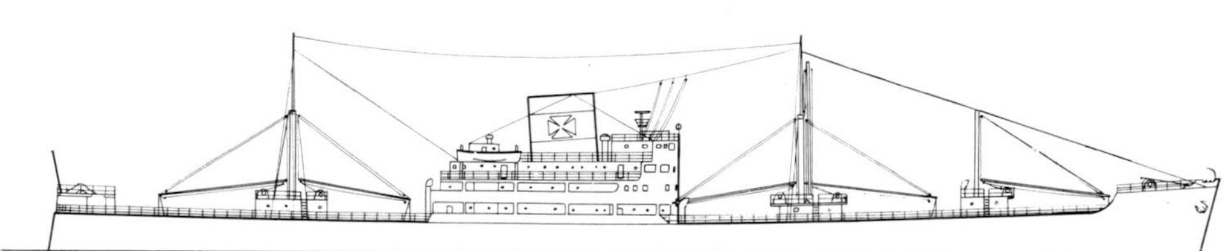

M.S. OSWESTRY GRANGE (1952)

Owners: Houlder Line Ltd.
Builders: Hawthorn Leslie & Co. Ltd.
Doxford diesel, 3,780 b.h.p.
Single screw
Service speed 12½ knots
Length overall 475 ft.
Beam 61·6 ft.
Deadweight tonnage 13,390

A refrigerated cargo liner running between London, Newport (Mon.), Sao Vicente and Buenos Aires. Outward bound the vessels of the Houlder Line carry a wide variety of general cargo, including chemicals, textiles, machinery, vehicles and agricultural tools and implements. Homeward, some of the cargo is refrigerated, but the most important item, beef, is chilled. It was found by experience that tissues of beef were damaged as a result of being frozen and this type of cargo is now carried at temperatures between 28° and 29·5°F. Chilled beef is also liable to loss of bloom, tarrib and mould, and scrupulous cleanliness in the holds is essential. Carcases are hung from overhead rails and even the hooks and chains are carefully sterilised before loading. As a result of this method of stowage the actual tonnages of meat carried are well below the deadweight capacity. During passage, air in the hold is frequently changed and the preservation of the meat is assisted by the injection of a proportion of CO_2.

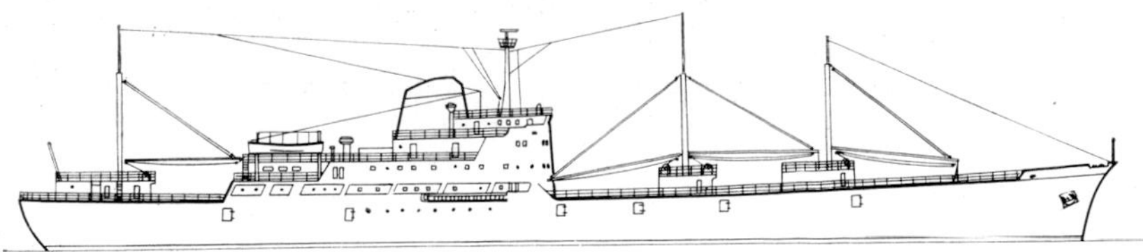

M.S. FORT TRINITE (1964)

Owners: French Line
Builders: Chantiers & Ateliers de Provence
Doxford diesel, 7,300 b.h.p.
Single screw
Service speed 19 knots
Length overall 410 ft.
Beam 56 ft.
Deadweight tonnage 4,900

The *Fort Trinite* is one of the most recent fruit ships built for the French Line. Like several other modern fruit ships, the refrigeration machinery can deal with both frozen and chilled meat.

The *Fort Trinite* runs in the French Line service between Hamburg, Antwerp, Le Havre and Pointe a Pitre, Fort de France, San Juan and Santa Domingo. The single voyage takes about 14 days and accommodation is provided for 12 passengers. All cabins have either a bath or a shower and most have private lavatories.

For part of the year the *Fort Trinite* is employed on the North Atlantic carrying meat cargoes eastward and general cargo westward.

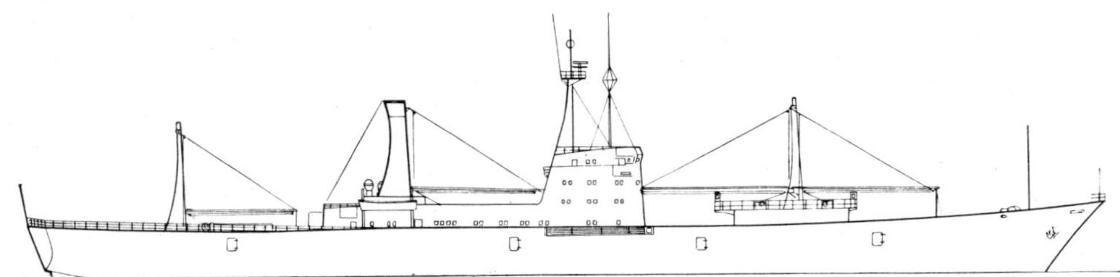

M.S. POLAR EQUADOR (1968)

Owners: Hamburg–South American Line
Builders: Blohm and Voss
Two Pielstick diesels
Single screw
Service speed 23·5 knots
Length overall 486 ft.
Beam 64 ft.
Deadweight tons 7,950

A modern fruit and meat ship running between Hamburg, Bremen, Rotterdam, Antwerp to various South American ports. Cargo is handled by fork lift trucks and horizontal conveyors are installed in the holds. The engine room is extensively automated and can be left unattended for periods of up to 16 hours per day.

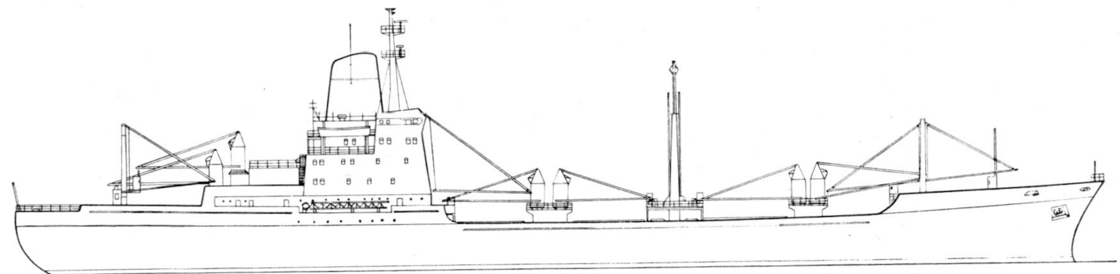

M.S. PRIAM (1966)

Owners: Blue Funnel Line
Builders: Vickers Ltd.
B. & W. diesel, 18,900 b.h.p.
Single screw
Service speed 21 knots
Length overall 563·6 ft.
Beam 77·6 ft.
Deadweight tonnage 11,200

The *Priam* is the first of a series of high-speed liners built in Japan and the U.K. for the Blue Funnel and Glen Lines. In addition to dry cargo, provision is made for refrigerated cargo, and chemicals and liquids in deep tanks.

Cargo is handled by cranes and derricks with capacities up to 5 tons and a Stulcken derrick of 60 tons capacity.

Through work study, automation of the main engine and planned maintenance the complement of this ship is 43 men, a considerable reduction over the earlier Glenlyon Class. The Glen ships employ Chinese ratings and the complement is consequently higher.

The *Priam* and her sister ships are employed on the express cargo service between the U.K. and the Far East. There is no provision for passengers.

CHAPTER 7 Crew Accommodation

MANY are the stories which have been related about the primitive living conditions suffered by sailors in sailing ships and, later on, in steam tramps. Unfortunately, most of them are true, although, judged against the general social conditions of the times, it is possible that shipowners were not always the monsters they are made out to have been. For many years minimum standards have been laid down by the Board of Trade. Some socially conscious owners made genuine attempts to improve upon these standards, but in the absence of the science and technology which is applied to problems today their efforts were bound to produce only limited results.

In the majority of ships the traditional location for the crew's quarters was the forecastle. Here, with the seamen on one side and the stokers on the other, a pretty miserable existence was endured. As often as not the seaman was expected to provide his own bedding. Heating in winter depended upon a coal stove, although steam heating was sometimes laid on. Condensation was excessive, and in bad weather water found its way in without difficulty. In summer this badly insulated and ill-ventilated space became hotter than a greenhouse and the occupants were often driven to sleeping on deck. Storage space for gear and personal possessions was almost nonexistent and the sum total of home comforts amounted to wooden benches and a mess table. Clothing could not be dried adequately and washing and toilet facilities were minimal. Food often had to be carried across open decks from the galley if no mess room had been provided in the main superstructure. Over and above all this, the forecastle was subjected to pounding in a seaway.

Quarters such as these persisted for a surprisingly long time and it was not really until the late '20s that noticeable improvements were made. The first substantial development occurred when the quarters were moved to the other end of the ship, either in the poop or at shelter deck level. Group rooms were provided and a degree of privacy at last became possible. A mess room was added and washing facilities had hot and cold water. A comparable improvement in lavatories was also made.

This standard of accommodation continued generally until the spate of new building got under way in the late '40s. Since then there has been a steady development, especially as it has become necessary to tempt young men to take up a career at sea. Modern cabins, usually designed for a single occupant, are very much like the accommodation provided for tourist class passengers in liners. They are well lit and pro-

The Captain's bedroom on the *Port Chalmers*.
Photo courtesy: Port Line Ltd.

A single-berth crew's cabin on the *Bencruachan*.
Photo courtesy: Ben Line Steamers Ltd.

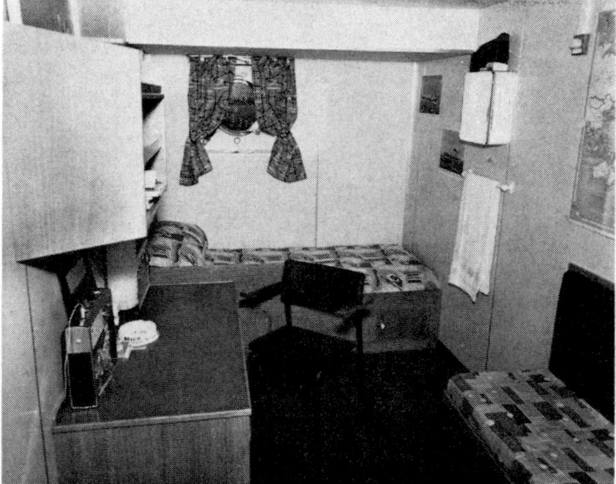

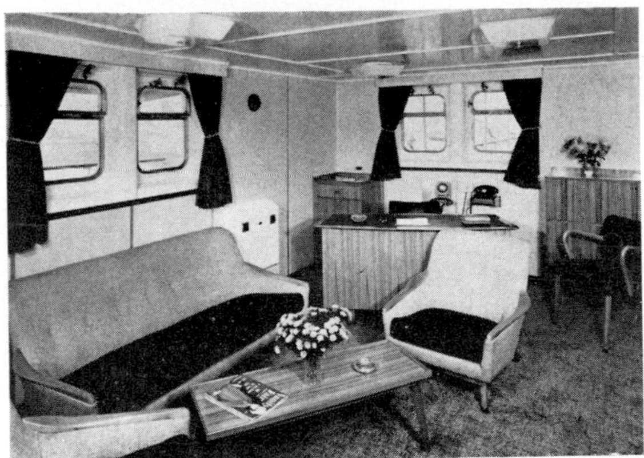

The Captain's dayroom on the *Mercury*.
Photo courtesy: Cable & Wireless Ltd.

The Junior Third Engineer's cabin on the *Mercury*.
Photo courtesy: Cable & Wireless Ltd.

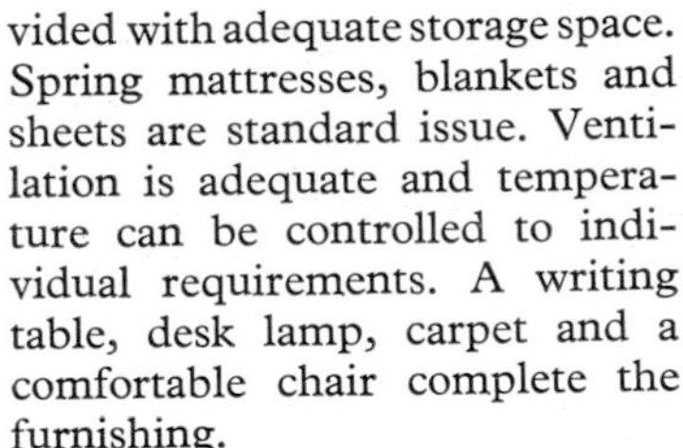

vided with adequate storage space. Spring mattresses, blankets and sheets are standard issue. Ventilation is adequate and temperature can be controlled to individual requirements. A writing table, desk lamp, carpet and a comfortable chair complete the furnishing.

Now that officers and men are housed in a single superstructure unit—the diehards predicted the complete failure of such an arrangement—the mess room is located adjacent to the galley. Laundry and drying rooms are provided and a recreation room is often available for communal activities. The final embellishment—at present only available in

The crew's recreation room on the *Port Chalmers*.
Photo courtesy: Port Line Ltd.

The officer's lounge on the *Mercury*.
Photo courtesy: Cable & Wireless Ltd.

A single-berth crew's cabin on the *Port Chalmers*.
Photo courtesy: Port Line Ltd.

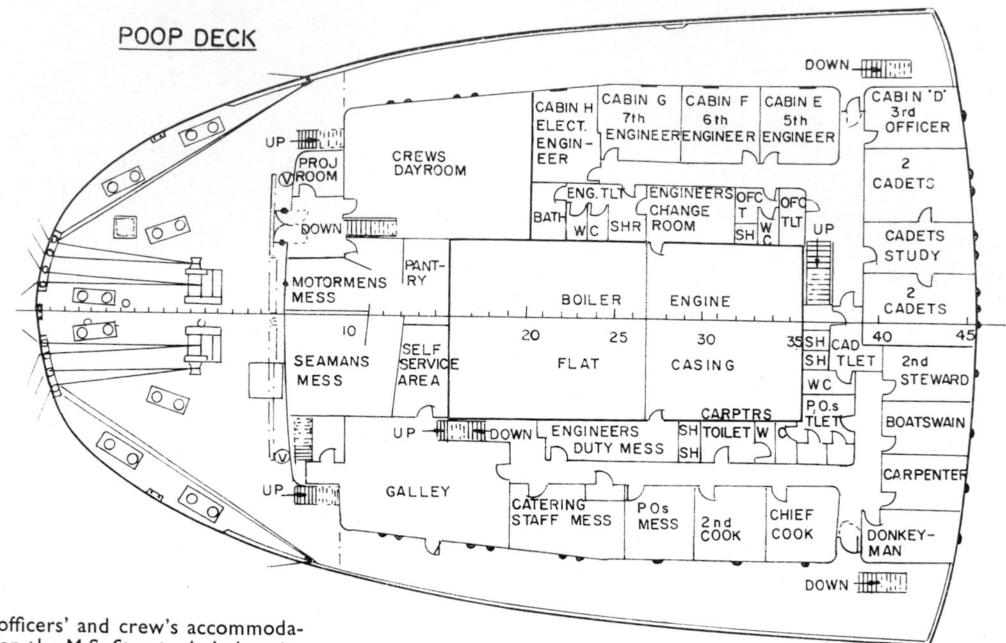

The officers' and crew's accommodation on the M.S. *Stonepool*. A description of this accommodation accompanies the account of the ship on page 28.

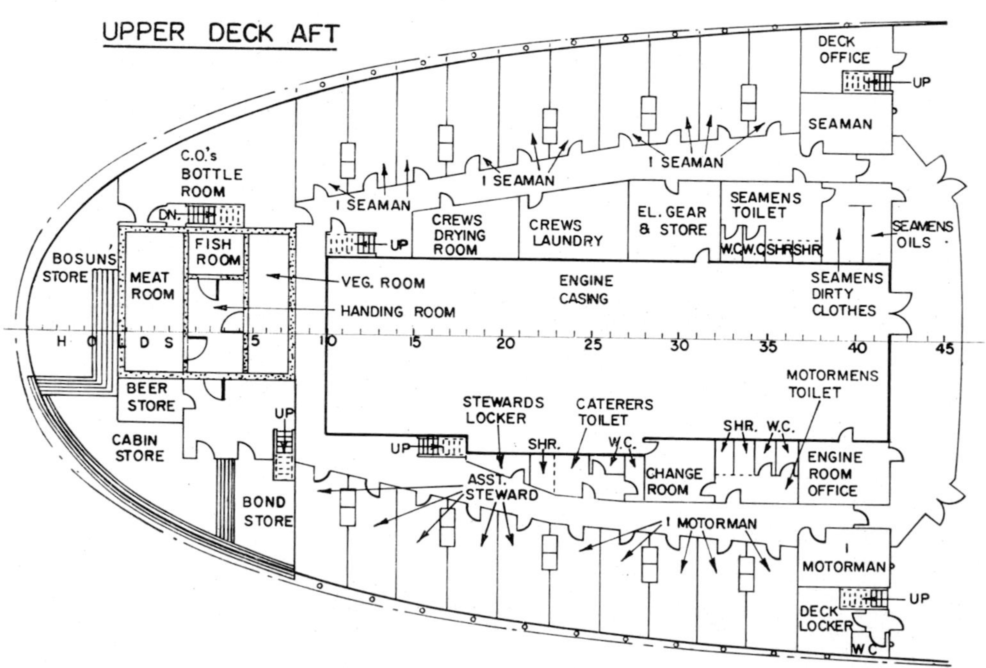

a few ships—is the provision of a swimming pool; not the canvas and pole variety, which for all its limitations provided any amount of fun, but a properly tiled sunken pool which would have been a feature of note in a liner in the not-so-distant past.

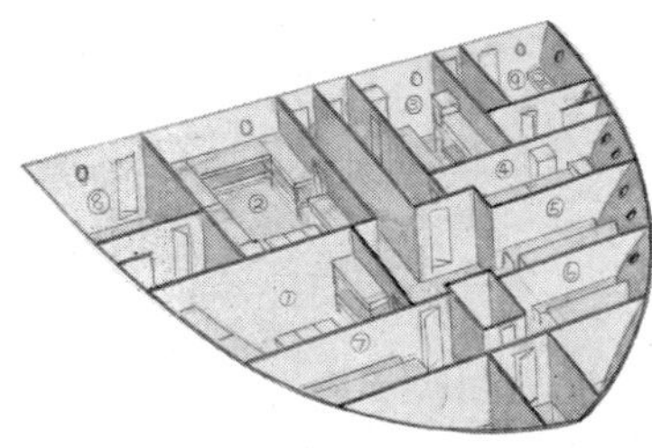

Crew Accommodation in High-Class Cargo Liners of 1921

(1) 6 seamen
(2) 8 seamen
(3) 4 stokers
(4) 4 stokers
(5) stokers' mess room
(6) seamen's mess room
(7) seamen's mess room
(8) seamen's washroom, 4 basins, 2 W.C.s, no bath provision
(9) stokers' washroom, 3 basins, 2 W.C.s, no bath provision

Length of forecastle 40 ft., beam of forecastle 56 ft.

Entrance to washrooms from shelter deck.

In stokers' room (4), each occupant had approximately 12 sq. ft. of standing space. Each seaman and stoker had a locker approximately 5 ft. high and 2 ft. square.

Mess rooms were furnished with scrubbed table and benches, with minimum provision for storage of crockery.

The galley was in the main superstructure about 150 ft. aft across open decks.

The boatswain, carpenter, donkeyman and oilers were berthed in very small cabins in the after end of the ship. Officers had small cabins and a saloon in the bridge structure.

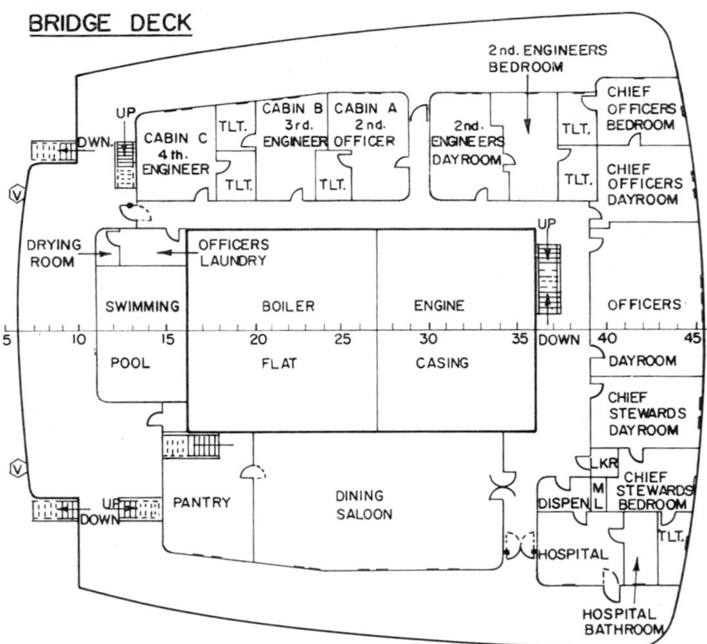

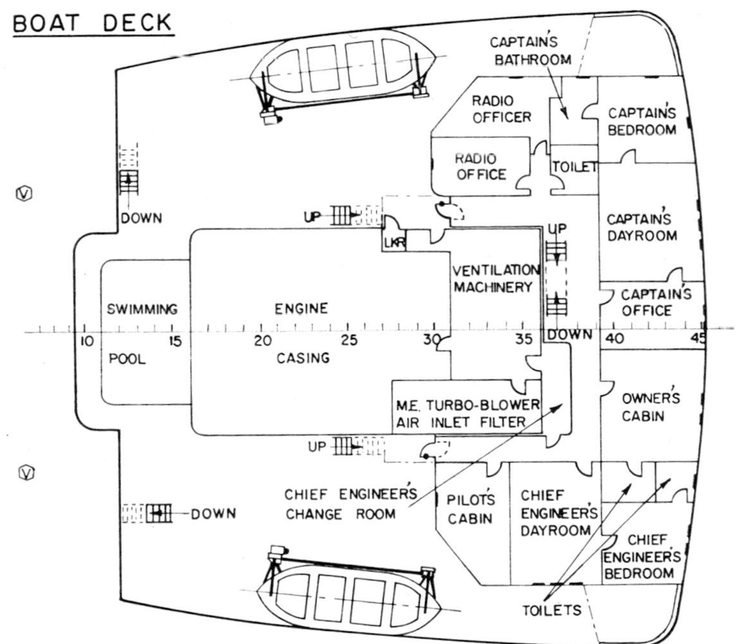

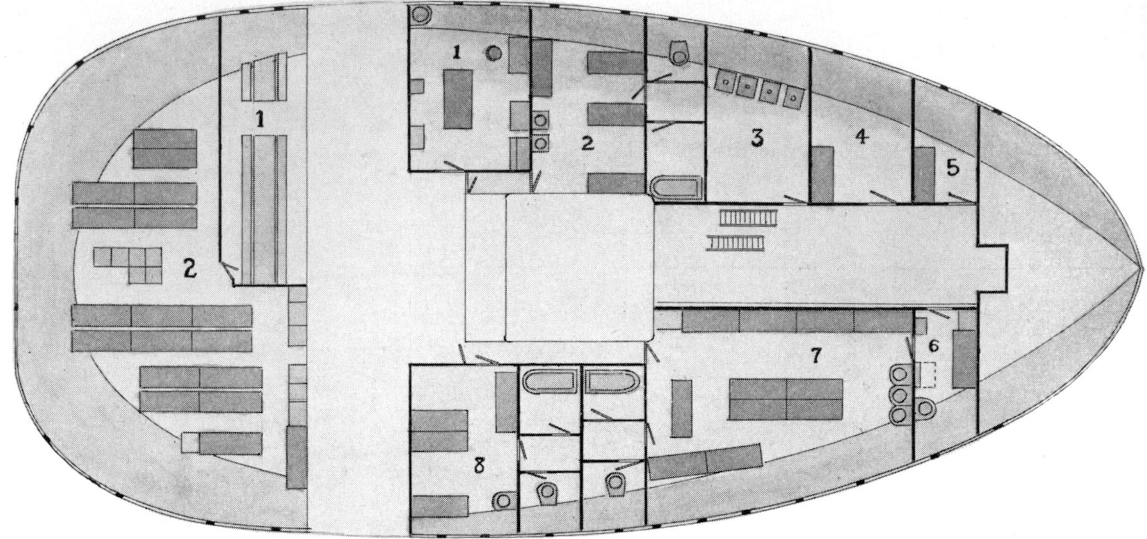

In 1911, the Société des Services Contractuels des Messageries Maritimes (Messageries Maritimes) built the S.S. *Paul Lecat* for their service from Marseilles to Indo China and Japan. The ship carried 90 First Class, 145 Second Class and 110 Third Class passengers, all of whom were accommodated in cabins. The ships of this fleet also carried units of soldiers and sailors to the French colonies, and the two sections of accommodation shown in the accompanying plan illustrate the seamen's quarters and the hospital, which appears to have had a generous number of beds in relation to the number of passengers carried.

The crew accommodation is typical of that found in many liners of the period. The location of these quarters was nearly always in the least profitable part of the ship, either right forward or right aft. Each man had a bunk and a locker with a capacity of about 8 cu. ft. As a result, the deck space, which was limited in any case, was further restricted by sea chests and other personal possessions. No laundry or drying room was available and oilskins and other gear were either stowed in the adjacent washrooms or around the bulkheads of the flat. Nevertheless, the crews of liners were usually better off than those in tramp steamers and sailing ships, for washroom facilities as well as living spaces were generally more adequate, dry and thoroughly ventilated with forced air supplied through louvres from trunking secured to the deckhead.

The ship's hospital was usually placed well aft. In this case it was as far forward as it was possible to locate it; it must have been extremely uncomfortable in heavy weather.

The scale of provision of beds in the male hospital was more generous than usual and it can only be assumed that the territories served produced more fever cases than elsewhere. The purpose of the ship's prison is, however, obvious, although it was unusual for a special cell to be provided for deportees. Ventilation was by forced air, and the decks of the hospital and the alleyways were probably covered with linoleum bonded to the bare steel with one of the adhesives then coming into use. Washrooms were usually tiled on a cement base.

Paul Lecat
Key to drawings
(1) Crew's mess room.
(2) Crew's accommodation—36 men.

(1) Consulting room with operating table.
(2) Isolation ward.
(3) Soldiers' w.c.'s.
(4) Prison.
(5) Cell for deportee.
(6) Nurse's cabin.
(7) Male hospital.
(8) Female hospital.

CHAPTER 8 Coastal Ships

COASTAL shipping has been in decline since the railways first carried goods and the roads were made passable for motor vehicles. Perhaps the effects were felt even before that when travellers were eventually able to make their way by stage coach rather than by slow and erratic sailing ships. As late as 1939 there were a few coastal passenger ships still at work, but they were patronised mainly by holiday makers and the services were not re-introduced after the war. Ships carrying 12 passengers continued, but even these are now few and far between.

In the '30s British coastal ships suffered from the inroads made into their trade by Dutch vessels, and it would seem that a complete recovery has never been achieved. Fewer and fewer general cargoes travel coastwise and the mainstream of activity centres on the carriage of coal and oil. The mainstay of the coal trade is the power stations and gas works, and a considerable number of ships are engaged in a round-the-clock supply operation. Chartered tonnage is employed in addition to ships owned by the various Boards. Further ships carry domestic coal, but this is a trade which has seen its best days. Small tankers, both company-owned and chartered, run on parallel courses to the colliers. At the moment it is a steady trade, but the extended use of pipe lines, such as that now being laid from Fawley to West London, may radically reduce the tonnage required.

Probably the most outstanding feature of the coal trade in the last 10 to 15 years has been the increase in the size of colliers. Some small harbours have been dredged and, in at least one case, a new lock has been constructed to permit the passage of larger ships, whilst the lower Thames power stations are now regularly discharging colliers of up to 8,000 tons. The largest colliers can also engage in international voyages.

Coastal tankers running between the main depots and the smaller outports have not increased in size to the same extent, although those ships which carry products from refinery to depots now range up to 19,000 tons.

Between 1918 and 1939, coasters of the type illustrated were almost standard equipment for coasting tramp companies in the U.K. They varied in length from about 150–250 ft. with deadweight tonnages up to about 2,500. There were a few larger vessels, mainly owned by the private gas and electricity undertakings, with tonnages up to 4,000 plus and these usually had three or four hatches. The number and arrangement of masts and derricks varied from ship to ship. Also worthy of mention was the group of N.E. Coast colliers which had their engines amidships.

Coasters were powered by triple expansion reciprocating engines, coal being the only fuel used. A typical ship had a master and two mates, who worked watch and watch about, five sea-

In 1946 it was decided to erect a new power station at Shoreham, Sussex. In order to ensure sufficient supplies of coal it was necessary to build a new lock (the third) which could handle ships of up to 4,500 tons.

Four colliers, each of 3,400 tons deadweight, were built for the service. They were the *James Rowan*, *Sir John Snell*, *Charles H. Merz* and *Sir William Walker*, 340 ft. long overall with a beam of 44 ft. The service speed is 11 knots and power is supplied by steam reciprocating engines. A fifth collier, the *Sir Johnstone Wright* of 4,200 tons deadweight, was also built for use on spring tides; at other times this vessel serves stations on the Thames estuary. In addition, chartered ships are used to supplement the C.E.G.B. vessels.

Each of the four vessels makes the voyage from Shoreham to the N.E. Coast in about 36 hours, and an average of 55 round trips are completed every year. The *Sir William Walker* was the first ship to use the new lock and the photograph shows her approaching the unloading wharf at the "B" station.

men, a steward and a cook. There were also a chief engineer, and one or two engineer officers. Three firemen who worked one watch in three completed the complement.

The officers and the steward had individual cabins, there also being a small saloon and pantry for the deck officers and an even smaller mess room for the engineers. Generally speaking, the earlier ships had forecastle quarters for the seamen and firemen, where conditions existed as described in Chapter 7. The galley was almost always located adjacent to the funnel casing.

Service speeds of these coasters ranged up to about 10 knots, but the engines rarely had much reserve power and head winds and seas soon slowed them down.

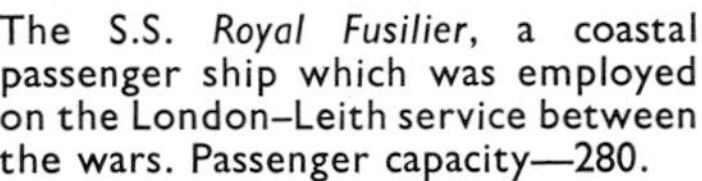

The S.S. *Royal Fusilier*, a coastal passenger ship which was employed on the London–Leith service between the wars. Passenger capacity—280.

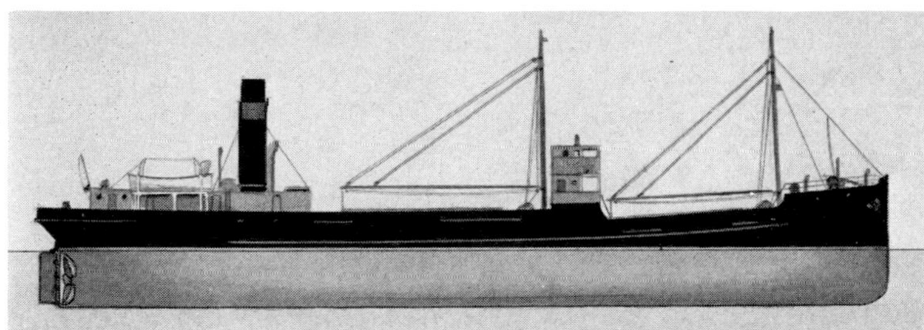

A typical British coasting ship of the mid '20s.

The method of steering was interesting and also applied to many deep-sea tramps and trawlers. A steam steering engine located in the wheelhouse—if there was one—or on the bridge, actuated a series of rods and chains which passed over steel sheaves and eventually linked on the open deck with the rudder quadrant. If a chain or rod parted it was necessary to steer the ship from aft by means of tackles. It was a highly unsatisfactory system and ships were lost through turning broadside to the seas (broaching) and capsizing before the ship's head could be turned again to head the waves.

Many of these ships were sunk in coastal convoys, particularly off the East Coast, and post-war replacements were mainly powered by diesel engines. Those that survived continued to trade, but economic conditions and old age had driven almost all of them to the shipbreakers' yards by the mid '50s.

In 1938 there were nearly 300 diesel powered coastal ships between 100 and 2,100 deadweight tons. This total, however, included coastal cargo liners such as those owned by Coast Lines Ltd., and the General Steam Navigation Co. Ltd. There were also the passenger vessels of the David MacBrayne Ltd. fleet (Clyde Estuary and the Western Isles) and the many coastal tankers owned by the principal oil companies.

By far the largest fleet of motor coasters was owned by F. T. Everard and Sons Ltd. (32 ships including tankers), followed by T. J. Metcalf (Metcalf Motor Coasters Ltd.) with 12 ships. Another company which saw at an early stage the advantages of

A packaged lumber cargo from the Baltic. The lengths of the packages are considerably shorter than those brought from Canada. The complete cargo was discharged by the two shore cranes.

M.S. KINGSNORTH FISHER (1966)

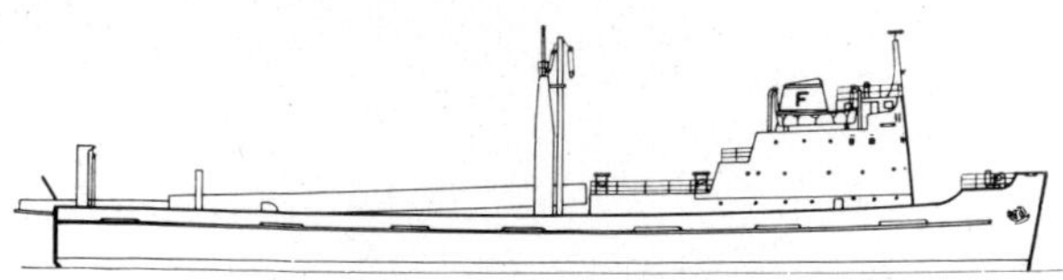

Owners: James Fisher & Sons Ltd.
Builders: Hall Russell & Co. Ltd.
Diesel electric, 1,100 b.h.p.
Twin screw
Service speed 11 knots
Length overall 284 ft.
Beam 53 ft.
Gross tonnage 2,355
Draught 12 ft.
Sister ship M.S. *Aberthaw Fisher*

Shallow draft coasters built expressly to carry heavy loads such as transformers and generators to sites of new power stations. Loads are taken on board on transporters via the adjustable link span and the ship's roadway. They are then lifted from the transporter by two 50-ton derricks and lowered to the hold by a hydraulic lift which is situated immediately aft of the superstructure. They are then moved to the position of stowage on adjustable trolleys.

Ballast systems are installed to keep the vessel on an even keel during loading operations and both the link span and roadway can be elevated by hydraulic jacks. A bow propeller is fitted to assist manoeuvring in restricted waters.

The *Kingsnorth Fisher* is on a long-term charter to the Central Electricity Generating Board.

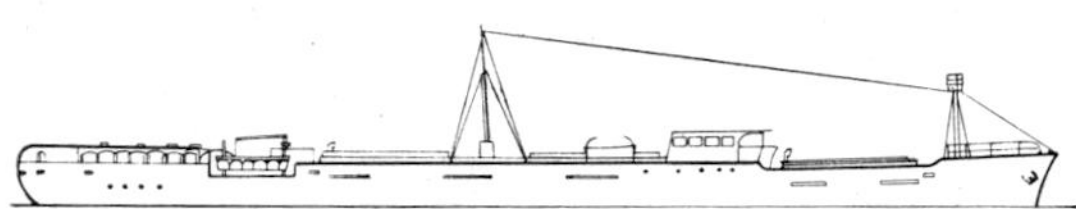

M.S. FULHAM VIII (1948)

Owners: Central Electricity Generating Board
Builders: Burntisland Shipbuilding Co. Ltd.
Geared diesels, 1,640 b.h.p.
Single screw
Service speed 11 knots
Length overall 270 ft.
Beam 39 ft. 6 in.
Deadweight tonnage 2,500 tons

"Flatiron" collier to serve power stations above Thames bridges. Both masts are telescopic.

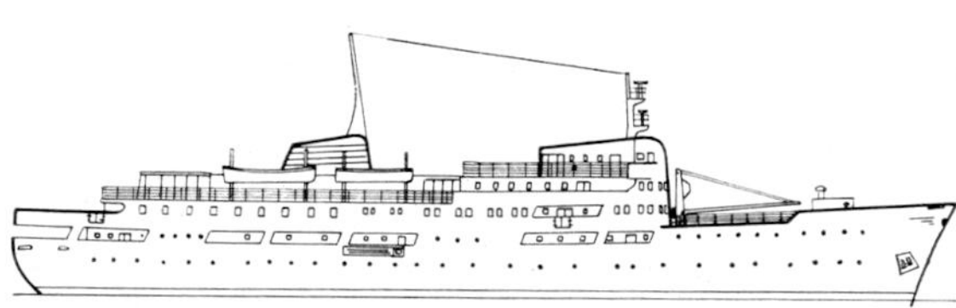

M.S. HARALD JARL (1960)

Owners: Det Nordenfjeldske Dampskibsselskab
Builders: A/S Trondhjems M/V
B. & W. diesel, 3,450 b.h.p.
Single screw
Service speed 16 knots
Length overall 286·75 ft.
Beam 43·58 ft.
Gross tonnage 2,568
Deadweight tonnage 750
54 First Class berths, 112 Second Class berths, 58 interchangeable berths

In Norway passenger shipping still maintains a position of considerable importance. The construction of new roads is changing the pattern of many fjord services and car ferries are taking the place of passenger ships. There are, however, still many communities which can only be reached conveniently by sea and the daily express passenger and cargo service between Bergen and Kirkenes is more vital than main line train services in the U.K. Several companies are concerned with this service and the *Harald Jarl* is a typical unit. The round trip of 2,500 miles from Bergen takes 11 days and 56 calls are made. It is probably the most interesting voyage from the scenic point of view in Europe. Cabins are reserved for holiday makers who wish to go on the round voyage. Apart from certain shore excursions no special facilities are provided and this is a true holiday voyage. Cargo is carried from Bergen to outports and between outports, and besides berthed passengers, deck passenger travel on short legs in the fashion of cross-channel steamers.

The *Harald Jarl* has been included in the Coastal section, but this and the other vessels are perfectly capable of undertaking deep-sea voyages. In the spring and summer these ships also sail to Spitzbergen, many hundreds of miles to the west and north of North Cape.

The principal ports called at are: Alesund, Kristiansund, Trondheim, Bodo, Svolvaer, Harstad, Tromso, Hammerfest and Kirkenes.

diesel propulsion was W. Robertson of Glasgow who owned nine vessels of this type.

M.S. CHELWOOD (1964)

Owners: FRANCE FENWICK & CO. LTD.
Builders: BARTRAM & SONS LTD.
6-cylinder stork diesel, 3,750 b.h.p.
Single screw
Service speed 14 knots
Length overall 370 ft.
Beam 53·5 ft.
Deadweight tonnage 7,200

The *Chelwood* is one of a group of colliers which have been built by four prominent coastal shipowners for long term charter to the Central Electricity Generating Board. Terms of charter and the design of the ships was agreed at a very early stage and this practice is becoming more common between charterers and owners of bulk carriers and tankers.

The *Chelwood* is much larger than previous colliers built for coastal work; she has been built to classification rules applicable to ocean-going ships.

The four ships serve three power stations in the lower reaches of the Thames, and a full cargo can be unloaded by grabs in 12 hours. The voyage to the East or North East coast is very short and an average of about one ship arrival per day is maintained.

M.S. *Chelwood.*
Photo courtesy: Wm. France Fenwick & Co. Ltd.

The accommodation provided for officers and crew is of a standard above that found in many larger ships. The Captain and Chief Engineer both have separate day and sleeping cabins with attached shower and lavatory. Other officers and crew have single-berth cabins. A dining room and lounge is provided for officers, a cafeteria and recreation room for the crew.

M.V. HEERENGRACHT

This Dutch coaster is owned by Spliethoff's Bevrachttingskantoor N.V. of Amsterdam. With a gross tonnage of 500 she is typical of the Continental "Paragraph Ships". Ships which do not exceed 500 tons gross and do not sail beyond the West of the U.K. are granted certain concessions which do not apply to larger ships. These are particularly concerned with manning, and considerable savings result. A large proportion of Dutch and German coastal ships are therefore built close to the 500 ton limit. Similar differences in manning scales between British home trade and foreign going ships exist, but the limits are not governed to the same extent by the tonnage of the ship.

M.V. ESSO HYTHE

The *Esso Hythe* has a deadweight tonnage of 1,285 tons. Her length overall is 208 ft. with a beam of 34 ft. She is designed as a fuel oil bunkering coaster carrying high flash products (over 150°F.) and with several similar ships is employed delivering fuel to ocean-going ships. Occasionally an oil cargo is delivered to a small shore storage installation.

Photo courtesy: An Esso Photograph.

M.S. *Esso Fawley*.
Photo courtesy: An Esso Photograph.

M.S. ESSO FAWLEY (1967)

Owners: ESSO PETROLEUM CO. LTD.
Builders: A/B LINDHOLMENS VARV., GOTHENBURG
Two Pielstick diesels, 5,040 b.h.p.
Single Kamewa screw
Service speed 16 knots
Kamewa bow thrust unit
Length overal 553 ft.
Beam 72 ft.
Deadweight tonnage 18,085

The *Esso Fawley* is a products tanker delivering various refined products from refineries to a number of distribution centres. She is classed by the company as a coastal ship, but she is equipped to undertake ocean voyages.

The welded hull is divided into four separate sections, each with its own loading and discharging system. One operator can control all operations from a central control point after certain master deck valves have been opened. Accommodation for a crew of 25 occupies four decks of the superstructure and all members of the crew have single cabins. The pitch of the propeller and the bow thrust unit are controlled from the bridge, which is equipped with a comprehensive range of navigational aids, including radar, Decca Navigator, radio direction finder and a VHF communications set.

M.S. GILLIAN EVERARD (1963)

Owners: F. T. EVERARD & SONS LTD.
Builders: CLELANDS SHIP BUILDING CO. LTD.
Nohab-Polar diesel, 1,500 b.h.p.
Single screw
Service speed 12 knots
Length overall 266 ft.
Beam 39 ft.
Deadweight tonnage 2,600

The *Gillian Everard* is one of the larger units of the Everard fleet. Everard's operate the largest fleet of British coasters, which range in size from about 3,500 tons deadweight down to small estuarial tankers and cargo vessels.

The *Gillian Everard* is designed to carry a wide variety of cargoes. Recently this vessel has been engaged in a series of voyages from Thurrock on the Thames to Glasgow with cement clinker. Other cargoes have been grain from Rotterdam and Antwerp to London and Liverpool, and potash from Ireland to a range of English and Scottish ports.

A coaster of the Everard fleet was the first ship to use the new Tilbury grain elevator.

M.S. *Gillian Everard*.
Photo courtesy: D. W. A. Mercer.

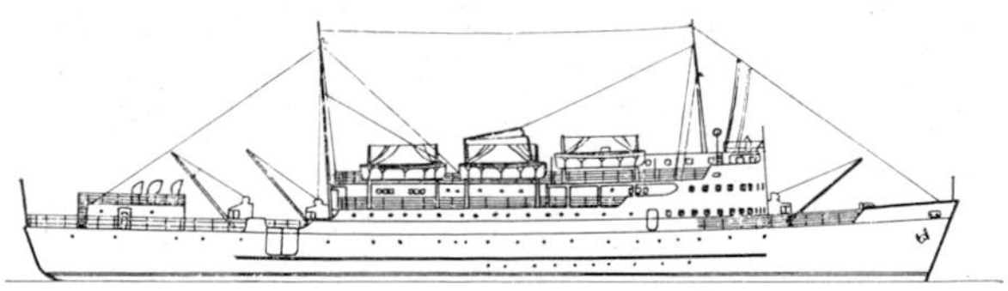

M.S. ST. NINIAN (1950)

Owners: North of Scotland and Orkney and Shetland Steam Navigation Co.
Builders: Caledon Ship Building and Engineering Co. Ltd.
Two British Polar diesels, 2,560 b.h.p.
Twin screw
Service speed 15 knots
Deadweight tonnage 945
Length overall 285 ft. 7 in.
Beam 46 ft.
Deadweight tonnage 945

The *St. Ninian* is employed on the passenger and cargo service between Leith, Aberdeen, Orkney and Shetland.

Passenger accommodation is provided for 160 First Class and 124 Second Class passengers. The First Class accommodation is surprisingly extensive and consists of a dining saloon, lounge, smoke room, bar and an observation verandah. Smaller rooms are available for Second Class passengers. Cabins are well appointed with hot and cold running water.

Cargo consists of the wide variety of things required by the islanders, and provision is also made for the carriage of cattle, sheep and horses.

Cargo is handled by three electric cranes. In 1950 there were few ocean-going vessels so equipped, but the companies concerned with coastal passenger lines and cargo liners have for very many years made use of this particular type of equipment.

The ships of this company are well known for the holiday voyages which are available during the spring and summer months.

Tens of thousands of naval men in both wars have travelled in this company's vessels across the Pentland Firth on their journeys to and from Scapa Flow.

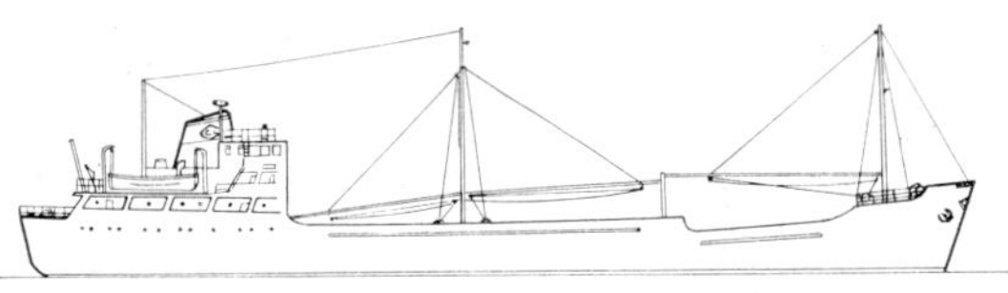

M.S. CORNISHBROOK (1961)

Owners: Comben Longstaff & Co. Ltd.
Builders: Clelands Shipbuilding Co. Ltd.
Deutz diesel, 1,210 b.h.p.
Single screw
Service speed 12 knots
Length overall 260·25 ft.
Beam 39 ft.
Deadweight tonnage 2,345

The Cornishbrook is a typical example of a tramp coaster, which can also meet the additional requirements for deep-sea voyages. Vessels of this type carry a wide variety of bulk commodities and also general cargoes when these are available. Some are engaged on medium- or long-term charters often interspersed with single-voyage charters.

For some time the *Cornishbrook* has been engaged on the following voyage pattern:

(a) Loads steel billets and steel coils at Antwerp. Loading time about one day.

(b) Sails to Birkenhead. Passage time three days, discharging time about one day.

(c) Sails in ballast to Newlyn where a cargo of granite chips from the company's quarries is loaded. Loading time eight hours by means of gravity chutes.

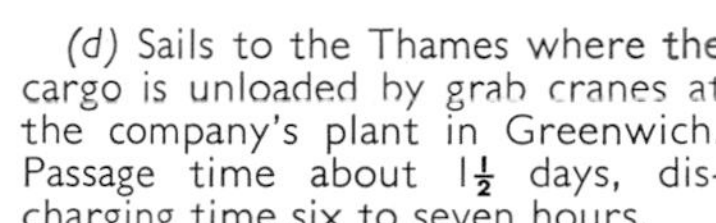

(d) Sails to the Thames where the cargo is unloaded by grab cranes at the company's plant in Greenwich. Passage time about $1\frac{1}{2}$ days, discharging time six to seven hours.

(e) Sails in ballast to Antwerp in about 12 hours. The process is then repeated.

Others of the company's ships are on charter to the Central Electricity Generating Board. Cargoes of coal are loaded at Blyth or Goole and the discharging port is usually Portishead. From time to time cargoes go to other generating stations on the Thames and the South Coast.

During the grain season bulk grain is loaded at French ports and at Rotterdam and conveyed to various U.K. ports. Comben Longstaff ships also carry potash from Rotterdam to Ireland. Other potash cargoes are carried from the Baltic to North Spanish ports, sulphur being loaded at Bayonne for the return trip.

The above voyages are but a few examples of the company's activities. They do indicate, however, the way in which the more enterprising owners are seeking business outside the diminishing traditional coastal areas.

CHAPTER 9 Tugs . . .

TUGS as we know them today are very much the creation of the age of steam. At first they were used in sheltered waters and estuaries, but gradually they extended their operations farther afield as engines improved and the knowledge of iron and, later, steel hulls developed. The stories of the early Thames tugs which ranged far down the Channel seeking a tow are well known, and even to this day the sight of a sea-going tug can conjure up visions of high adventure and danger.

Deep sea towage has more than kept pace with the requirements of the shipping industry, and almost anything that floats can be delivered to any destination. Floating docks, crippled ships, dredgers, for example, are towed over vast distances of ocean, and as recently as 1968 a French battleship was towed to the breaker's yard by ocean-going tugs. Oil rigs have lately provided a new source of business, and anything more ungainly and vicious in a seaway is hard to imagine.

The International Drilling Company's drilling rig *Orion*, leaving the Clyde under tow by the *Pacific*. Two tugs of the Clyde Shipping Co. Ltd., are secured alongside the rig to assist steering in restricted waters. The *Orion* was leased for a period by the Gas Council and Amoco. Eleven holes were sunk, eight of which were productive.

The *Pacific* was built in 1963 and is owned by Bugsier Reederei-Und Bergungs G.m.b.H., a leading salvage and ocean towing company. This vessel has a length overall of 236·8 ft. and a beam of 39·25 ft. Two 12-cylinder Deutz diesels deliver 8,500 b.h.p. and drive the ship at 18 knots on a single screw. The crew includes two divers and extensive pumping, cutting and other salvage gear is carried.

Photo courtesy: Gas Council.

The second function of most of the ocean-going tugs is salvage. Stationed at strategic ports throughout the world they play out a game which alternates between weeks or months of inactivity and short periods of intense activity when they leave harbour to answer a distress call. Speed at this time is essential, for it is not unusual for tugs of rival companies to be in the vicinity, and the first ship to arrive on the scene and settle terms with the master of the disabled ship may be on the way to receiving salvage payments which will more than meet the cost of maintaining the tug on station. "May" is, however, the operative word, for it is not unusual for the ship in tow to sink before it can be beached or anchored in harbour. If the internationally accepted form of salvage agreement is then in operation, the salvage tug receives nothing and it returns to start again the patient vigil which is ended either by the arrival of a relief tug or the transmission of yet another "Mayday" call.

Harbour tugs, some of which are equipped to undertake coastal towage, need little description. Through the years their basic layout has remained unchanged, although hull, propeller and engine design have improved their efficiency to a quite remarkable extent. Yet it is in the world of tugs that the paddle still finds a use. Several paddle tugs were put into service by the Admiralty in 1957 and 1958 for the specific purpose of berthing and unberthing aircraft carriers.

The largest ports in the U.K. have, in addition to ship-handling tugs, a fleet of still smaller vessels whose function is to tow barges. The most famous of these are undoubtedly the Thames tugs, which can be seen on any day from the Embankment working the tides between the Port of London and depots far up the river.

"Smit" is the name which immediately comes to mind when ocean towage is mentioned. At any time about 20 tugs are on salvage station or crossing the oceans of the world with a variety of tows. The two smallest of these tugs, built in 1946 and 1949, have engines of 1,000 h.p. Each new group has generally been larger and more powerful than its predecessors, and the *Zwarte Zee* (1963), *Witte Zee* (1966) and *Rode Zee* (1968) have engines which develop 9,000 h.p.

In addition to ocean-going tugs this company operates a fleet of over 20 coastal and harbour tugs with horsepower between 150 and 600. The associate N.V. Nieuwe Rotterdamse Sleepdienst has eight or more tugs for operating in the North Sea and the Europoort.

Tugs owned by the Overseas Towage and Salvage Co. Ltd. (Milford Haven Tug Service Ltd.), are operated in close co-operation with Smit's ocean-going tugs.

Through another affiliated company, W. A. Van Den Tak's Bergingsbedrijf N.V., Smits have an interest in a fleet which operates seven sea-going salvage vessels, coastal and inland salvage craft, salvage tugs, floating sheerlegs, a crane barge and pontoon barges.

Smits are also concerned with the Smit-Lloyd N.V. oil rig supply ships. The company was registered in 1964 and within a year a fleet of seven supply vessels and one crew boat were operating in the North Sea and the Mediterranean. The fleet now numbers more than 12 ships serving oil rigs on a world-wide basis.

In 1968, a new department was set up to develop the towage of cargo and heavy industrial equipment by barge. This type of transport is new to Northern Europe, and Tak barges and Smit tugs have already delivered two large cranes which were loaded and unloaded under their own power, a method which will be particularly useful in ports where unloading facilities are not available. Barges can also carry material which is too bulky to be carried in ordinary ships. The possibilities of carrying bulk cargoes of oil, grain and other commodities are being investigated. Successful operations of this type have already been carried out by Moran tugs.

The widespread and varied activities of the big Smit tugs can be shown by brief accounts of individual ships' movements over a period of six months.

Witte Zee

This tug towed a derrick-barge from Bordeaux to Melbourne. A suction dredger was delivered at Dampier from Fremantle. A similar tow was completed between Singapore and Port Hedland.

Orinoco

The *Orinoco* was stationed in the North Sea. She towed a supply vessel from Bordeaux to Rotterdam, and towed the disabled *Athellaird* from the Bay of Biscay to Liverpool. The *Orinoco* then proceeded to Kure, Japan, and towed a crane barge to Brunei. Next she delivered a dredger from Port Hedland to Singapore and continued to the company's salvage station at Bahrain.

Oostzee

Towed the disabled Liberian vessel *Atlantic Knight* from the Moçambique Channel into Lourenço Marques. The *Oostzee* then carried out several tows with dredging material from Durban to Capetown. A motor vessel was delivered to Durban from Port Elizabeth. The Iranian ship *Cyrus II*, which was drifting disabled in the Arabian Sea, was towed to Diego Suarez. Next, the *Oostzee* completed a tow from Port Latta to Cape Cuvier, N.W. Australia, and then sailed to Singapore where a salvage station is maintained.

The *Englishman* has comfortable accommodation for officers in single cabins and crew in two-berth cabins. There is also a cabin for six runner crew (the seamen who man a tow on a long ocean voyage). All of the accommodation is air-conditioned. Two fire-fighting monitors are located on the platform between the bridge and the twin exhaust uptakes.

As the *Englishman* was designed for international towage, the wheelhouse is equipped with a comprehensive outfit of radio transmitting and receiving equipment. There is also a direction-finder, radar and echo sounder. Remote control positions for the main engines are located on the flying bridge and in the wheelhouse. The towing winch can also be operated from the latter position. In addition to salvage and towing, the *Englishman* has been designed to service oil rigs.

M.T. ENGLISHMAN (1965)

Photo courtesy: United Towing Co. Ltd.

Owners: UNITED TOWING CO. LTD., HULL
Builders: COCHRANE & SONS LTD., SELBY
6-cylinder Ruston and Hornsby diesels, 4,100 b.h.p.
Twin screw
Free running speed 14 knots
Length overall 145 ft.
Beam 33 ft.

The *Englishman* is one of three powerful tugs which this company has built since 1965. The vessel is equipped with twin rudders, and during trials recorded a bollard pull of 32 tons. The main towing winch is located under the shelter of the boat deck and a towing hook tested to 45 tons static load is mounted on a table aft of the winch. The towing winch can hold 400 fathoms (2,400 ft.) of 5-in. circumference wire rope.

The United Towing Company has been engaged in towing for nearly 50 years and has achieved an international reputation. The larger tugs of the fleet, which now number 13, are engaged in all forms of ocean towage and logged over 150,000 miles in a period of 12 months. Oil rigs, crane barges, pipe-laying barges, disabled ships and dry docks can be handled by one or two of these tugs working together, and plans are now being studied for a much larger vessel which will be able to tow the largest merchant ship without assistance.

Photos courtesy: Moran International Towing Corporation.

M.T. ALICE L. MORAN (1966)

Owners: MORAN INTERNATIONAL TOWING CORPORATION
Builders: KURE SHIP BUILDING AND ENGINEERING CO.
Four General Motors diesels, 9,600 b.h.p.
Twin screws
Trial speed 16·5 knots
Length overall 211 ft.
Beam 42 ft.

At the time of her entry into service the *Alice L. Moran* was the largest ocean-going tug in the world, and also one of the few U.S. registered ships built in a foreign country since the war.

The *Alice L. Moran* has a conventional appearance and single-handed is capable of towing oil rigs and other awkward tows. Immediately after commissioning she commenced her long journeys, crossing the Atlantic four times and the Pacific three times. A tow from Texas to Peru was also completed.

The tug has a cruising range of over 15,000 miles. Tows are controlled by an automatic winch which maintains a safe tension on the tow wire and permits the maintenance of a higher average speed in heavy weather. Towing equipment consists of 3,600 ft. of $2\frac{1}{2}$-in. and 3,600 ft. of $2\frac{1}{4}$-in. wire rope. The crew accommodation is fully air-conditioned with individual cabin control.

The *Alice L. Moran* is now on long-term bareboat charter to the United Towing Co. Ltd., and has been re-named *Statesman.*

The Moran Corporation runs about 100 tugs and barges. Some operate in New York harbour and on the Erie Canal, whilst others, operating under the names of affiliated companies, work in the harbours of Philadelphia, Baltimore and Norfolk (Curtis Bay Towing Co.) Portland, Maine (Central Wharf Towing Co.) and Port Arthur, Texas (Picton Towing Co.).

Moran have also been pioneering in the field of giant tug-propelled barges. Included in a growing fleet are the 17,000 ton *Caribbean,* which carries sugar between Puerto Rico and the East Coast of the U.S., three 15,000 ton cement barges, which operate out of Ravenna, N.Y., to Boston, Jacksonville and intermediate ports, and several 6,000 ton barges which carry coal on Long Island Sound.

A Moran tug alongside the *Ponce de Leon*. This new ship is 700 ft. long with a gross tonnage of 24,000. She is owned by Transamerican Trailer Transport and with a speed of 26 knots is one of the fastest merchant ships afloat. Cargo consists of 260 trailers and 300 cars. The *Ponce de Leon* operates on a weekly service between New York and San Juan, Puerto Rico.

The photograph illustrates clearly the way in which ship tonnages have increased in the last ten years, with consequent problems for tug operators. The *Ponce de Leon* is by no means the largest ship in the world—some modern tankers are over half as long again—and in many of the principal ports of the world larger tugs are being built to cope with the handling of ships in light condition, or with extremely high freeboards and superstructures, are subjected to tremendous wind pressure.

Photo courtesy: Walter Fussey & Son.

M.T. DINGLE BAY

In 1968 the tug owning company of R. and J. H. Rea set up the Bantry Bay Towing Company Ltd. This company is registered in Eire and it now operates four similar tugs to service the *Universe Ireland* and the other large tankers which use the Bantry Bay terminal.

These tugs, the *Dingle Bay*, *Brandon Bay*, *Bantry Bay* and *Tralee Bay*, are distinctive vessels with unusually high bridge structures. They are 127 ft. long overall and are propelled by Mirrlees diesel engines generating a power of 2,500 b.h.p. The propellers operate in Kort nozzles to increase the towing power of the tugs and they are also equipped with two towing hooks. All four vessels are needed to berth and unberth the 312,000 ton tankers and each tug has extensive fire-fighting equipment and oil spill dispersal units. The *Dingle Bay* was built at the Hessle Yard of Richard Dunston. The total building cost of these four tugs was more than £1,500,000.

R. and J. H. Rea have for many years operated harbour tugs at Avonmouth, Bristol, Portishead, Sharpness, Cardiff and Barry. At the present time they have 11 tugs at these ports and over half of them are fitted with Kort nozzles. In 1959 a fleet of four tugs was established at Milford Haven to service the tankers using the new facilities there and there are now seven tugs in operation. All of them have diesel machinery of 1,300 b.h.p. Over the years the size of the tankers entering Milford Haven has steadily increased and the company now have on order a further three tugs similar in dimensions and power to the *Dingle Bay*.

In sheltered waters the tug's bow fits into a "V" notch in the barge's stern, thus permitting the most advantageous use of the tug's power. At sea average speeds of 8 knots are maintained on tow. Anchor, lights and temperature control of the barge holds are effected by radio control.

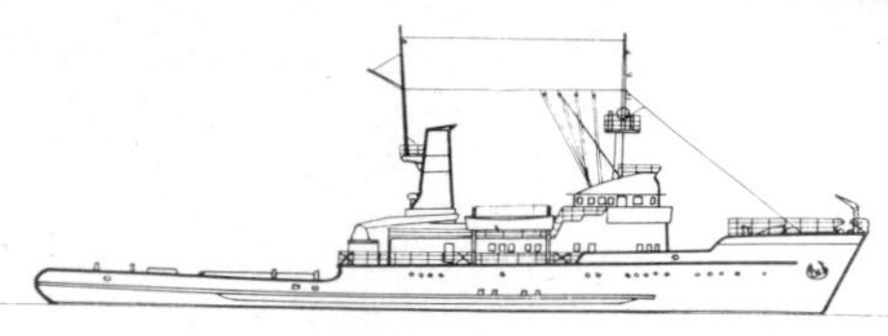

M.T. RODE ZEE (1969)

Owners: L. Smit & Co.'s Internationale Sleepdienst
Builders: N.V. Scheepswerf en Machinefabriek "De Merwede"
Two Werkspoor diesels, 9,000 i.h.p.
Single screw
Free-running speed 15 knots
Length overall 224 ft.
Beam approx. 40 ft.

The *Rode Zee* is the third 9,000 i.h.p. tug built for this owner. Unlike her sisters, the *Zwarte Zee* and *Witte Zee*, the *Rode Zee* has been designed primarily for contract towing rather than salvage work and her speed is three knots less. In order to achieve maximum efficiency when towing the controllable pitch propeller operates in a nozzle.

The towing winch, which has two drums, has a capacity of 1,000 metres of $7\frac{1}{4}$ in. and $6\frac{1}{2}$ in. steel wire rope. Extensive spare towing ropes are carried on mechanically operated drums. A further two-drum winch is installed at the after end of the ship. Extensive fire-fighting and salvage equipment is carried and a special work boat is designed to transport portable salvage gear.

The *Rode Zee* has twin funnels and the wheelhouse has all-round vision.

Officers and crew are housed in exceptionally high class air-conditioned accommodation.

D.E.P.T. GRIPER (1958)

Owners: Ministry of Defence
Four Paxman diesels, B.T.H. generator, 1,600 h.p.
Chain drive to paddles
Free running speed 13 knots

One of a series of paddle tugs built by the Admiralty in 1957 and 1958 for harbour duties. As such they are some of the most powerful tugs in harbour service In addition, the independent paddles make them tremendously manoeuvrable and idealy suited to the conditions in which they are required to work. Subsequent tugs built for the Ministry of Defence have been screw vessels.

The latest barge, which will operate between the Gulf of Mexico, Philadelphia and Sewaren, N.J., then by canal to Toronto and Cleveland, has specially coated caustic-resistant tanks which will carry any of the following products: cyclohexane, ethyl alcohol, ethylene alcohol, glycerine, hexylene glycol, isopropyl alcohol, methyl ethyl ketone and methyl isobutyl ketone.

The barge concerned, the *Artemis*, is fitted with two Schottel-designed rudder propellers. These are sufficiently powerful to eliminate the "negative skeg" or drag factor and also improve the "following" characteristics of the barge. This will simplify navigation of canals and also increase sea speeds. The two units can also be used for manoeuvring the barge alongside quays.

Since 1961 Moran has built 12 diesel tugs of more than 3,100 h.p., four of which deliver 4,290 h.p. All of these vessels are part of the fleet of more than 40 tugs operating in New York harbour. They are also capable of ocean towage and have been involved from time to time in salvage work. One, the *Edmond Moran*, has made several trips to Vietnam with drydocks, power plants and dumb barges. The significance of this development is that whereas it took 12 tugs to berth the *Queen Elizabeth* on her maiden voyage in 1940, four were able to do the job when she arrived for the last time in 1968.

One interesting aspect of the Moran salvage work is that disabled ships are towed to harbour on the basis of an ordinary agreement as applicable to normal coastal and harbour work. The company does not rely on salvage law, neither do the tugs carry Lloyd's open form. The philosophy behind this policy is that a ship in trouble is more than likely to have been a customer of the company at one time or another and that advantage should not be taken of a piece of bad luck.

Salvage Tugs

The work of salvage tugs can be gauged to some extent from the following casualty returns reproduced by permission of the Liverpool Underwriters Association.

The figures relate to the month ended 31st August 1968, and include steam and motor vessels of 500 tons gross register and upwards which were posted in the Loss Book. Comparative figures for previous years are also given.

After a collision in fog off Beachy Head, the British Rail tug *Meeching* towed the *Crystal Jewel* into the safety of Seaford Bay. Badly holed and with the bridge structure crumpled and bodily displaced, the *Crystal Jewel* looked in a sorry state. Within a few days, however, she was towed to Rotterdam for repairs and was back in service within a month.

Photos courtesy: Evening Argus, Brighton.

Another incident in the Channel. The M.S. *Saale* was in collision and went on fire. Two tugs went to the assistance of the abandoned ship and brought her into safety. This vessel, too, was returned to service within a very short time. The tug on the port side of the *Saale* is a small harbour tug which is using a manually operated hose to fight the fire. The other tug is the large German salvage vessel *Seefalke*. She was built in 1924 as a steamer and later re-engined with two Deutz diesels delivering 3,0000 h.p. and a free-running speed of 13 knots.

Photo courtesy: Evening Argus, Brighton.

Nature of Casualty	*British Commonwealth*		*Foreign*		*Results*		
	Total Loss	Partial Loss	Total Loss	Partial Loss	Total Losses	Partial Losses	Total
Weather damage	—	8	1	39	1	47	48
Founderings and abandonments	—	—	3	—	3	—	3
Strandings	—	13	2	54	2	67	69
Collisions	—	34	2	132	2	166	168
Contact damage	1	23	—	96	1	119	120
Fires and explosions	—	11	2	19	2	30	32
Missing	—	—	—	—	—	—	—
Damage to machinery, shafts and propellers	—	38	—	125	—	163	163
Other casualties	—	21	1	49	1	70	71
Totals June, 1969	1	148	11	514	12	662	674
June, 1968	2	109	12	541	14	650	664
June, 1967	4	152	22	495	26	647	673
June, 1966	4	132	9	545	13	677	690
June, 1965	2	154	14	522	16	676	692

By no means all of the above casualties required the services of salvage tugs, and descriptions of some of them indicate the various perils which still face ships in the routine performance of their duties:

Yellowstone (New Orleans–Inchon). Disabled at sea with boiler trouble. Towed to Manzanillo, Mexico, by tug *Alice L. Moran*. Repaired and later sailed for Korea.

Gothic (Wellington–U.K.). On fire at sea. Heavy damage to superstructure including bridge and navigational equipment. Four passengers and three crew killed. Returned 800 miles to Wellington under own power. Sailed after temporary repairs.

Captain G. (Kosseir–Shanghai). Reported damage to engines during typhoon "Shirley". Tugs despatched to area. No trace of vessel found, but wreckage later discovered. Master and 24 crew members rescued by Chinese vessel.

Hai An. (Hualien–Kaohsiung). Aground off T'ai Tung. Constructive total loss.

Kolubara (Galatz–Brindisi). Aground off Cape Papas. Refloated with tug assistance and proceeded to destination.

Ugo Fiorelli (ex-Gela). While tank cleaning 5 miles out from port of Gela, explosion occurred, followed by fire. Ship abandoned with heavy damage. Fire extinguished with aid of tugs and other vessels. Towed into Gela Roads. Eight crew members reported dead.

Eagle Courier (Seattle–San Francisco). Collision in fog 4 miles off Estevan Point (W. Coast Vancouver Island) with ship *Seattle*. Leaky and with extensive bow damage. Latter also sustained bow damage. Both vessels later arrived at Todd's Shipyard, Seattle.

Phryne (New Orleans–Puerto Cabello). Whilst at Kingston, Jamaica, fire in No. 2 hold was extinguished. Later, fires broke out in Nos. 3 and 4 holds, extinguished but overheating again detected. Salvage vessel *Rescue* towed the *Phryne* 8 miles out to sea where affected cargo was dumped. Vessel later returned to Kingston for repairs (cargo consisted of Alfalfa pellets, etc.).

Connecting up the tow is often the most dangerous part of salvage towing operations. This picture shows a Dutch harbour tug passing a line to a product and chemical tanker which went ashore on the northern mole of the New Waterway after attempting to enter in rough weather without a pilot.
Photo courtesy: L. Smit & Co.

Eventually the *Zwarte Zee*, the *Witte Zee* and a flotilla of harbour tugs managed to extricate the tanker from its perilous situation.
Photo courtesy: L. Smit & Co.

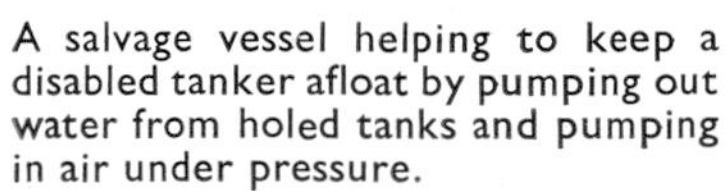

A salvage vessel helping to keep a disabled tanker afloat by pumping out water from holed tanks and pumping in air under pressure.
Photo courtesy: L. Smit & Co.

M.S. BRITONIA

Owners: OVERSEAS TOWAGE AND SALVAGE CO. LTD.
Builders: APPLEDORE SHIPBUILDERS LTD.
Polar diesel, 2,000 b.h.p.
Single screw
Free running speed 14 knots
Length overall 157 ft. 6 in.
Beam 31 ft. 6 in.

Salvage and ocean-going tug equipped with a powered towing winch capable of handling 400 fathoms of 5-in. circular steel-wire rope and 540 fathoms of $4\frac{1}{2}$-in. steel-wire rope. In addition the *Britonia* is equipped with a comprehensive outfit of salvage gear and fire-fighting monitors.

The *Britonia* is the largest salvage tug owned in the U.K., and this vessel and the *Neptunia* work in close association with the tugs of L. Smit & Co.'s Internationale Sleepdienst.

The salvage tug *Britonia*.
Photo courtesy: Victor Studio, Hong Kong.

Ocean-Going Tugs

Ocean-going tugs are able to tow the most unusual pieces of equipment. In 1966 a number of vessels were built in the U.K. for an Indian harbour development scheme. The large ones went under their own power, the small ones were loaded on cargo ships. The medium sized equipment: pontoons, barges and tugs had to go by other means. Three pontoons—part of the order—were linked together and the other craft—seven in number—were lashed and secured on the pontoons. The voyage of 6,500 miles to India was completed in two months.

The delivery of tin dredgers has been a feature of ocean towage for very many years, but it can still be hazardous work. When the *Ierse Zee* took charge of the dredger *Bangka I* from Scotland to Indonesia, a force 10 S. Easterly gale was encountered in St. George's Channel. So powerful was the wind that tug and tow drifted towards the Irish coast. After a series of adventures, which included the parting of the tow wire, the dredger was eventually towed clear of the dangerous lee shore and taken to Gibraltar, where a completely new set of emergency anchor gear was installed to replace that lost during the gale.

During the operations of this type the vessel or equipment towed is manned by a crew of seamen called "Runners". This is a particularly unpleasant and often perilous task since once the tug has lost control of the tow, the Runners are almost completely at the mercy of the sea. In coastal waters it is possible to anchor the tow, but even this cannot be done when deep water is reached.

Two Rotterdam tugs at the bow of the Holland America Line's *Rotterdam*. With two tugs at the stem and two at the stern, the liner is pulled out into the New Waterway. The two heading tugs then tow until their charge has adequate steering way. It is also usual for one of the tugs to stand by until the congested upper reaches have been cleared.

The tug *Fairplay IV* of Hamburg. Both the *Castelsardo* and the *Fairplay IV* are used, amongst other things, for berthing and unberthing large passenger liners.
Photo courtesy: D. W. A. Mercer.

The Italian tug *Castelsardo* of Genoa.
Photo courtesy: D. W. A. Mercer.

The *Betty Smith*, a New Orleans harbour tug owned by the Crescent Towing Co. American tugs are distinctive craft because of the practice of placing the towing hook well aft. This allows a longer deckhouse and they usually have a "piled up" look about them.
Photo courtesy: Collection of Eric Johnson, New Orleans.

The Alexandra Towing Co. Ltd. steam tug *Gladstone*. Based at Southampton, the *Gladstone* handles ocean liners. The Alexandra Towing Co. also maintains fleets at Manchester and the Mersey, Swansea and Port Talbot.
Photo courtesy: D. W. A. Mercer.

The most powerful salvage tugs in the world are the twin sister ships *Oceanic* and *Arctic* owned by the Bugsier-Reederei-und Bergungs-Aktiengesellschaft of Hamburg.

The *Oceanic* is powered by Deutz diesel engines producing 17,500 i.h.p. and a free running speed of 22 knots. She has twin controllable pitch propellers and a bow thrust unit has been provided to increase manoeuvrability. The bollard pull is 150 tons. These performance figures clearly indicate the type of vessel which these owners consider to be necessary to handle the largest bulk carriers and tankers.

In general appearance the *Oceanic* follows traditional lines, but there are innovations in the form of a hospital and cabins for rescued crews. Large inflatable fenders have been provided to reduce the risk of damage when going alongside another ship. The cruising range is 20,000 miles.

M.S. BEVER

Owners: W. A. VAN DEN TAK'S SALVAGE CO. LTD.
Diesel, 300 b.h.p.
Service speed 8·5 knots
Length overall 130 ft. 5 in.
Beam 33 ft. 11 in.
Gross tonnage 347

The *Bever* is an ocean-going salvage vessel belonging to an affiliated company of L. Smit & Co.'s Internationale Sleepdienst. The equipment of this vessel includes powerful anchor windlasses, capstans, guy winches and a central winch with two drums exerting a pull of 7 tons each, and a third with a pulling capacity of 7 tons. In addition, there is a 20-ton derrick and bow rollers to handle heavy anchor cables; these rollers can withstand a pressure of 50 tons.

The *Bever* is equipped with an air compressor for two divers and a fire pump with a capacity of 164 tons per hour. 2,260 litres of foam are also carried.

Other equipment includes patching material, salvage anchors, a centrifugal sandpump and two diesel water pumps with associated hoses, pipes and couplings. There are also various types of diving gear, electrical underwater welding and cutting apparatus.

An impression of the M.T. *Zwarte Zee.*

The salvage vessel *Bever.*
Photo courtesy: L. Smit & Co.

Fyffes Line *Camito* alongside the banana discharging berth at Southampton Docks.

Photo courtesy: Elders & Fyffes Ltd.

CHAPTER 10

Cargo Handling

General Cargo

FROM the earliest days of iron-hulled steam ships cargo has been handled by derricks. The simple steam tramps, which led the way to British supremacy at sea, had two masts, often wood. Two derricks, again often of wooden construction, were rigged on each mast and four rudimentary steam winches were provided to work them.

Each time a parcel of cargo was lifted from the hold the derrick had to be swung across to plumb the jetty or lighter by means of derrick guys. This method achieved quite a remarkable work rate, but it was expensive of man-power, punishing on the gear and sometimes perilous to the cargo.

By the turn of the century steel masts with strong crosstrees had led to the setting up of two widely-spaced derricks on each side of the mast. In addition a winch could be placed in line with each derrick and the system known as the "Union Purchase" came into being. Its use has not yet ceased. With this system, one derrick is plumbed over the hatch, the other is secured plumbing over the side of the ship. The cargo runners are shackled together and two winchmen acting in concert can lift and sling outboard a parcel of cargo without any further movement of the derricks.

Since the earliest days steam winches have improved out of all recognition. D.C. and A.C. remote control winches have done much to improve work rates. Nevertheless the fixed position of the derrick over the hold meant that cargo had to be manhandled from its place of stowage and, until recently, the speed with which this could be done determined the actual rate of progress.

Two inventions have helped the derrick in its traditional form to remain competitive: the fork lift truck and the pallet which it carries. The use of a fork lift truck in the hold and 'tween decks has accelerated the rate of stowage quite dramatically and the stevedore has been relieved of arduous work. Much general cargo, however, is not susceptible to this kind of handling and much research has been carried out to improve existing gear and develop new methods.

Cranes first made their appearance in any number about 1958, and since that time several manufacturers have entered the market with their own particular versions. Their advantages over the derrick are obvious, but so far not many ships have a complete outfit of them.

The Hallen swinging derrick gear is in principle a reversion to the single derrick which has been mentioned earlier. In operation, however, it is radically different. Every operation is powered and one man can operate the derrick, which can plumb any part of the hatch and handle 30-ton loads with ease.

Another recent development, which owes much to a rapidly expanding knowledge of the strength of ship structure, is the the incorporation of twin and

The method of raising and lowering a derrick which remained in use from the introduction of steam cargo winches until about 20 years ago. The topping life "A" is led to the barrel end of the winch "B". Turns are taken round the barrel end and the derrick raised to the required angle. The chain stopper "C" is then set up and the topping lift eased back until it takes the strain. The topping lift is then cast off from the winch and secured to the cleat "D".

In older ships a wire pennant was sometimes spliced to the topping lift and a chain at the other end. Upon the derrick reaching a certain height the chain was shackled to a fitting at the base of the mast and this took the weight. With this system it was not possible to adjust the angle of the derrick and the pennant was positioned so that the derrick plumbed the centre of the hatch.

In all modern ships the raising of a derrick is a simple and safe operation, made so by the topping winch. This is a drum around which the topping lift is rove. The free end is taken to the winch and the derrick raised. A simple rachet device on the rim of the topping winch drum prevents the topping lift running back and the operation is completed by throwing off the turns on the barrel ends. When lowering the derrick, the strain is first taken by the winch. The ratchet is then released and the derrick lowered. A further precaution when the derrick is raised is the insertion of a bar through the frames of the winch and the ratchet.

Below:
The S.S. *Beldis* of the Christen Smith Shipping Co. (Belships).

triple hatches. These span nearly the whole width of the ship, and when the covers are removed direct vertical access is available to almost every part of the 'tween decks and hold.

Heavy Derricks

The pioneers of the heavy derrick were the Christen Smith Shipping Co. of Oslo (Belships). After experiments with strengthening ordinary ships the first heavy lift ship—the *Beldis*—appeared in 1924. Her first cargo consisted of 17 complete locomotives and tenders which were loaded and later discharged in the Argentine with a 100-ton capacity derrick. Other companies also became interested at the same time in what was obviously to become a lucrative trade and the Clan Line, for instance, installed heavy lift derricks in their regular cargo liners.

The Belships design was used as a basis for a standard heavy lift ship during the war and cargo ships were fitted out with heavy derricks as a matter of routine. The practice was continued when shipowners rebuilt their fleets after 1945.

Another recent development, the Stulken derrick, has been quickly accepted. One derrick can serve either of two hatches and this tremendous unit can be seen on many cargo liners. The *Australia Star* of the Blue Star Line has a Stulken derrick with a working load of 300 tons.

Bulk Cargoes

The handling of bulk cargoes involves the sophisticated use of simple processes and, on occasion, the use of derricks and winches.

Loading ports vary between the fully mechanised to the near primitive. A ship may be loaded in a matter of hours by gravity or giant grabs, or on the other hand may be required to lift with its own gear a complete cargo from dockside or lighter.

In discharging bulk cargoes the following systems have been almost universally adopted: grab cranes, magnetism, pumping, suction and conveyor belts. Coal, other minerals and sugar are grabbed and either passed directly into railway wagons or to storage dumps. Oil is pumped ashore into storage tanks. Scrap metal is moved by magnetic grabs and baled pulp is discharged by the combined efforts of magnetism acting on the steel bands, and suction pads. Grain is sucked from the holds and discharged by gravity into barges or by conveyor belts to storage silos.

SINGLE DERRICK: Once the cargo has been lifted (1) the derrick must be swung across by the guys (indicated by arrowed lines) and secured before the cargo can be lowered. When using this form of derrick it is usual to prevent the cargo swinging by means of manually controlled lines.

UNION PURCHASE: When the cargo is raised high enough by wire (1A) then wire B begins to pull across. At the same time wire A is held taut until the strain is held equally by wires A and B (2) Wire A is then slacked away and the cargo is lowered when wire B is vertical (diagram 3). In practice the movements between (1), (2) and (3) overlap and surprising rates of cargo movement can be achieved. The derrick guys remain secured in the same position throughout the operation.

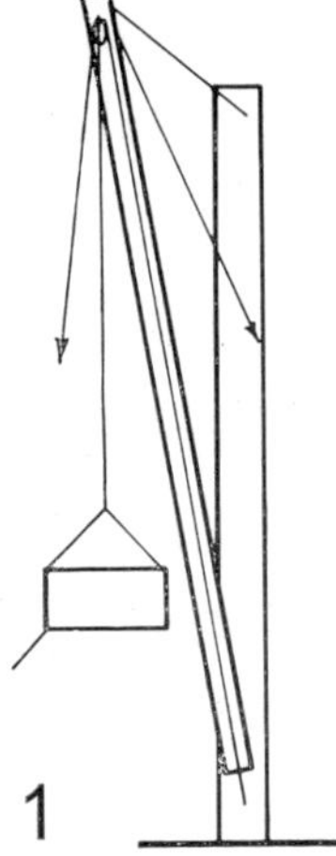

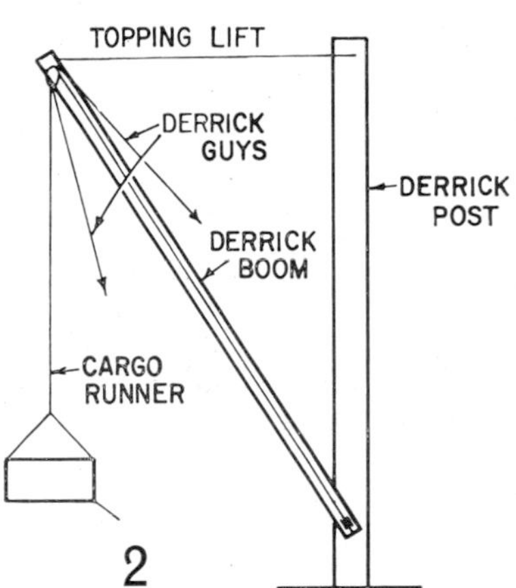

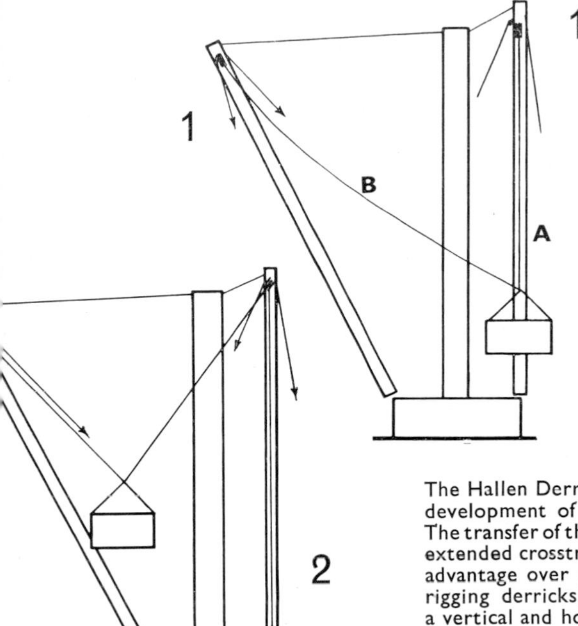

General Cargo

It is usually fastest and cheapest to unload general cargoes by shore cranes and where they are available a ship will rarely be called upon to use its own gear. Occasionally, when working cargoes such as timber, ships' derricks or cranes will be used at one or more hatches to supplement the shore facilities. However, the practice varies from port to port and depends upon factors

The Hallen Derrick is a sophisticated development of the simple derrick. The transfer of the derrick guys to the extended crosstrees has an enormous advantage over previous methods of rigging derricks, as they operate in a vertical and horizontal plane above the boom and the downward pull exerted by conventional guys is eliminated. In addition, the derrick guys have been adapted to function as topping lifts. When the derrick is topped or lowered in the outboard position, the guy pennants traverse the rounded surfaces of the "D" plates, and protection is given to the spiral coil wire inner pennants by an inner covering of brass rings and an outer covering of galvanised steel rings. Three power units are incorporated, one each for the guys and one for the hoisting tackle. The slewing and topping of the derrick is controlled by a "joy stick". Movement to left or rights slews the derrick, whilst movement fore and aft tops or lowers the derrick. A second lever controls the hoisting tackle. One man can operate the derrick and two consoles are provided, one to port and one to starboard, so that the operator can work in the most advantageous position.

Hallen derricks in New Zealand Shipping Co. vessels can be rigged to handle loads of up to 30 tons. The hoisting tackle shown—a single wire —has a safe working load of 3 tons.

The single Stulcken heavy lift derrick, like the Hallen derrick, combines topping lift and derrick guys and also has the advantage over the conventional heavy lift derrick in that it can be used at either of two hatches without dismantling the very heavy gear and lifting the derrick boom around the mast. Furthermore, the angle at which the posts are set eliminates the need for stays. Its disadvantage is that it adds considerable top weight to the ship.

In the dual 500 ton set-up illustrated, four topping lifts are used. The derrick booms are linked together by a complex series of swivels and synchronisation of the two cargo runners is achieved by spreading the load through six interlinked sheaves.

The *Uhenfels* belongs to the "Hansa" Company and the derrick is shown under test at maximum outreach.

Photo courtesy: Blohm & Voss.

which are apparent only to those concerned with the operation.

Similarly, it is difficult to understand why such a wide variety of shipborne gear is being used, even by ships engaged on the same routes and carrying basically the same cargoes. Many things are taken into consideration before the final decision is made. The overall cost is the first factor and this must be judged against the number of days in a year that the equipment may be expected to be used. The time taken on an average voyage will also be considered, since the installation of high efficiency gear in a ship travelling at 12 knots is—unless there are other factors—an uneconomic proposition. Also taken into consideration are the speed with which cargo can be brought to the ship's side and the ability of the dock workers to clear discharged cargo at a rate sufficient to prevent bottlenecks and the subsequent slow-down in the speed of operation of the gear. Many ports are still tied to manual methods and a ship engaged primarily in voyages between such ports will be fitted with the simplest and cheapest equipment. Finally, there is still possibly an element of conservatism amongst shipowners which reacts against new methods, and also the salesmanship which is obviously brought to bear in one of the most competitive sectors of industry in the world.

Cargo liners, which up until about 1950 presented an almost uniform appearance, are now notable for the wide variety of cargo handling gear which they carry. The following are some examples:

Complete outfit of conventional derricks.
Part derricks and part cranes.
Complete outfit of Hallen derricks.
Part cranes, part Hallen derricks.
Complete outfit of cranes.

Bulk Carriers

Similarly, and for much the same reasons already mentioned, bulk carriers are equipped with a variety of gear. Unlike cargo liners, however, only the same type of equipment is usually installed in one ship. At the present time these ships have either conventional derricks, cranes or gantry cranes such as the Munck-loader. At large ports it is possible to see ships carrying similar cargoes using any of these methods of cargo handling.

Oil

As with ores, oil is found in a wide variety of terrain, and often the problem of piping it to the sea is a major undertaking. For example, oil was recently discovered in Alaska and it will require a 900-mile pipeline to reach the nearest port which is ice-free throughout the year. Loading points therefore vary from quays alongside refineries, which were built as close as possible to the fields, to jetties built miles out to sea with the oil being pumped through submarine pipelines. At the moment the *Universe Ireland* can load a full cargo at only one place in the Persian Gulf; at a jetty 10 miles off the coast of Kuwait, which is equipped with hose gantries sufficiently high to deal with the rise and fall of the tide and the difference in height of the loading deck which arrives empty and leaves loaded.

Off Das Island, in the Abu

The *Clan Sutherland* loading a 152-ton stator for Sydney. Also included in the same shipment was a 162-ton stator for Melbourne and a 91-ton turbo-alternator for Fremantle. The *Clan Sutherland*'s heavy lift derrick has a safe working load of 165 tons and the photograph clearly shows the massive construction of such a derrick. The main post is heavily stayed with steel rods and massive slings are shackled to lugs on the stator. Two winches are coupled together to raise the topping lift and two winches are also used to power the cargo runner. Single winches operate the derrick guys.

Photo courtesy: Cayser, Irvine & Co. Ltd.

Dhabi area, a jetty has been completed which can handle the 200,000-ton BP tankers. At Kharg Island the consortium of companies operating in Iran have built a loading jetty with 60–70 ft. of water and able to handle tankers with tonnages considerably in excess of 200,000 tons. The cost of this installation is estimated to have been more than £65,000,000. Similar facilities are being provided at Forcados in Nigeria, also for BP.

Two methods of overcoming the problem of depth of water have been developed for use in areas where good weather conditions can be expected for most of the year. They are:

1. The fixed-point mooring device, a steel tower fitted with a loading arm to which tankers can moor and swing with wind and tide. The oil reaches the loading point by submarine pipes, and flexible pipes make the connecting link with the tankers' loading hoses.
2. A similar device, but in the form of a buoy which is very securely moored.

Both of these loading points stand in very deep water and can therefore be used by tankers of any size—subject to sufficient sea-room in which to swing. Considerable experiment has been carried out with these devices, and it is considered that they can be made sufficiently large and strong to provide moorings for storage hulks and the necessary machinery to pump oil from underwater wells to hulks and then to tanker, thereby eliminating the present procedure of pumping the oil to tank farms ashore and then to more conventional loading installations.

With the exception of certain installations where large tankers discharge into smaller tankers, oil is almost always discharged in close proximity to storage tanks or refineries. The installations are

The all-weather meat loading conveyors at Bluff Harbour, Southland, New Zealand. The five loaders are adjusted to the hatches of the ship being loaded, although it is necessary to supplement these with the ship's gear in vessels with six or more hatches.

Photo courtesy: High Commissioner for New Zealand.

Inside the meat loader shed. The conveyors are loaded from insulated railway wagons and the holds are cooled down to the minimum possible temperature before loading commences.

Photo courtesy: High Commissioner for New Zealand.

similar in all respects to the loading jetties.

A mooring buoy, with pipelines to the shore, is to be moored off Durban so that 200,000-ton tankers can discharge full loads.

An experiment has been carried out in connection with the discovery of oil in Alaska. A large tanker which had been converted into an icebreaker successfully forced the North West Passage. The use of this route will obviate the use of pipelines across Canada, and a special fleet of icebreaking tankers is now being planned.

The Munckloader

Munckloader is the trade name for a ship-mounted gantry bridge crane developed and manufactured by Munck International A/S, Bergen, Norway.

In principle, the ship can be completely loaded or unloaded by the crane operator only—eliminating all manpower in the holds or on deck. In practice unions are not always prepared to agree to this, but technically the problems have been solved.

The cranes travel on rails along the deck and have hinged jibs projecting over the ship's side in order to make it possible to pick up or place loads on the quay or in barges.

The operator's cabin is suspended under the trolley, giving the operator visual control of the load in all positions as well as in the cargo holds.

The Munckloader can be fitted with roof and curtains to permit operation under any weather conditions.

During a voyage the cranes are parked on special stowage brackets and two men need about 15 minutes to park or rig them.

Safe working loads vary between 10 and 50 tons. A variety of cargoes can be handled and the following special equipment can be used (normally only the 40-ton crane is suitable for containers).

By May 1969, 83 Munckloaders had been fitted or were on order for 49 ships.

Coal

Coal is loaded by gravity. In the N.E. of England advantage has been taken of the high, steep river banks, and platforms (staithes) have been built out over the water. Railway hopper wagons are run on to the staithes (by gravity) and the coal is discharged through the bottom of the wagons into chutes.

At Goole, coal from the West Riding collieries is brought down the river in barges. Each barge, with a capacity of 40 tons, is in fact a rectangular floating container. Barges are chain linked together and after rounding curves

Discharging a cargo of packaged timber at a South Wales port. At the forward end of the ship fork lift trucks are placing the packages for easy access by the derrick. On the quay several packages are moved at one time to storage by heavy fork lift trucks or onto semi-trailers for onward carriage.

The derricks are working in union purchase and are unusual in that the derrick guys are operated by individual powered winches. A further development is the placing of the winch controls so that one man can operate both cargo runners.

Immediately ahead and to the left of the ship is one of the ore carriers chartered to the British Iron and Steel Company and running regularly to South Wales.

Photo courtesy: British Transport Docks Board.

in the river they are straightened by buffers. On arrival at Goole the compartments are floated individually into a submerged cage, lifted by an elevator, turned over and the coal shot into a chute.

In South Wales, the elevator system is used, but with rail wagons again as the link with the collieries. The wagons, which are fitted with hinged ends, are run onto a traverser which moves them under the elevator. The wagons are lifted, tipped, and the coal discharged into a chute. Empty wagons are run onto a second road parallel with the loading road.

All coal chutes are fitted with baffles to control the rate of feed into the ship and to prevent loss through breakage.

At industrial plants, coal is discharged by crane and grab. Most domestic coal depots are also equipped with cranes and the coal is discharged into large hoppers, whence it can be weighed and sacked or loaded into bulk lorries. At very small ports coal is still unloaded by ship's derrick and the old-fashioned trip bucket.

Meat

For many years meat has been loaded by cranes and slings, but recently equipment has been devised to speed up this process. Pocket belt elevators have been installed at Bluff and Timaru. Considerable reductions in loading times have been achieved, and an unusual feature of this system is that unlike most others it is still possible to use the ship's gear and attain still faster loading rates.

A new battery of mechanical unloaders at the Royal Victoria Docks is expected to handle 9,000 carcases or 300 tons of cartons per hour. In the majority of ports, however, meat continues to be unloaded by shore crane or ship's derricks and slings.

Packaged timber being unloaded at Tilbury. All operations on the quay, including receiving from ship, sorting, piling, unpiling and delivery to transport are carried out by a shed crew of 20 men, all of whom are able to drive the mechanical equipment on the berth (fork lift trucks and side loaders) and all jobs are interchangeable.

The vessel being unloaded, unlike that in the previous illustration, has a full set of cranes. The centre line bulk head dividing the hold is carried down for several feet. This, together with the high hatch coamings allows the ship to be loaded with grain without the use of shifting boards.

Photo courtesy: Port of London Authority.

Sugar

The following information relates to the plant at the Thames refinery of Messrs. Tate and Lyle Ltd.

Bulk sugar carriers are moored to an L-shaped jetty. Barges and coasters may be berthed on the shore face.

Two 12½-ton electro-hydraulic level-luffing travelling cranes are accommodated on the crane deck and have a discharge capacity of up to 400 tons per hour. 12½-ton and 7½-ton grabs with a sugar capacity of approximately 6½ and 4 tons respectively, deliver the sugar on to a 48-in. wide conveyor along the crane deck. This conveyor passes through a 10-ft. diameter steel tube to the weighing and sampling machines. The sugar is then carried on another conveyor belt into the 20,000-ton raw sugar shed and the 10,000-ton raw sugar silos.

Lumber

The Canadian lumber trade has been subjected to radical development during the last few years, and this can best be illustrated by the activities of the Seaboard Shipping Co. Ltd., established in 1936 to control and improve the efficiency of lumber shipments made by its affiliate, the Seaboard Lumber Sales Co. Ltd. This company handles the products of over 50 saw mills, plywood and other lumber product plants on the coast of British Columbia.

In 1961 the first Canadian shipment of packaged lumber was made and in 1964 the port of Hull received the first such cargo to arrive in the U.K. In 1968 the company had about 20 ships on charters of up to five years, many of which had been built to their specifications. In the same year the Indian M.S. *Chennai Ookkam* left Vancouver with timber, plywood and shingles totalling 20,463,000 f.b.m. The deck cargo was stacked 20 ft. high, and this alone weighed more than the complete cargo of a Libery ship. By reducing the number of loading and discharging ports, the Seaboard Shipping Co. calculates that the following economies have been achieved:

The M.S. *Chennai Ookam.*

The M.S. *Hove*. Hundreds of cargoes such as this arrive at ports all around the United Kingdom during the summer and autumn. Deck cargoes of loose timbers are supported between baulks of timber which fit into slots on the bulwarks. Chains are passed across the cargo and secured with quick release gear for use in an emergency.

	1963	1968
	No. of days for 5,000,000 f.b.m.	No. of days for 10,000,000 f.b.m.
Loading	20	10
Sailing time	40	28
Discharging	25	12
Total	85	50

There is, however, a limit to the number of ships which can use the ports able to receive the larger bulk carriers—the company mentioned is not, of course, the only organisation operating these ships—and cargoes are also despatched to smaller ports in smaller ships; four recently chartered (also built to specification) by the Seaboard Shipping Co. have a capacity of about 11,000,000 f.b.m. A typical cargo for one of these ships is 10,400,000 f.b.m. of timber and other wood products for delivery to Nantes, Antwerp and Amsterdam. The international nature of shipping is demonstrated by these ships. One is Norwegian, two are British while the fourth is registered under the Liberian flag and carries a Chinese Master and crew.

The ships of the Seaboard Co. are equipped with cranes of 5- or 8-ton capacity, but many bulk carriers engaged in the lumber trade have conventional derricks; a few are fitted with Munck-loaders. Loading is almost always by ship's gear from jetty or barge. Discharging in the U.K. is by shore crane, sometimes supplemented by ship's cranes or derricks, or entirely by ship's gear.

Scandinavian and Russian timber continues in the main to arrive as loose cargo and, although larger ships are now coming from Russia, the majority are short-sea trade vessels often carrying as little as 400–500 tons to the small outports. The procedure for loading and discharging is similar to that for the large bulk carriers.

NOTES:

1. "Lumber" is a general term for wood products and includes sawn timber, plywood and shingles.
2. In relation to the Canadian trade "logs" means squared off baulks of timber. Under Canadian law, the export of unworked tree trunks is prohibited.

Bananas

The method of loading and discharging bananas described is that followed by Messrs. Elders and Fyffes Ltd.

Plantations are advised in advance of the quantity of fruit

A loose timber cargo aboard an old steamship. The planks are stowed as closely as possible to the winches and the derricks remain topped during the voyage.

required to be loaded into a particular ship. Bananas are cut on the same day that they are loaded. The traditional head-carrying loading still exists, and at some ports the ships are required to lay off and receive their cargo from barges carrying between 500 and 1,000 cartons. The method being increasingly used, however, is the conveyance of the fruit by conveyor belt and gravity rollers to the ship's side, where the cartons are passed by hand through side doors.

At ports in the U.K. all Fyffes bananas are unloaded by electrically-operated pocket conveyor belts and transferred directly into insulated goods wagons.

China Clay

China clay, the product of the quarries around St. Austell, is exported from the small harbour of Par and from Fowey.

At Par, the clay, in fine powder form, arrives in 15- to 17-ton (net) tipping lorries. This is unloaded on to portable elevators and thence by chute into the ship's hold. A high output rate is maintained and it is normal for a ship loading 600–900 tons to be completed in a day.

At Fowey, ships up to 10,000 tons deadweight are loaded by conveyor and chute from railway wagons. Whilst waiting to berth, ships are moored with both bower anchors and lines from the stern to a buoy.

Ships from Par take china clay coastwise and to a wide variety of Continental and Mediterranean ports. The larger ships from Fowey take their cargoes to ports all over the world. The following figures indicate the tremendous increase in exports since 1948 and also the number of ships which enter Fowey and Par during the course of a year.

	Par			*Fowey*
	Foreign	Coastal	Total Tons	Total Tons
1948	62,530	86,977	149,507	N/A
1954	118,785	103,497	222,282	536,543 (1956)
1960	438,485	171,577	610,062	540,629
1967	783,282	146,156	929,438	740,558

The M.S. *Viking I*. Built by Kaldnes M/V A/S, Tonsberg, in 1961. Length overall 324·8 ft., beam 60 ft. Two Pielstick diesels, 11,060 b.h.p., twin screw, service speed 20 knots. The first car ferry in service from the U.K. with bow and stern doors. 800 passengers and about 150 cars.
Photo courtesy: D. W. A. Mercer.

Iron Ore

Ore deposits are often found in remote and mountainous regions, and one of the major considerations in deciding whether or not to exploit the deposit is the cost of transport, and sometimes the possibility of organising transport at all. Ore is, however, such a valuable source of raw material that considerable trouble is taken to provide an outlet. To develop the deposits in Western Australia new roads and townships were built. A 70-mile standard gauge railway was built to the coast and at Finucane Island, one of three ports constructed, over 8,000,000 cubic yards of solid rock was removed to allow ships of 60,000 tons to reach the point at which the loading facilities were constructed.

Iron ore is loaded by conveyor belts and gravity and the installation at Finucane Island, illustrated on page 160, is typical of general practice. When more than one chute is used, the largest bulk carriers can be loaded in a matter of hours.

Iron ore is discharged by means of grabs which can unload either on to a conveyor belt for conveyance to storage dumps or into smaller storage hoppers from which railway trucks can be loaded. The vessel being unloaded at Port Kembla, N.S.W. (page 161), is the *Iron Flinders* which was purpose-built for the voyage to this port from Whyalla, South Australia.

The pyramids of ore can be clearly seen and, as this ship was built solely for the carriage of this product, it is able to load in each hold. Also visible are the wing tanks which are filled with water to trim the ship and produce an easier motion in a seaway. The hatch covers are of the "single pull" type and automatically stack away into the stowage positions. The reverse action covers the hatches in a few minutes.

The *British Admiral* discharging at BP's Angle Bay Ocean Terminal. The crane on board is used for handling the large flexible hoses.

The curved topsides of the hull are a feature of modern tankers and bulk carriers, and greatly add to the longitudinal strength, besides dispensing with long runs of welded joints. The *British Admiral*, although a large ship, will be small in comparison with the new BP tankers being built; these have deadweight tonnages of over 200,000 tons.

Photo courtesy: British Petroleum Co. Ltd.

Port of London

At the end of the 18th century and the beginning of the 19th century, congestion of shipping in the London river had produced conditions of near chaos. Pilfering and stealing from cargoes had reached enormous proportions, and, in an effort to relieve the situation, private companies built enclosed docks as close as possible to the city area. These were the London Docks (commenced in 1802), the East India Dock (1806) and St. Katherine's Dock (opened in 1828). The West India Docks were opened in 1802 by William Pitt.

These measures did much to safeguard and speed up the handling of cargoes, but the expansion of trade following the introduction of steamship services led to the need for still more facilities and in 1868 the Millwall Docks were built. The Surrey Commercial Docks were also developed at this time. 1855 saw the opening of the Royal Victoria Docks, to be followed in 1880 by the Royal Albert Dock. In 1886 a dock system was excavated at Tilbury.

In 1908 the Port of London Authority was set up by Act of Parliament to assume overall control of the enclosed docks and tidal stretches of the river—a distance of 69 miles.

The first major project undertaken by the P.L.A. was the construction of the King George V Dock in 1921. This dock, together with the Victoria and Albert Docks constitutes one of the largest enclosed docks in the world, and for many years it has handled vast quantities of meat, grain, sugar and general cargo, part of it being discharged into coasters and barges for distribution to outports and up-river depots and factories. Export cargoes go to all parts of the world and ships of every important British shipping company, and foreign ones as well, can be seen there.

Constant development and enlargement of facilities have been a feature of the P.L.A.'s operations since they first took over from the many independent and sometimes inefficient companies, and in recent years new warehouses and open storage areas have been provided for palletised and unitised cargoes. Containers pass through several of these dock systems although they must be lifted by ordinary cranes or ship's equipment. Nevertheless, the continued expansion of trade, the move towards mammoth ships, the inability to expand docks in areas encircled by industrial undertakings and out-dated road and rail systems led the P.L.A. to the decision to develop Tilbury at an initial cost of about £30,000,000. Here was the space required for a really modern dock system, and a basin connected with the older docks has berths and large back areas for container ships, bulk timber carriers and roll on/roll off ferries. On the riverside a new grain terminal has been built and the new jetty will be able to berth 65,000-ton bulk carriers. Discharge will be into the granary for storage, or into coasters, barges, bulk grain lorries or rail wagons.

Shippers have not been slow to take advantage of the new facilities and the United States Lines inaugurated a weekly service. Some of the largest timber shipments received in the U.K. have been discharged here. A container service to Rotterdam is now fully established and the decision of the OCL and ACT Consortia to adopt Tilbury has ensured that London will be Britain's premier port for many years to come.

Simultaneously with the Tilbury developments, major dredging projects have been carried out in the estuary. Existing channels have been re-aligned and a completely new channel—the Knock John—provides 48 ft. of water at high water neaps and 51 ft. at highwater springs. Tankers of over 100,000 tons deadweight are now entering the river and a recent cargo topped the 130,000-ton mark. Research into the pattern of tides and currents higher up the river has not only enabled the P.L.A. to re-align and deepen river channels, but has also led to the remarkable reduction in maintenance dredging from 500,000 to 10,000 hopper tons annually.

The P.L.A. maintains a fleet of ship-handling tugs and a comprehensive range of salvage tugs and wreck-raising gear. Dry docking facilities are available at several points on the river and the new Tilbury dry dock recently accommodated a tanker of nearly 60,000 tons deadweight. Private ship-repairing yards provide first-rate facilities, and the P.L.A.'s own police force patrols dock areas and the river.

The Port of London handles 33% of the U.K.'s exports and 27% of her imports. Total cargo handled amounts to about 60,000,000 tons—48,000,000 tons of this total being accounted for by imports. A breakdown of the principal items in the import figures gives the following:

	Millions of tons
Petroleum and products	29·0
Coal	10·0
Cereals	1·5
Timber	1·75
Sugar	1·0
Paper pulp	0·75
Paper and paper board	1·0
Meat	0·5
Metallic ores	0·5
Iron	0·5
Steel	0·5

The River above London Bridge

London Bridge is the upper limit of navigation for large ships, and those vessels which proceed above it are limited in size by the depth of water, clearance under bridges and the turning areas available in the higher stretches of the river.

The first movement seen on the flood tide is usually that of the smallest oil lighters which pass Westminster from about one hour after low water. Larger lighters follow and until about an hour before high water 10 or more of these craft will pass. During the same time tugs with anything between one and six barges in tow can also be seen. About two hours before high water the large "flat iron" colliers make their way up, preceded by the sea aggregate dredgers which berth just below Battersea.

For an hour or so on either side of high water there is little movement, but once the ebb begins to flow the oil lighters begin to make their way down river. Tugs which are usually engaged on a shuttle service also get under way, and for a period of about three hours there is a steady flow of traffic. Again at low water there is little movement except for the pleasure craft, which during the spring and summer run services between Westminster, the Upper Pool and Greenwich. In addition to the types of craft already mentioned there is a limited traffic of coasters, usually varying in size between 200 and 500 tons, and a small number of self-propelled cargo lighters.

This is the general pattern of shipping which repeats itself every day throughout the year, although there is a considerable reduction in tug traffic over the weekend. Whenever possible vessels take advantage of the tide, and only occasionally will a tug, usually running free, or an oil lighter make its way against the current. The other exceptions are the colliers, dredgers and larger coasters which come downstream about 1–2 hours after the onset of the flood tide.

With few exceptions, towage on the Thames is carried out by contract and it is therefore difficult to determine what particular activity a tug is engaged upon at any given time. There are two distinct types of contract, the first in which a tug and barges will be used exclusively by one particular organisation or company, the other in which tugs and barges will be carrying the products of various companies according to immediate requirements.

The *Tudorose* is engaged in the former capacity. She is owned by Flower and Everett Ltd., who hold a contract with the Greater London Council, one part of which involves the removal of refuse from the City of Westminster. Sixteen barges are used in the operation and these are taken from Grosvenor Dock, up to six at a time, by the *Tudorose*. On occasions another tug is involved. The loaded barges are towed down river on the ebb tide to Pitsea where the refuse is used to reclaim marsh land. Empty barges are returned on the flood tide and during a year more than 180,000 tons of refuse is moved in this way. Refuse from the City of London is similarly dealt with from Wallbrook Wharf.

M.T. *Charlock.*

M.T. *Ine.*

The motor tug *Charlock* is owned by Charrington Lighterage Co. Ltd., and is employed on a wide variety of tasks. The photograph shows her towing two oil barges loaded with domestic fuel oil en route from Coryton to the distributing centre at Isleworth. The *Charlock* can, however, also be seen as far down the river as Tilbury, towing barges from ship's side to riverside wharves and between the enormous number of wharves which line the river and creeks.

Unfortunately the lighterage industry on the Thames is declining and this is noticeable in the amount of traffic passing above London Bridge. On a normal day, however, at least ten tugs will pass Waterloo Bridge on a single tide and the products moved by water include meat (in insulated barges), timber, waste paper, scrap iron, grain and limited amounts of general cargo. Daily consignments of cement are towed from cement works on the lower reaches of the river to Hurlingham by tugs owned by the Blue Circle Portland Cement Co. Ltd., and carrying that company's funnel insignia.

The *Charbrook* works a five-day week with a limited amount of overtime, and will be in continuous employment for more than eleven months in the year.

The crew consists of Master, Mate and Engineer.

The *Ine* (250 deadweight tons) is typical of a large number of West German and Dutch coasters.

The motor dredger *Yolanda* was one of the dredgers employed in deepening the Sea Reach channel and creating the new Knock John Channel.
Photo courtesy: Port of London Authority.

The *Yolanda* was built in Holland in 1966 and is owned by the Westminster Dredging Company. She is 315 ft. long overall with a beam of 55 ft. The maximum dredging depth is over 65 ft. and the hopper well has a capacity of nearly 4,000 tons of spoil. Dredged material is sucked on-board mixed with water through the long dredging pipe and is deposited as the water is forced through channels in the hopper. A full load is taken aboard in an hour and this can either be dumped through hopper doors or pumped ashore. When working in the estuary the dredged material was used in reclamation work at the new Tilbury Docks.

The controllable pitch propellers and all dredging operations are controlled from the bridge and the vessel moves ahead at about 3 knots; free running speed is about 14 knots. Two crews are carried and work carries on for 24 hours a day.

M.T. *Tudor Rose.*

They are some of the smallest cargo ships to make crossings of the North Sea and the Channel, and their limited dimensions permit extreme flexibility of operation. They can be seen on the rivers and canals of Northern Europe and they are able to penetrate some of the smallest rivers around the coast of the U.K.

The *Ine* has been chartered to Freight Express Ltd. for the past seventeen years and is employed between near Continental ports and London. The photograph shows her en route to Fulham, where she discharges cargoes of grain, stone and asbestos. Outward bound the *Ine* carries scrap iron and waste paper, loading mainly at Fulham and Bow Creek.

The dredging of aggregate (gravel, sand and shingle) from the sea bed is very much a post-war development, and there are now several companies occupied in supplying an industry which makes ever-increasing demands for raw materials.

The *Bowbelle* is owned by British Dredging (London) Ltd. and operates from the company's installation at Nine Elms. Subject to fog and other adverse weather conditions this vessel and the larger *Bowsprite* operate a 36-hour cycle from despatch to despatch; 24 hours are spent on passage and dredging, 12 hours being discharged by shore grab and cranes. In normal conditions four round voyages are completed in one week, five in the second.

M.T. *Bowbelle*

The aggregates are dredged from various grounds off the Essex coast, but mainly in the Shipwash. A small dredger is continuously employed seeking fresh deposits of workable material. When a suitable area has been discovered and the Crown Commissioner's consent obtained, the larger dredgers move in. These vessels make use of a 36-in. diameter suction pipe which can operate in depths up to 50 ft. By the use of screens the material

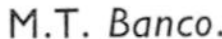

M.T. *Banco.*

M.T. *Conformity*.

taken on board can be varied between pure sand or stones. In practice the cargo brought back normally consists of 80% stones and 20% sand. Like the colliers the *Bowbelle* leaves Nine Elms about one hour after low water and will come up river about two hours or so before high water.

Oil is carried up river in large quantities on every tide and most of the major oil companies are concerned in this operation.

The lighters employed, which are suitable for estuary and river work, vary between about 200 tons and 900 tons, and all of them are equipped with power discharging pumps.

Oil is loaded at the Isle of Grain, Thames Haven, Shell Haven, Purfleet and Dagenham and the time taken on the voyage to the concentration of depots between Battersea and Hammersmith will vary. However, as an example the lighters operated by Shell B.P. take 3½ hours from Shell Haven or Thames Haven. They arrive before high water, pump out and return on the ebb. This is repeated on a basis of three tides on duty and one off and the lighters are only withdrawn from service for overhaul for up to one month each year. The largest vessels carry a crew of Master, Mate, two engineers and two deckhands; the smallest, Master, Mate and Engineer. At the moment working conditions for the crews vary from company to company.

The photographs show the *Banco*, one of the largest lighters owned by Beagle Shipping Ltd., and the Everard coastal tanker *Conformity*.

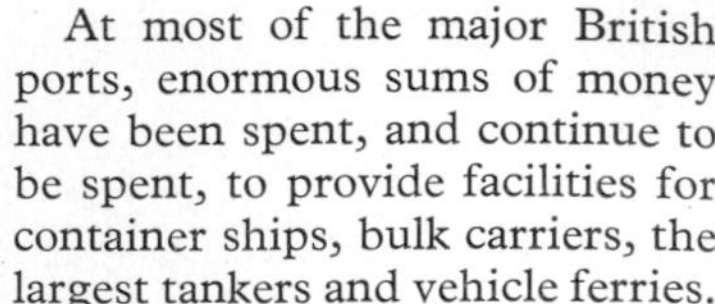

At most of the major British ports, enormous sums of money have been spent, and continue to be spent, to provide facilities for container ships, bulk carriers, the largest tankers and vehicle ferries.

The first major container facilities were provided at Felixstowe and Grangemouth for the ships of Sea-Land Service Inc., running from Rotterdam to New York and Baltimore, with connecting services to Florida, Texas, Puerto Rico and the West Coast of the U.S.A.

Container facilities have also been provided at Greenock. Liverpool has provided a container area, and further container installations and additional deep-water berths are in course of construction. Southampton has developed a container area on reclaimed land to receive vessels of the Atlantic Container Line, the United States Line and the Dart Container Line (Armement Deppe S.A. (Antwerp) and Bristol City Line of Steamships Ltd.); two Paceco-Vickers Portainer cranes have been installed on the 1,000 ft. berth.

Various ports are carrying out detailed studies of currents and tides to determine the most economical method of developing deep channels for the largest tankers and a project is planned for the Humber to export coal in

The loading jetties at Shell's Cardon Refinery on the Paraguana Peninsular. This installation is the largest in Venezuela and processes over 8 million tons of crude oil every year. As in many other parts of the world a township has been built with medical services, schools, stores and social amenities for refinery employees and their families.

Photo courtesy: Shell Petroleum Co. Ltd.

On facing page 153:

The Royal Group of Docks, London (*above*). Tilbury (*below*).

Photos courtesy: Port of London Authority.

Photos courtesy: Port of London Authority.

A development in one of the older dock systems. P Berth of the Millwall Docks has been completely rebuilt to provide extensive shed facilities and unobstructed approaches to the ship's side. During the winter months the car ferries *Black Watch* and *Black Prince* run between London and the Canary Islands. Their car decks become cargo holds and once a week large quantities of tomatoes, vegetables and fruit arrive. The cargo is handled by fork lift trucks, both inside the ship and on the dockside and about 300 tons an hour can be delivered either to the sheds or directly on to lorries.

During the summer months the *Black Watch* runs between Newcastle and Bergen as the *Jupiter*; this vessel is jointly owned by the Bergen Line and the Fred Olsen Line. The *Black Prince* leaves London during the summer and sails between Harwich, Kristiansand and Amsterdam.

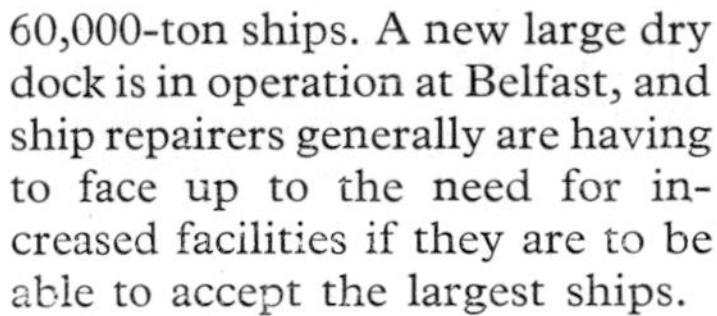
60,000-ton ships. A new large dry dock is in operation at Belfast, and ship repairers generally are having to face up to the need for increased facilities if they are to be able to accept the largest ships.

At Southampton the Princess Alexandra Dock, which was used by the cross-channel ships of British Rail, has been turned into roll on/roll off berths for ferry services to France and Spain. Illustrations (page 158) show how the inner dock was filled in and modern facilities built on the reclaimed land. At the berths are the Swedish Lloyd Line's *Patricia*, which runs every four or five days to Bilbao, one of the Normandy Ferry's ships, which operate a frequent service to Le Havre, and one of Thoresen's ferries which provide a daily summer service to Le Havre and Cherbourg. The vessel in the foreground is the *Viking IV*, which is used to convey export cargoes and does not carry passengers. In winter the *Viking III* is transferred to the Harwich–Bremerhaven service of Prins Ferries.

(1) *Electro hydraulic grab for coal*
The grab has an effective payload of 11 tons. The crane operates at 50 cycles per hour but with a hopper on deck and a conveyor belt to shore, the speed of operation can be increased to 75 cycles per hour; an hourly discharge rate of 900 tons is achieved.

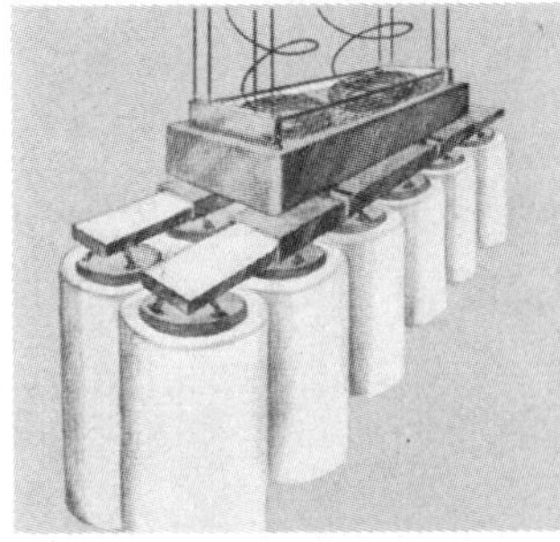

(2) *Vacuum clamp for newsprint and kraft*
12 rolls of newsprint are handled at a time at 42 cycles per hour. In the Norwegian M.S. *Rondeggen* (9,180 tons deadweight) the three Munckloaders can completely discharge the holds in about 10 hours.

(3) *Fork handling for packaged lumber*
On the same ship up to 1,200,000 f.b.m. are carried as deck cargo. Only one crane at a time is used for discharging this cargo and the whole operation can be carried out at the rate of 400 tons per hour with one man in the crane and two men on deck to help, if required, to get the fork into position.

(4) *Container handling*
A special strong back is fitted for handling containers. It is estimated that with adequate shore facilities, 25 60,000-lb. containers can be unloaded and a similar number loaded within 75 minutes.

From one to three Munckloaders are usually installed in a ship, the reasons for the variation being similar to those mentioned in the paragraph about cargo gear selection.

In the recently developed Munckloaders the two main beams and four legs of the standard crane have been replaced by a single main beam and two curved legs. This construction allows longer loads to be handled, and where two of these type are installed they can be operated in tandem any required distance apart, thus allowing long and heavy loads to be handled (up to twice the lifting capacity of each crane). The two cranes can also be locked together electrically and driven as one unit by a single crane operator from one or other of the cranes.

View of main deck with 25-ton Munckloader.
Photo courtesy: Shipping World & Shipbuilder.

The Port of Rotterdam

Rotterdam is the largest port in the world. Originally it was a small town situated on a series of shallow waterways, many of them silted up at the mouth and few of them deep enough to carry ocean-going sailing ships. Various measures were taken to open up the port, and the turning point in Rotterdam's prosperity was the construction of the Nieuwe Waterweg (New Waterway).

The first dock—the Binnenhaven—was dug in the 1870's, and developments, which are still proceeding, have been carried out in the order shown on the map. Some harbours, however, have been enlarged at various times as the need for particular facilities arose.

Rotterdam has always been a port closely concerned with bulk cargoes and the demands of the growing Ruhr industries did much to account for this. The recession of the '30s clearly indicated that a port so dependent upon the political and economic circumstances of other countries was not firmly based, and post-war plans to develop the port further laid great emphasis on the attraction of industry to the large area of immediately available and potential sites around the harbours.

The first big development after the war was the Botlek complex which provided for ships up to 65,000 tons deadweight. The movement of bulk cargoes from Waalhaven to Botlek enabled the former system to be used for general cargo ships. At the same time extensions and reconstructions in the Eemhaven, Prinses Margriethaven and Prinses Beatrixhaven produced an extra eight miles of berths for similar purposes.

The proposal to construct the Europoort was adopted in 1957, and by 1967 ships of 140,000 tons deadweight were entering. As in the case of London, new projects at sea were required to match the port development, and a 12-mile channel with a depth of 75 ft. was completed by 1966. These works, together with the extensions to Europoort at Maasvlakte will make possible the acceptance of vessels up to 250,000 tons deadweight at any state of the tide and at any time of day or night, for there is not a lock gate in the whole length of the system from the Hook of Holland to Rotterdam.

Further developments include the excavation of a new complex on the North Bank immediately opposite Europoort. Here the increasing roll on/roll off trade will be handled, and it is estimated that by 1976 some 20,000,000 tons of cargo will pass through each year. In this system, too, a terminal will be provided for the passenger ships which make scheduled calls at Rotterdam.

The plan to attract industry has been highly successful and many firms concerned with petrochemicals have built plants close alongside the jetties and quays. Basic to the future of Rotterdam's industrial prosperity is the continued and increasing need for oil, grain, coal, timber and various ores. On the completion of Maasvlakte, the Shell Oil plant will have an annual capacity of 25,000,000 tons. BP are to make this port the centre of a European depot supplying 20,000,000 tons annually. Esso's output will be 16,000,000 tons and other companies to use Europoort will be Caltex/Esso, Gulf Oil, Konam and Mobil Oil.

Rotterdam is also the hub of a pipeline system which extends as far down the Rhine Valley as Frankfurt. Several large German refineries receive their supplies in this way and an increasing number of Dutch industrial undertakings are linked to the line. During 1966 the pipeline to the Rhine Valley itself accounted for 12,000,000 tons of crude oil and the overall capacity is scheduled to reach 40,000,000 tons, with the possibility of still further increases. Approval in principal from the Belgian Government has also been received to the construction of a pipeline to Antwerp.

The following figures indicate the magnitude of business handled by the port:

Year 1967

Over 30,000 sea-going vessels passed through the port and about 250,000 calls were made by inland craft. Seaborne cargoes amounted to 141·4 million tons; international Rhine traffic 45·0 million tons.

General cargo: 22,500,000 tons.

Bulk cargoes: 40,200,000 tons (7,200,000 tons grain, 17,800,000 tons ore and 6,400,000 tons coal).

Oil: 78,700,000 tons.

Subsequent years have shown a steady general increase of business to the order of over 10% annually. (In 1968 over 114,000 containers were loaded or unloaded in the port.)

Ship repairing and shipbuilding yards with 31 floating docks with a lifting capacity of 400–54,000 tons, 6 construction docks and 18 slipways.

Approximately 675,000 passengers land or embark.

The tanker *Molda* berthing in the Europoort. The *Molda*, which has a deadweight tonnage of 143,620 on an overall length of 932 ft. and a beam of 142 ft. is owned by A/S J. Ludwig Mowinckels Rederei of Norway.

The tug *Steenbank*, with a h.p. of 1,250, belongs to the N.V. Nieuwe Rotterdamse Sleepdienst and was specially built to operate in the Europoort and the North Sea. The tug on the left is the *Azie* of the same company and also has a h.p. of 1,250.

Photo courtesy: Port of Rotterdam.

This illustration of an Atlantic Container Line vessel loading in the Prinses Margriethaven gives a fine impression of the size of these ships and the equipment needed to handle the shore ramp.

Photo courtesy: Port of Rotterdam.

A Sea Land container ship unloading containers with a gantry crane in the Prinses Beatrixhaven. The semi trailers in the foreground are examples of the type of equipment developed for the road transport of containers.

Photo courtesy: Port of Rotterdam.

Discharging grain with floating elevators on each side of the ship. The barges, which are loaded simultaneously, find their way to many inland European ports through complicated systems of canals.

Photo courtesy: Port of Rotterdam.

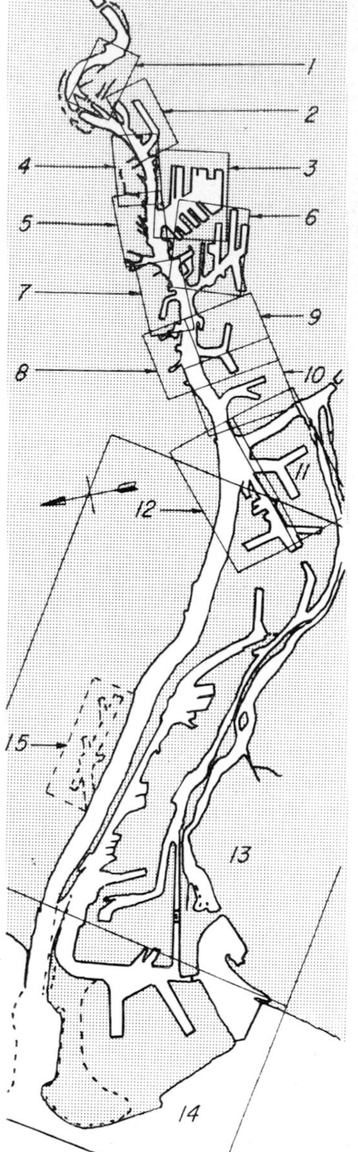

THE HARBOURS OF ROTTERDAM

1. Binnenhaven 1878; Entrepothaven 1879; Spoorweghaven 1879; Persoonshaven 1901; Noordereiland. **2.** Rijnhaven 1887-94; Wilhelminakade 1714-1915; 1e Katendrechtse haven 1887-88; 2e Katendrechtse haven 1895-96; Maashaven 1898-1905. **3.** Waalhaven 1907; **4.** Parkhaven/Parkkade 1890; Westerkade St. Jobshaven/St. Jobskade 1890; Lloydkade; Schiehaven/Middenkous 1890-1909; Westzeedijk. **5.** Ijselhaven/Ijselkade 1910-15; Lekhaven/Lekkade 1910-15; Keilehaven 1910-15; Merwehaven 1923-32. **6.** Eemhaven 1942; 1e Eemhaven; 2e Eemhaven; Prinses Beatrixhaven 1964; Prinses Margriethaven 1967; Prins Willem-Alexanderhaven. **7.** Wilhelmshaven 1914-15;Wiltonhaven 1924.**8.** Vulcaanhaven 1913; Kon. Wilhelminahaven 1905. **9/10.** 2e Petroleumhaven 1940-55; 1e Petroleumhaven 1929. **11/12.** 3e Petroleumhaven; Chemiehaven; Botlek; St. Laurenshaven 1954-57. **13.** Europort; Seinehaven; Brittanniehaven; Calandkanaal; 7e Petroleumhaven; 5e Petroleumhaven; 4e Petroleumhaven; Scheurhaven; Beneluxhaven; Beerkanaal; Petroleumhaven 1958-68. **14.** Maasvlakte, continuing. **15.** Rijnpoorte, continuing.

Outer Dock Southampton before development.

Photo courtesy: British Transport Docks Board.

Aerial view of Princess Alexandra Dock, Southampton, showing roll-on/roll-off berths used for services to France and Spain for passengers, freight and accompanied cars. This development has been carried out by the British Transport Docks Board at a total cost of £2½ million.

Photo courtesy: British Transport Dock Board.

The Shell Refinery at night.
Photo courtesy: Port of Rotterdam.

Cars
Traditionally, cars have been carried by cargo liners, but the rapid rise in exports has led shippers to find additional shipping space. This has been achieved by equipping bulk carriers with portable decks, which stow away flush with the ship's side when they are required to load a bulk cargo. Some years ago a shipment of 500 cars was considered as something remarkable, but in May 1968, the Ford Motor Company Ltd. exported a consignment of 2,000. The ship employed was the *Thorbjorg* of 22,000 tons and the illustration shows a battery of cranes on the quayside at Dagenham lifting the cars on board with a type of sling which has long been in use for this particular operation.

Assuming a steady development of the export trade in cars, there is little doubt that consignments will also become larger. The Japanese are building a drive on/drive off carrier which will carry 4,000 cars and they are confident that this ship will find full cargoes.
Photo courtesy: Ford Motor Co. Ltd.

Loading bulk clay into the ship's hold by means of a mobile conveyor at the company's Port of Par.
Photo courtesy: English China Clay Groups

Floating elevators and shore elevators discharging grain from the *Francois L.D.* in the Bollekhaven at Rotterdam.

The *Francois L.D.* was built in 1962 and is engaged in world-wide tramping. Her owners, Louis Dreyfus et Cie., are one of the leading French companies concerned with tramp ships and bulk carriers.

Photo courtesy: Port of Rotterdam.

At the new deepwater port at Finucane Island, Western Australia, the 30,000-ton *Harvey S. Mudd* takes on a load of iron ore from Mount Goldsworthy.

Photo courtesy: High Commissioner for Australia.

Shoreham (Sussex) "B" Station is typical of the discharging plants used by electric power stations in the U.K. Two coal unloaders and one Kangaroo crane, each rated at 300 tons/hour, unload the colliers and weigh the coal before loading conveyors transport it to the boiler bunkers or stocking-out yard. Each grab has a capacity of 6 tons and a 3,400 deadweight tons collier can be discharged in 9½ hours—i.e. under favourable conditions a ship can be "turned round" in a tide.

Photo courtesy: Central Electricity Generating Board.

The 19,100-ton iron ore carrier *Iron Flinders* was designed and built in the Broken Hill Pty. Co. Ltd. Shipyard at Whyalla, South Australia.

Photo courtesy: High Commissioner for Australia.

Coal hoists at Swansea. The *Marwick Head* is a vessel of 1,786 gross tons and was built in 1952. She is owned by Henry and Macgregor Ltd. of Leith. The *Marwick Head* is equipped with a full set of derricks and is capable of carrying a wide variety of bagged and bulk cargoes. The second ship is the *Deerwood*, owned by France, Fenwick & Co. This vessel has a deadweight tonnage of 8,140 and can engage in coastal or international voyages.

Photo courtesy: British Transport Docks Board.

The Port of New Orleans

The Port of New Orleans is the second largest port in the U.S.A. and is located about 110 miles above the two principal entrances to the Mississippi River. A third, and new entrance, the "Tide-water Channel", enters the Gulf to the west of the other two entrances and reduces the sailing distance by over 30 miles.

Each year about 90,000,000 tons of cargo passes through the port, and more than 25,000,000 tons of this total is accounted for by imports and exports involving over 5,000 ships. The balance represents the tonnage carried on the inter-coastal and inland waterway systems.

Imports consist mainly of coffee, lumber, sugar, molasses, hemp, bauxite, bananas, burlap, refined oil products, sisal, jute and general commodities. Exports are sulphur, machinery, grain and meals, cotton, chemicals, fertilisers and refined oil products. The grain exports from New Orleans are the largest in the U.S. and account for a large proportion of export cargoes.

New Orleans has over 70 miles of deep-water berths for ocean-going ships and a further 100 miles of quays for inland waterway craft. The port is also served by seven independent trunk railways, feeding into a "Public Belt Railroad" which distributes wagons to the various quays and storage areas. The nature of general cargo handling is indicated by the fact that the wagons which arrive from the north with export cars are often loaded on the return journey with a similar number of cars imported from Europe.

This port has world-wide cargo liner connections and 1,200 scheduled sailings each year are provided by more than 100 companies. Containers are handled in increasing numbers and the provision of special facilities is under way. It is estimated that by 1970, 288,000 containers will be in use and regularly passing through the port.

There are 18,000 miles of inland waterways radiating from New Orleans, and they are divided into the Mississippi River System and the Gulf Intra-coastal Waterway. The latter system stretches westward to Corpus Christi and Brownsville on the Mexican border. Eastward it reaches Apalachicola, from which port ocean-going barges continue to Tampa in Florida. Similar ocean-going barge tows sail direct from New Orleans across the Gulf to Tampa.

The main inland waterway system embraces the Rivers Mississippi, Ohio, Allegheny, Monogahela and Kanawha. These rivers and linking canals permit navigation as far north as Chicago, where connection is made with the Great Lakes and the St. Lawrence Seaway. In winter months, cargo normally exported by the St. Lawrence is carried in barges to New Orleans. Car manufacturers at Detroit regularly use New Orleans as the port of export.

Some of the many cities served by the waterways are: Cincinnati (Ohio), St. Paul (Minnesota), Pittsburgh (Pennsylvania), St. Louis (Missouri), Omaha (Nebraska), Kansas City (Kansas), and Memphis (Tennessee).

Cargoes are carried between the principal cities on scheduled services or on voyage or period charter as required. The vast extent of this system is indicated by the following average voyage times:

From New Orleans to:

Louisville	11 days
Cincinnati	13 days
Chicago	14 days
Pittsburgh	16 days
Minneapolis	17–18 days

To New Orleans from:

Louisville	5 days
Cincinnati	9 days
Chicago	11 days
Pittsburgh	13 days
Minneapolis	11 days

These figures are based on towage performances with barges of mixed cargo. Specially designed barges in integrated tows attain much higher speeds. Average progress upstream is about 8 knots, covering about 100 miles per day; 150–200 miles per day is normal progress downstream.

The barges vary in size considerably, the largest being about 300 ft. long. Barges of this size are operated by Esso and they are towed five at a time. The overall length of such a tow is 1,195 ft., which enables the whole unit to pass without difficulty through the largest locks which are 1,200 ft. in length.

Tugs as well vary considerably in dimensions and power. The small "harbour" tugs can be in the 50–60 ft. range, whilst the largest are about 175 ft. long with an engine output of 6,000 h.p. These particular tugs can tow without difficulty up to 37 barges. In all, the total weight carried equals that of a medium sized bulk carrier.

Hundreds of tugs and literally thousands of barges find employment on the system. One company, for instance, operates 23 tugs and 520 barges.

A wide variety of cargoes is carried in bulk, the following being the principal commodities:

oil, coal, pig iron, sand, grain, chemicals, liquid and natural sulphur, salt, potash, fertilisers, sugar, steel, coke, lumber, cars, shells, anhydrous ammonia, newsprint, cement, fluorspar, butane, bricks, ores and piping.

In addition enormous tonnages of general cargo are carried.

It should be noted that on the Mississippi tugs are often known as "tug boats" and whilst the word "tow" continues to be used, the majority of barges are now pushed.

New Orleans is also a centre for the manufacture of drilling mud. Several companies offering off-shore services to oil rigs are also based in the port.

This photograph shows how the tugs push the barges. Larger tows are secured three or four abreast.
Photo courtesy: Collection of Eric Johnson.

The tug *Mobile*, owned by Coyle Lines, tied up alongside the tow at the river bank.
Photo courtesy: Collection of Eric Johnson.

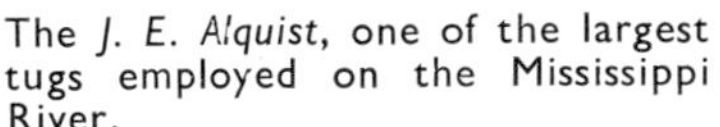

The *J. E. Alquist*, one of the largest tugs employed on the Mississippi River.
Photo courtesy: Collection of Eric Johnson.

A "stern wheeler", the *Gen. John Newton*, of the Corps of Engineers, New Orleans District. The Corps of Engineers are responsible for dredging and many other maintenance duties in U.S. harbours.

Photo courtesy: Collection of Eric Johnson.

The *President* which takes sightseers on daily tours of the harbour. The *President* is a modern vessel and is probably one of the finest of its type in the world.

Photo courtesy: Collection of Eric Johnson.

An off-shore mooring–loading buoy. This particular installation carries two cargo lines and a third for bunker oil.

Photo courtesy: Shell Petroleum Co. Ltd.

The Shell tanker *Sivella* loading crude oil at the Halul Island buoy. The flexible pipes are buoyed and are lifted onboard by crane, or, as in this case, a derrick. The *Sivella*, which was built in 1963 and has a deadweight tonnage of 79,327, was one of the last Shell tankers to have the bridge and officers' accommodation amidships. This vessel flies the French flag and is employed on voyages from the Persian Gulf to French refineries. Other Shell tankers are registered in the U.K., Bermuda, Holland, the Dutch East Indies, Venezuela, Germany and Argentina. Vessels flying the flag of Liberia are on bareboat charter but carry traditional Shell names.
Photo courtesy: Shell Petroleum Co. Ltd.

Another view of BP's terminal in Milford Haven. Jetties have to be of extraordinarily strong construction to withstand the pressure of large tankers. The extensions to the jetty are "dolphins" to which mooring lines are secured.

Berthing the largest tankers is a delicate operation, and it has been calculated that a safe approach speed should not exceed 18 ft. a minute. Such progress is almost impossible to judge accurately by eye and Esso, in collaboration with the Royal Radar Establishment, have developed a low-velocity measuring radar device. A pilot model is now in use at the Company's Milford Haven Terminal as a berthing aid for all ships over 150,000 deadweight tons; it has proved to be particularly valuable at night.

The tugs in attendance belong to the fleet of R. and J. H. Rea Ltd. and were especially constructed for service in the Haven. All of them have comprehensive outfits of fire-fighting equipment including monitors which can deliver water at high pressure.
Photo courtesy: British Petroleum Co. Ltd.

Grain

The loading and discharge of grain follows a standard procedure. The grain arrives at the dockside by high-speed conveyor belts and is transferred into pipes which shoot it into the holds by gravity. Several tubes are sited at each berth and are flexibly mounted so that all holds can be loaded simultaneously.

Discharging is carried out by floating or shore elevators. The grain is pneumatically sucked from the holds, whence it is moved by conveyor belt to storage. All holds are discharged at the same time.

Modern elevators can achieve discharge rates of up to 1,600 tons per hour.

The bulk grain terminal at Geelong in the State of Victoria. Exports from Australia go mainly to mainland China, U.S.S.R., Japan, Germany and India.

The Greek tramp steamer alongside is typical of ships which were built in the early '50s and before the advent of the bulk carrier.

Photo courtesy: High Commissioner for Australia.

The Ports of London and Rotterdam are concerned mainly with the export of manufactured goods and the import of bulk products from every part of the world.

Vancouver is primarily an exporter of raw materials and the following figures give an idea of the trade of such a port and the markets which it serves:

March 1968 (other than grain)

Commodity	*Tonnage Exported* (thousand tons)	*No. of Countries of Cargo Destination*
Lumber	105·6	12
Logs, poles, ties	26·7	12
Flour	1·8	6
Milled cereals	4·1	7
Tallow	0·9	1
Canned or preserved fish	1·4	20
Distilled alcoholic beverages	0·03	6
Apples	0·008	2
Raw hides and skins	0·5	4
Potash	125·3	5
Nickel and alloys	0·2	8
Zinc and alloys	0·9	2
Lead and alloys	0·06	1
Copper and alloys	0·004	1
Copper in ores, concentrates	16·0	1
Other metals in ores, concentrates	2·0	5
Coal (bituminous)	109·5	1
Coal (anthracite)	20·8	1
Sulphur	111·4	6
Rapeseed	20·0	2
Mustard seed	0·01	1
Flax seed	10·7	4
Asbestos	5·8	14
Inorganic chemicals	0·4	9
Paper	15·0	13
Newsprint	0·8	5
Wood pulp	42·0	13
Plywood and veneer	3·9	9

The total lumber export of 105,600 tons was the equivalent of 70,408,650 f.b.m. One f.b.m. equals a volume of 12 × 1 × 1 in.

One standard equals 1,980 f.b.m.

1,400 tons of canned or preserved fish was made up of 105,712 cases.

Vancouver Exports of Grain for April 1968 *in Bushels*

Vessel	*Destination*	*Bushels loaded*
To U.K./Continent:		
Kotor	Italy	1,470,000
Paola d'Amico	Spain	74,189
Cheshire	Holland	45,023
Georgi Benkovski	Italy } Malta }	193,512
		1,782,724
To Orient:		
Grand Integrity	Japan	633,291
Deltadrecht	China	1,332,837
Eirini L.	Japan	520,800
Otowasan Maru	Japan	339,734
Romandie	China	1,120,000
Amstelveen	China	646,987
Himmerland	Japan	820,849
Bronxville	Hong Kong }	35,840
	Malaysia }	35,840
Pleiades	China	494,667
Atlantic Sunbeam	Japan	496,267
Ancora	Japan	180,880
Hollands Burcht	China	858,667
Ever Peace	Japan	621,133
Yannis	China	575,680
Ever Sureness	Japan	499,333
Atlantic Freedom	Japan	551,122
Atlantic Fury	Japan	688,903
Gudrun Bakke	Hong Kong	72,240
King Minos	Japan	533,867
Tai Lung	Taiwan }	169,792
	Korea }	41,557
Kanangoora	Japan	688,903
Eiho Maru	Japan	1,701,120
Britta	China	1,542,613
		15,202,922
To Central and South America:		
Fernbank	Venezuela	77,131
Ithica Island	Venezuela	124,133
		201,264
To Others:		
Ola	U.S.S.R.	479,733
Otradnoe	U.S.S.R.	493,173
Orehkov	U.S.S.R.	493,733
Ithica Island	Jamaica	246,400
Ostrogozhsk	U.S.S.R.	492,800
Zagorsk	U.S.S.R.	198,427
		2,404,266

Wheat pouring into the hold of a ship. Owing to the danger of the cargo shifting and capsizing the ship, holds must be fitted with shifting boards unless deep longitudinal bulkheads are fitted. In older ships the boards formed a complete bulkhead, the top of which can be seen in the open hatch. Strengthening was added by wire pennants between the supporting pillars and the ship's side.
Photo courtesy: High Commissioner for Australia.

Total for one month, over 19·5 million bushels in 34 ships.

For the month of March total inward cargo amounted to 138,117 tons. During April, 149 deep-sea vessels entered the port, 151 cleared outwards.

CHAPTER 11

12-Passenger Cargo Liners

TRAVEL in 12-passenger cargo liners has been possible for very many years. Prior to 1939, the accommodation provided was often very simple and, even allowing for rises in prices, probably relatively cheaper than it is today. £1 per day, and occasionally even less, was considered to be adequate for a passage anywhere in the world. The present popularity of this type of travel is not therefore the direct result of the withdrawal of passenger liners.

The S.S. *Bencruachan*, the latest ship in the fleet of the Ben Line (managers: Wm. Thomson & Co., Edinburgh) and the first large British cargo liner to have twin funnels. In 1959 the *Benloyal* entered service and was the first of a series of ships of similar tonnage and a service speed of 20 knots. In 1966 the *Benwyvis* was built with a service speed of 21 knots, and was followed by the *Benalbanach* in 1967 and the *Bencruachan* in 1968.

The *Bencruachan* is powered by a turbine as opposed to the diesels of earlier ships. With a deadweight tonnage of 14,650 she becomes one of the largest ships trading to the Far East.

Twelve passengers are carried on weekly sailings from London, Southampton or Hull to various Far East ports. For the time being the ships are routed via the Cape and calls are made at Singapore, Hong Kong, Pusan, Yokohama and Kobe on the express service. Other services call at ports such as Port Swettenham, Bangkok, Labuan, Kota Kinabalu, Sandakan and Tawau. The *Benervachan* has sailed from Japan to London in under 26 days.

Photo courtesy: Ben Line Steamers Ltd.

The Blue Star cargo liner *Wellington Star*, 12,539 gross tons. All ships of this company's fleet carry up to 12 passengers on various routes to South Africa, Australia and New Zealand. Three ships also maintain a service between Glasgow, the U.S.A. and the North Pacific coast of Canada.

A full passenger service with accommodation for about 50, all First Class, operates between London and Buenos Aires. Calls are made at Lisbon, Las Palmas/Santa Cruz de Tenerife, Rio de Janeiro, Santos and Montevideo. On the return Las Palmas and Santa Cruz are omitted. The round voyage takes approximately 47 days.

Photo courtesy: Blue Star Line Ltd.

Shipowners themselves have always held definite views on fitting out ships for 12 passengers. On the one hand the opinion is held that little, if any, profit arises from this activity, that the claims of cargo and passengers cannot be reconciled, and that passengers should travel by liners where these are available. Other companies have accommodation in all their cargo liners and consider that the undertaking is profitable. One or two passenger/cargo companies not only provide facilities in their cargo ships, but advertise them alongside their passenger ships.

In modern ships the accommodation provided is of exceptional quality and everything possible is done for the passengers' comfort. Nevertheless there are restrictions. Very few of these ships carry doctors or stewardesses and it is not unusual for companies to decline to accept people over the age of 70. In certain circumstances a certificate of good health is considered to be sufficient. In addition, passengers must provide their own entertainment, since no staff is carried for this purpose.

Passengers also have to accept

BOAT DECK

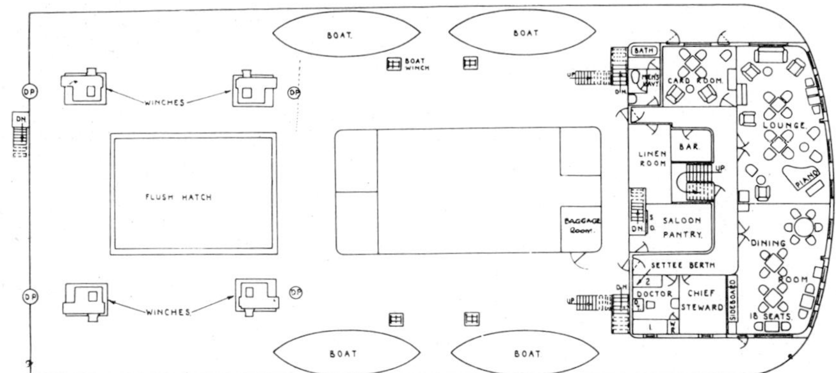

PASSENGER DECK

The accommodation on the *Wellington Star*. Each cabin has its own private bath or shower and lavatory. Passengers have the use of the boat deck where there is adequate space for deck games.

Photo courtesy: Blue Star Line Ltd.

that the ship's business is primarily cargo carrying and for this reason the actual date of departure cannot generally be notified more than two or three weeks in advance. Ports en route may be changed and no guarantee can be given as to the time to be spent in particular ports at the end of the outward voyage. Nevertheless schedules are followed reasonably faithfully and arrival at the home port is usually on the advertised day or very near to it.

The effect which container ships will have on 12-passenger cargo liners is difficult to estimate. Clearly with turn-round time of as little as two days and schedules which contain no more than three ports, there is no point in travelling in these ships, and accommodation has not been provided. It is also possible that the number of berths will decline as several companies who have hitherto provided accommodation in their short sea passage ships are building new vessels without passenger provision. However, passages will be available to most of the world's principal ports for some years to come and during that time the waiting lists of prospective passengers will no doubt get longer and longer.

Examples of Services with Passenger Accommodation

Marseilles–Genoa–Fremantle–Adelaide – Melbourne – Sydney – Brisbane–Noumea (Messageries Maritimes, 4–5 passengers, "Velay" Class ships).

Mombasa–ports to Capetown, then Fremantle, other Australian ports, and return via Mauritius (Royal Interocean Lines, 10–12 passengers).

Amsterdam – Cristobal – Los Angeles – San Francisco – Vancouver, returning via Seattle or Portland, San Francisco and Los

A single-berth cabin. All the accommodation is air-conditioned with individual controls in the cabins.

The main passenger lounge, *Bencruachan*. The Ben Line is noted for the standard of its service, which is equal to that usually found in large passenger liners.

Photos courtesy: Ben Line Steamers Ltd.

The dining saloon of the *Ben Cruacher* which is shared with the ships' officers. Asian stewards are employed in all the company's vessels. A permanent swimming pool is located within a screened area at the after end of the superstructure.
Photo courtesy: Ben Line Steamers Ltd.

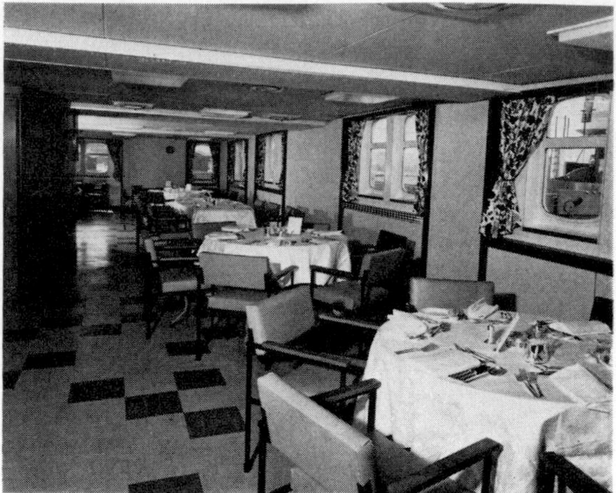

The dining saloon on the *Port Chalmers*, The previous *Port Chalmers*, built in 1933, also carried a similar number of passengers. The cabins were comfortable and fitted with hot and cold water, but bathrooms, of which there were three, were provided for general use.
Photo courtesy Port Line Ltd.

Angeles (North German Lloyd, 12 passengers).

Portland / Vancouver / Seattle – Yokohama – Kobe / Osaka – Pusan, Inchon – Okinawa – Keelung – Manila–Hong Kong–Yokohama–Seattle (American Mail Line, 8–12 passengers, "American Mail" Class ships, de luxe for 12 passengers on "Washington Mail" Class ships).

New York–Tenerife, Las Palmas, Dakar, then several West African ports to Douala. Return via same ports to New York (Farrell Lines, 12 passengers, "African Crescent" and "African Glade" Class ships).

Hamburg/Bremen–Rotterdam, Antwerp, Patras, Piraeus, Salonika, Izmir, Istanbul, Burgas, Constanta (German-Orient Line, 2-10 passengers depending upon ship).

London – Marseilles, Genoa, Leghorn, Naples, Palermo, London (Currie Line Ltd., 12 passengers, *Zealand*).

Liverpool–Dublin, Cork, Lisbon, Barbados, Trinidad, Belem, Manaus. Return via Belem, Fortaleza, Lisbon, Leixões, Le Havre, Rotterdam, U.K. port (Booth Line, 4–6 passengers, "Clement" Class or *Dominic*).

The *Port Chalmers* of 1933 had a deadweight tonnage of 11,600 on dimensions of 492 ft. overall and a beam of 65 ft.
Photo courtesy: D. W. A. Mercer.

The sail training ship *Nippon Maru*.

Photo courtesy Collection of Eric Johnson, New Orleans.

CHAPTER 12 Miscellaneous Ships

The Assembly Hall.

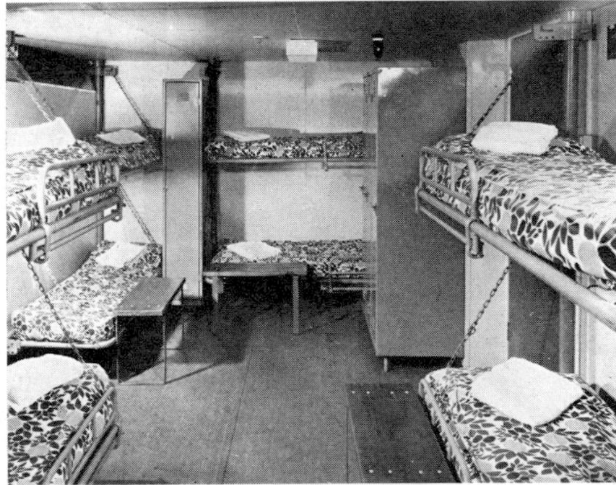

A Students' Dormitory.

Photo courtesy: B.I.S.N. Co. Ltd.

The School Ship

WHEN it was announced in Parliament that the rapidly contracting overseas commitments of the armed forces had made the continuing use of troopships an uneconomic proposition and that the Government had decided that existing charters would not be renewed and future troop movements would be carried out by air lifts, the British India Line, whose connections with trooping stretched back unbroken to the Indian Mutiny, were faced with the immediate problem of finding employment for the *Dunera.*

In the '30s B.I. troopships had undertaken cruises during the summer months and one particular charter by the School Journeys Association had proved to be particularly successful. On the strength of this experience and the outcome of some swift but concentrated research, the decision was made to inaugurate an entirely new form of sea travel—educational cruising. The *Dunera* was refitted and, complete with hall, schoolrooms, dormitories, a cafeteria and accommodation for a permanent staff of teachers, she carried out the first cruise in 1961. It was known at the time that only experience would show whether

The Cafeteria.

A Lecture Room.

Photo courtesy: B.I.S.N. Co. Ltd.

The S.S. *Uganda*. During refit, considerable additions were made to the superstructure. With the exception of derricks for handling stores, all cargo gear was removed. Additional lifeboats, including launches, were fitted.
Photo courtesy: B.I.S.N. Co. Ltd.

The S.S. *Neuralia*. The *Nevasa* was an identical sister ship.

such an enterprise could be continued through the winter months, but the company was sufficiently encouraged by results to place a second ship—the *Devonia*—in service in 1962.

Both the *Dunera* and the *Devonia* have now been scrapped, but their place has been taken by a third troopship—the *Nevasa*—and the *Uganda*, which had been withdrawn from the East African service. Some indication of the financial problems attendant upon the operation of these ships is afforded by the fact that the refit of the *Uganda* exceeded the original building cost by about £700,000.

S.S. UGANDA (1952)

Owners: BRITISH INDIA STEAM NAVIGATION CO. LTD.
Builders: BARCLAY, CURLE & CO. LTD.
Steam turbines
Twin screw
Service speed 16 knots
Length overall 540 ft.
Beam 71 ft.
Gross tonnage 14,430

The *Uganda* was designed for the company's U.K./East and South Africa Cargo/Passenger service, and by the time of her withdrawal in 1966 had completed 52 round voyages and carried over 42,000 passengers and nearly 750,000 tons of cargo.

After conversion to a Schoolship, accommodation was provided for 304 Cabin Class passengers (previously 200 First Class and 100 Tourist) and 920 students.

Facilities for Cabin passengers include a music room, dining saloon, smoking room, card room, writing room, two cocktail bars, shops and hairdressing saloon and a covered verandah leading to a swimming pool.

Students are berthed in 43 dormitories with two-tier bunks. The mess hall seats 300 at one time and is fitted for double cafeteria service. In addition, students have the use of 14 lecture rooms and a library/map and information room. A large common room is provided, also a swimming pool, launderettes, photographic room and hair-drying rooms.

Both Cabin passengers and students share the use of the assembly hall/cinema which seats over 400 people. A hospital block, staffed by two surgeons and two nurses, has four wards and an operating theatre.

The ship's company comprises 366 officers, petty officers and ratings, and includes a Director of Education, two Deputies and six matrons.

In 1961 the *Dunera* carried out 16 cruises and carried 1,436 Cabin passengers and 8,268 students. In 1967 the *Dunera, Devonia* and *Nevasa* completed 56 cruises and carried 11,065 Cabin passengers and 44,360 students.

A wide variety of cruises is offered, and itineraries include places as far apart as the Norwegian fjords, Leningrad, Stockholm to Alexandria (for Cairo), Haifa (for Jerusalem), Antalya (Turkey) and Madeira.

These educational cruises have become widely known, and have been joined by students from the U.S.A., Canada, several European countries and even Japan.

M.S. LADY DELIA (1966)

Owners: INTERNATIONAL OFFSHORE SERVICES
Builders: BROOKE MARINE LTD.
Two 8-cylinder Blackstone diesels, 1,600 b.h.p.
Twin screw
Service speed 12 knots
145 h.p. bow thrust unit
Length overall 170 ft.
Beam 37 ft.
Deadweight tonnage 730

The arrival in the North Sea of a number of drilling rigs has led to the need for an entirely new type of ship—the oil rig supply vessel.

The *Lady Delia* is typical of all the ships in this fleet and is equipped to carry out a number of functions.

Probably the most important is that of laying out anchors when rigs are moved to new locations. This can amount to taking on board and relaying up to eight anchors, and the crew of the near sister ship *Lady Alison* have moored a rig in 6½ hours, no small feat when it is borne in mind that each anchor weighs 15 tons. The earlier vessels had "A" brackets at the stern for lifting anchors, but newer vessels have a stern roller which has proved to be more successful.

The *Lady Delia* transports to the rigs everything that is needed. She has tanks which hold 66 tons of drinking water, 310 tons of industrial water, cement and barytes. There is also a freezing room with a capacity of 100 cu. ft., and food is carried in containers on the main deck. The crew totals 12 and there is additional accommodation for 12 passengers in three cabins. General cargo carried includes several hundred tons weight of conductor pipes.

The *Lady Delia*, like the other ships in the fleet, is classed at Lloyds for world-wide trading, and rigs have been serviced off the West African coast, the South Australian coast and in the Arabian Gulf. This vessel is completely air conditioned and the accommodation can be kept at a reasonable temperature in any weather conditions.

The largest vessels in the fleet, with 3,000 b.h.p., are also used to tow rigs and they are capable of steaming for more than 12,000 miles without refuelling.

The M.S. *Lady Delia*. The twin funnels allow a heavy duty winch to be worked under cover of the forecastle deck. This vessel is fitted with a Flume stability tank. The main engines, bow thrust unit, windlass and mooring winches can be remotely controlled from the bridge. The *Lady Delia* is also equipped with automatic gyro pilot, radar, echo sounder, direction finder, VHF and MF radio telephone and searchlight.
Photo courtesy: P. & O.

R.R.S. JOHN BISCOE

Owners: BRITISH ANTARCTIC SURVEY
Builders: FLEMING & FERGUSON
National diesel-electric motors, 1,450 s.h.p.
Single screw
Service speed 12 knots
Length overall 219 ft.
Beam 40 ft.
Strengthened for navigation in ice
Complement: 33 officers and crew, 34 scientific personnel

The R.R.S. *John Biscoe*.
Photo courtesy: British Antarctic Survey.

Special features of this vessel include the strengthening of the bow, the use of intermediate framing to stiffen the sides of the hull and the use of special steel which is resistant to sub-zero temperatures and impact with ice. Ice fins protect the propeller and rudder whilst the ship is moving ahead and an ice knife gives similar protection when working astern.

Every year in October, the *John Biscoe*, the R.S.S. *Shackleton* and a chartered ship of the Danish J. Lauritzen Line leave Southampton for Montevideo and Stanley, Falkland Islands. For the following five months they are engaged in relieving personnel and supplying stores to the stations maintained by the British Antarctic Survey in and around the Grahamland Peninsula.

The stores carried in these ships include, food, fuel, small aircraft which have insufficient endurance to make the flight South, sledges, snow cats, medical supplies and huts. The dogs for hauling sledges are bred in the South, but occasionally a few are brought in to introduce new blood.

The approach to a station is often a slow and arduous business, for although strengthened against ice, the *Biscoe* must take advantage of open channels or stretches of broken ice and can only force a way through solid ice of limited thickness. The ship is conned from the crow's nest on the foremast. Working on a coast can bring its perils and a change of wind can quickly build up pack ice. In these conditions progress is often brought to a standstill and it rests with the Master to decide whether to pull out or face the risk of total encirclement and consequent damage to the ship. On one occasion, when the *Biscoe* became trapped in this way, it became necessary to seek the assistance of a U.S. icebreaker to force a passage through otherwise inpenetrable ice. However, ice navigation has recently been made less hazardous by the use of satellite photography. Satellites photograph the whole of the British territory at regular intervals. Transmissions from the satellites to London are interpreted by experts and "ice forecasts" are prepared in much the same way as our own weather forecasts. The forecasts are then

Unloading a crate of stores onto a sledge. Note the use of the union purchase.
Photo courtesy: British Antarctic Survey.

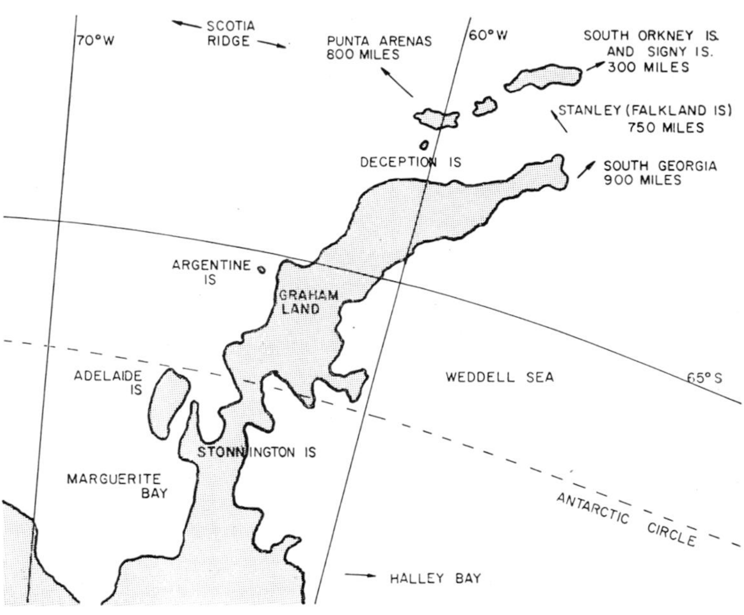

The area of operations of the *John Biscoe*.

transmitted to the *John Biscoe* via South America, and the Master is advised about suitable ways of approaching the bases. This system has proved to be most successful and much time has been saved as a result.

Another innovation of great use to the scientists engaged in surveying the Scotia Ridge is the system of satellite navigation. Bearings are taken of satellites and complex equipment turns the readings into latitude and longitude. The fix obtained is known to position the ship within a square of 200 yards.

On arrival at a station the stores and equipment are unloaded under the most primitive conditions and the *John Biscoe* carries two scows for ferry work between ship and shore. Occasionally it is possible to moor the ship alongside an ice face and the cargo is then discharged by derricks straight on to sledges.

Throughout the ship's stay in the South, ship-borne scientists are carrying out investigations and surveys, and it will be seen from the accompanying voyage schedule that some time is set apart for work on the Scotia Ridge, one of the world's most interesting submarine formations.

Voyage Schedule

14 Oct. –18 Nov.	Southampton–Montevideo–Stanley.
22 Nov.–29 Nov.	Stanley–Punta Arenas–Deception.
14 Dec.–30 Dec.	Deception–Scotia Ridge (geophysics)–Deception.
31 Dec.– 8 Jan.	Deception–island landings–Deception.
9 Jan. –17 Jan.	Deception–Punta Arenas–Stanley.
20 Jan. –31 Jan.	Stanley–Signy–Deception, Argentine Islands.
2 Feb. –18 Mar.	Argentine Islands–Marguerite Bay area–Argentine Islands.
20 Mar.–29 Mar.	Argentine Islands–Deception–Stanley.
31 Mar.–15 Apr.	Stanley–South Georgia–Signy–Stanley.
20 Apr. –18 May	Stanley–Montevideo–Southampton.

The *Biscoe*'s scientists, together with those who man the shore stations for a two-year period, are concerned with every aspect of physical science, whilst medical personnel investigate the effects on the human body and mind of long periods of physical and often mental strain.

Teamwork is the key to successful expedition work and the officers and men of the *John Biscoe*, who are recruited from the ranks of the Merchant Service, are vetted to ensure as far as possible that they have the

The M.S. *Kista Dan*, one of J. Lauritzan's ice strengthened ships. In this photograph, the hull is painted black and the funnel carries the device of this line. Antarctic ships now have red hulls and funnels so that they show up well against the ice.
Photo courtesy: British Antarctic Survey.

physical ability and temperament to face the arduous and often dangerous conditions encountered.

On return to the United Kingdom, the *Biscoe* refits and lays up at Southampton until the time arrives to store and work up for another voyage.

SAIL TRAINING SHIP NIPPON MARU

Owners: NAUTICAL TRAINING INSTITUTION OF THE JAPANESE MINISTRY OF EDUCATION
Builders: KAWASKI DOCKYARD CO. LTD., KOBE
Four-masted auxiliary barque
Two diesels, 1,200 b.h.p.
Speed on engines 11 knots
Length between perpendiculars 260 ft.
Beam 42 ft.

The recent "Tall Ship" races have done much to re-awaken interest in sail and the beneficial effects which can result from a spell in a sailing ship. However, a distinction has to be made between these ships which exist for the purpose of character training, such as the *Winston Churchill*, and those which have the serious purpose of training naval or merchant navy cadets. The *Nippon Maru* belongs to the latter group, and whilst some accept that service in such a ship produces benefits, there are many who claim that it is quite irrelevant to the navigation of modern ships.

There is no sail training ship of the size of the *Nippon Maru* in the U.K. and service on such a ship is not a prerequisite to obtaining a mate's ticket. Some countries do require such service and sail training ships are likely to continue in existence for some years to come.

The *Nippon Maru* has accommodation for 120 cadets and a permanent crew of 66 officers and men. Cadets have eight-berth dormitories and the use of a dining room fitted with tables and benches. The crew quarters are of extremely high standard, the officers being housed at the after end of the long poop deck. A dining room with cabins leading off is lit by a skylight.

The vessel can be steered from two positions: the forebridge and at the after end of the poop—in true sailing ship style.

Apart from the fitting of an additional bridge and wheelhouse above the main bridge, the *Nippon Maru* has remained unaltered externally in 39 years. It has not been possible to find out whether the internal arrangements remain the same, but there is no reason to believe that the information given above is incorrect.

C.S. MERCURY (1962)

Owners: CABLE AND WIRELESS LTD.
Builders: CAMMELL LAIRD & CO. (SHIPBUILDERS AND ENGINEERS) LTD.
Diesel electric, 6,000 s.h.p.
Twin screw
Service speed 14·5 knots
Steaming range 8,000 miles (60 days)
Length overall 473 ft.
Beam 58 ft. 6 in.
Gross tonnage 8,962
Deadweight tonnage 5,817
Lightweight cable capacity 1,300 miles in three tanks. Also approximately 162 repeaters on deck. Also able to handle larger-capacity coaxial cable.

The *Mercury* is the cable layer in the Cable and Wireless fleet of one cable layer and five

Final stowage of cable in one of the storage tanks.
Photo courtesy: Cable & Wireless Ltd.

T.H.S. VEDETTE

Corporation of Trinity House.
One of two 40-ft. 20-knot diesel launches which operate the pilot service from Folkestone. These launches are extremely versatile and have proved their worth during more than 12 months' rigorous service. They have continued to operate in a Force 9 gale, but experience has shown that a larger vessel—the *Lodesman*—was required for extended service in such conditions.

The *Evi Livanos* was built in 1957 and has a deadweight tonnage of 20,124.

Pilots still board ships by rope ladder and a requirement of a pilot cutter is a clear uncluttered deck area from which the pilot can board.
Photo courtesy: Trinity House.

The C.S. *Mercury*. The twin-funnel uptakes have allowed the provision of a completely unimpeded working deck. The centre forward sheave is used for paying out cable. The other two are used for picking up damaged cable. The *Mercury* is strengthened for navigation in ice.
Photo courtesy: Cable & Wireless Ltd.

cable repair ships. Built at a cost of £2,000,000, this vessel has bow sheaves and stern chute. The forward gear can lay armoured cable in shallow water at speeds up to 8 knots and can exert a pull of 30 tons when picking up. The aft cable machinery can pay out cable at 8 knots and sustain a load of 6 tons. It is also capable of picking up cable at one knot against a pull of 10 tons and withstanding a surge of 20 tons.

During cable operations the vessel can be controlled from the bridge, or the bow/stern paying-out positions. Controls for the main engine, transverse propulsion unit and steering gear, together with instrumentation, are also fitted in "houses" near the bow and stern operating positions.

Navigating instruments include one shallow-water and two deep-water echo sounders, a submerged log, side-streaming log, a wire sounding machine for cable work, two radar sets, Decca Navigator, Loran, weather recorder and a radio direction finder. Two optical range finders are also fitted on the wheelhouse top.

The nerve centre of the electrical side of the cable operations is the transmission test room on the upper deck where cables and repeaters are tested and the positions of faults or breaks in the existing cables determined. On the lower deck is a large electrical workshop.

Cable layers can work in any part of the world in conditions varying from arctic cold to tropical heat. The accommodation for officers and crew of the *Mercury* has been planned to provide comfortable living quarters under these extremes, and high velocity "Colvinaire" air conditioning fan units have been installed in all living spaces and cabins. Air can be supplied warm, cooled or at atmospheric temperature, and the cable working space on the upper deck can also be warmed during cold weather.

The Captain, senior officers and senior cable representatives have private suites consisting of day-room and bedroom. The other officers are accommodated in large single-berth cabins on the boat and bridge decks. Single-berth petty officers' cabins are on the upper deck, with two-berth cabins on the main deck for ratings. Facilities for the crew include a laundry, deck tennis court and a swimming pool.

The crew of the *Mercury*, apart from the officers, are Spaniards recruited from the Vigo and La Linea areas.

The forward end of the working deck of the *Mercury*. The ship is approaching the buoyed shore end of the Capetown–Ascension Island Cable and is about to make the final splice.
Photo courtesy: Cable & Wireless Ltd.

The crew of 159 officers, petty officers and ratings is made up as follows:

Officers

- Captain
- 8 Deck Officers
- 9 Engineer Officers
- 3 Electrical Engineers
- 5 Cable Engineers
- 2 Submarine Cable Technicians
- 2 Pursers
- Surgeon
- (plus 6 spare berths)

Petty Officers

- Bosun
- Assistant Bosun
- 2 Bosun's Mates
- Carpenter

Chief Steward
2 Deck Engine Drivers
Fitter
Engine Room Storekeeper
Deck Storekeeper
Workshop Assistant
Assistant Deck Engine Driver
(plus 2 spare berths)

Crew

8 Quartermasters
40 Deck Ratings
16 Engine Room Ratings
25 Catering Ratings

Since commissioning in 1962, the *Mercury* has steamed over 270,000 miles and laid nearly 10,000 miles of cable. In 1963 she was in the Pacific for the cable link between Canada and Australia and in the following two years laid the SEACOM link between Singapore, Sabah, Hong Kong, Guam, New Guinea and Australia. The *Mercury* later laid the cable system between Bermuda and Tortola, B.W.I.

Cable layers can follow no set pattern of work. When not engaged on cable laying, the *Mercury* acts as relief ship for the cable repair ships which are located at strategic positions on the world's cable network and is ready at a minute's notice to sail, locate and repair a fault or break in a cable.

Cables and repeaters being loaded.
Photo courtesy: Cable & Wireless Ltd.

The following account of the *Mercury*'s activities between March 1967 and April 1968 indicates the variety of work undertaken:

On 6th March 1967 the *Mercury* arrived at Gibraltar after a passage of 1,071 miles, during which she had undertaken cable repairs. From that date until 10th October she was constantly engaged on repair work, having visited Vigo, Southampton, Plymouth and Malta. Passages included runs of 2,938, 1,813, 1,229 and 2,117 miles. During this time the *Mercury* was also in dock for a special survey and refit lasting about a month. Total distance steamed during this period was 17,445 miles.

The after deck cable machinery. In order to achieve infinitely variable speed control for all conditions of paying out cable, electro-hydraulic drive and braking was selected. Operated in conjunction with the aft cable gear is a taut wire machine made by Submarine Cables Ltd., which pays out piano wire simultaneously with the cable and indicates the actual mileage covered by the vessel over the ocean bed. This gives a reliable check on the percentage of slack laid in the cable to suit the contours of the ocean bottom.
Photo courtesy: Cable & Wireless Ltd.

		Miles
1967		
10 Oct. –15 Nov.	At Southampton. Loading approximately 1,300 miles of cable and 138 repeaters for the Capetown/Ascension Island cable.	
15 Nov.– 5 Dec.	On passage to Capetown.	6,319
5 Dec.– 7 Dec.	At Capetown.	
7 Dec.–18 Dec.	Laying cable.	
19 Dec.– 1 Jan.	On passage to Vigo.	4,140
1968		
1 Jan. – 3 Jan.	At Vigo.	
3 Jan. – 5 Jan.	On passage to Southampton.	617
5 Jan. –27 Jan.	At Southampton. Loading approximately 1,300 miles of cable and 137 repeaters for second stage of cable.	
27 Jan. –12 Feb.	On passage to cable ground.	4,721
12 Feb.–20 Feb.	Laying cable. At this point the cable was cut and buoyed-off to repair fault in earlier section of cable.	
20 Feb.–27 Feb.	On passage to Capetown.	2,083
27 Feb.	Called Capetown.	
27 Feb.– 1 Mar.	Passage and cable repair.	25
1 Mar.– 8 Mar.	On passage to cable ground.	2,081
8 Mar.–11 Mar.	Laying cable and completing final splice at Ascension.	900
11 Mar.	At Ascension.	
11 Mar.–21 Mar.	On passage to Vigo.	3,095
22 Mar.	At Vigo.	
22 Mar.–24 Mar.	On passage to Southampton.	643
24 Mar.– 7 Apr.	At Southampton, including dry-docking.	

M.V. JOHN ASHLEY (1958)

Owners: THE MISSIONS TO SEAMEN
Length overall 75 ft.
Beam 18 ft.

The parish of the *John Ashley* is a 70-mile stretch of river between Tower Bridge and the Medway ports. The Padre/Skipper visits the crews of colliers lying at buoys awaiting berths or carrying cargoes which are discharged into lighters and therefore do not come alongside.

The *John Ashley* is a floating club and chapel. She has a well-stocked library and film shows are given when requested. She is constantly used as a post office for sending messages and remittances and is often employed taking a sick man to hospital.

The core of these activities is the spiritual care of seafaring men, and the Padre receives a steady stream of men who wish to discuss their problems with a man of understanding. The routine of the *John Ashley* is to stay out for three days and return to base on the third night. Thus it is possible to tie up alongside ships at night, when the men are free to board the *John Ashley*. After family prayers, the men are invited to Holy Communion which is held at 7.45 before they turn to. From time to time seamen are prepared for baptism by the Padre and when they are baptised they are usually well supported by their shipmates.

The *John Ashley*, which is named after the founder of the Missions to Seamen, is maintained by voluntary contributions.

T.H.V. STELLA

Owners: CORPORATION OF TRINITY HOUSE
Builders: J. SAMUEL WHITE & CO. LTD.
Diesel electric, four 6-cylinder diesels by English Electric, 1,450 b.h.p.
Twin screw
Service speed 10 knots
Length overall 221 ft.
Beam 37·9 ft.

This vessel is fitted with an electrically powered towing winch, and triple headed capstan

The M.V. *John Ashley*.
Photo courtesy: Missions to Seamen.

The T.H.V. *Lodesman*.
Photo courtesy: Trinity House.

on the forecastle to facilitate the lifting and handling of buoys. A heavy derrick is also fitted to lift buoys which are normally 20 ft. long, 10 ft. in diameter and over 5 tons in weight. Moorings can weigh another 5 tons and the cost of a complete unit can be as much as £3,000. Carried in gravity davits are lifeboats and two heavy work boats, and crews of lighthouse tenders are probably the most proficient of any merchant navy personnel in small-boat work.

Accommodation is provided for the ship's company and also for the relief crews of light vessels and lighthouses.

The *Stella* is at present stationed at Penzance and is principally concerned with servicing the many lights around the South West Coast of England, including such famous names as the Bishops Rock, Longships and Wolf Rock lights and the Sevenstones Light vessel.

T.H.V. LODESMAN

Owners: CORPORATION OF TRINITY HOUSE
Builders: R. S. STOKVIS AND ZONEN, ROTTERDAM
Two Gardner type 8L3B 4-stroke diesels, 460 b.h.p.
Twin screw
Service speed 10 knots
Length overall 71 ft.
Beam 18 ft.

The *Lodesman* is the heavy-weather pilot launch which operates in the Channel when weather conditions are too severe for the 40-ft. launches.

In heavy weather speed is not the most important criterion, and considerable attention has been given to sea-keeping qualities, safety and the conditions to be experienced when laying alongside a larger ship for the transfer of the pilot.

The plan of the *Lodesman* has been specially adapted by Trinity House in conjunction with the consultants, Burness, Corlett and Partners Ltd., from the design of the R.N.L.I.'s 70-ft. all-weather lifeboat. Considerable modifications have been made to the deck and internal layout to the make the design suitable for pilotage purposes. In addition, the gunwales have been protected by extra heavy fendering, and twin screws and twin rudders have been incorporated to improve manoeuvreability. All engine controls are centred in the wheelhouse and the rudder is controlled by a conventional wheel, an electric power lever control and a remote wandering lead control.

Accommodation is provided for one officer and two crew. Seating is available for 12 pilots.

The T.H.V. *Stella*.
Photo courtesy: Trinity House.

M.S. THE LADY PATRICIA (1962)

The M.S. *The Lady Patricia* at Dublin. The cylindrical containers can be seen on the quay and is about to be loaded into No. 1 hatch by crane.

Photo courtesy: Arthur Guiness, Son & Co. (Dublin) Ltd.

Owners: ARTHUR GUINNESS, SON & CO. (DUBLIN) LTD.
Builders: CHARLES HILL & SONS LTD., BRISTOL
British Polar diesel, 1,210 b.h.p.
Single screw
Service speed 11·5 knots
Length overall 213 ft.
Beam 36·5 ft.
Gross tonnage 1,181

Messrs. Arthur Guinness, Son & Co. Ltd. were the pioneers of the bulk carriage of beer by sea, and commenced this type of operation in 1952 with the first purpose built ship, *The Lady Grania. The Lady Gwendoline* followed in 1953, to be joined by *The Lady Patricia* in 1962.

The Lady Patricia has a Sterne Freon refrigeration compressor which is capable of maintaining the required hold temperature in both summer and winter without hold insulation. The crew are accommodated in single cabins and the ventilation of this accommodation and the engine room is by a mechanical system.

The large bridge windows give all-round visibility and radar, echo sounder, Decca Navigator, Arkas automatic pilot and radio telephones are fitted.

The hull is protected by rubber belting. Two 4-ton electric cranes manufactured by Clark Chapman & Co. are fitted, and these handle the cargo at all ports.

Guinness is carried in aluminium or stainless steel tanks, each with a capacity of approximately 500 gallons. Full tanks, which weigh 2¾ tons, are designed for both fork lift and crane handling. The internal beer container is heavily reinforced and the bottom of each tank is recessed to rest on top of another.

Working both holds at once the ship can be loaded or discharged in under 10 hours and the ship can be turned around in one day if necessary.

The round trip to Liverpool from Dublin is 250 miles and to Manchester 320 miles. The pattern of sailings for the three ships is as follows:

	Departure from Dublin for *Ship A*	*Ship B*	*Ship C*
Monday			
Tuesday	Liverpool	Manchester	
Wednesday			
Thursday	Liverpool		
Friday			
Saturday		Manchester	Liverpool

The next week Ship A will follow Ship B's schedule and so on. Sometimes a Wednesday sailing to Liverpool is substituted instead of the Tuesday and Thursday sailings.

S.S. METHANE PRINCESS (1964)

Owners: BRITISH METHANE LTD.
Managers: SHELL TANKERS (U.K.) LTD.
Builders: VICKERS-ARMSTRONGS (SHIPBUILDERS) LTD.
Two Vickers-Armstrongs-Pametrada geared turbines, 12,5000 s.h.p.
Single screw
Service speed 17·25 knots
Length overall 621 ft.
Beam 81·75 ft.
Deadweight tonnage 12,200

The *Methane Princess* has a low deadweight capacity in relation to her overall dimensions. The reason for this is that the specific gravity of liquid methane is only about one half of that of crude oil. In addition, a considerable volume of the hull is taken up by the provision of ballast tanks and insulation. A crude oil tanker of similar dimensions would carry about 28,000 tons. The cost of the *Methane Princess* was £4,750,000, about double that of a conventional tanker.

The nine cargo tanks, which are made of a special aluminium alloy, are divided into three equal groups, each separated by a cofferdam which carries ballast. Throughout the length of the holds, the hull is of double construction, the spaces between the skins also being used for ballast.

The S.S. *Methane Princess.*
Photo courtesy: Gas Council.

The insulation of the holds consists mainly of balsa panels faced with plywood. The bottom of the holds is insulated entirely with high density balsa which carries the full weight of tanks and cargo. The side insulating panels are augmented by a layer of glass fibre.

The insulation serves a dual purpose. It prevents the absorption of heat from the atmosphere into the cargo. It also protects the steel hull from exposure to the cargo, which is carried at -258°F. (-161°C.). In the event of an accident, the insulation will effectively prevent the escape of gas for up to ten days. Further protection to the insulation is effected by keeping the hold spaces perfectly dry by the injection of nitrogen at slightly positive pressure.

No refrigerating plant is carried in the ship and in order to minimise the vaporisation of the liquid a high service speed is maintained. During the voyage there is a vaporisation of 0·3% per day of the cargo. This "boil off" is collected by centrifugal compressors and fed to the boilers which can burn either oil or gas. In this way, one-third of the ship's fuel requirements are met.

The degree of instrumentation and automatic control is extensive. The main hull temperatures are monitored and gas detectors are located in the holds, compressor house and elsewhere. There are remote control pumps and automatic valve closing controls, and the nitrogen blanket around the tanks is continuously monitored for traces of hydrocarbon gases, so that a possible leakage of gas can be immediately detected.

The liquid methane—about 12,000 tons by the end of a voyage—is pumped ashore at Canvey Island into specially designed storage tanks. On completion of discharge natural gas is pumped into the tanks to keep them under pressure of gas during the return voyage to Arzew in Algeria. Loading is completed in about 15 hours and the *Methane Princess* and the identical sister ship, *Methane Progress,* deliver cargoes at about five- to six-day intervals.

The idea of conveying liquid gas by sea first arose from experiments which had been carried out in the U.S.A. to determine the feasibility of constructing adequately insulated barges for river transport. The two companies who were pioneering this work formed a company—The Constock Liquid Methane Company—to develop the project with particular emphasis on ocean transportation. At this stage the Gas Council entered into partnership with Constock, and after further exhaustive experiments

The *Methane Pioneer* has been acquired by Antarctic Gas and under the new name of *Aristotle* is still carrying cargoes of liquid methane.
Photo courtesy: Gas Council.

and trials, the *Methane Pioneer*, a converted 5,000 ton merchant ship, arrived at Canvey Island with a cargo of liquid methane in February 1959.

The success of this and subsequent trial voyages led to the submission for Government approval of a scheme to import liquid methane from Algeria. Approval was received during the same year, 1961, and a long-term contract for the import of 700,000 tons per year was negotiated. At the same time plans were drawn up for the construction of the *Methane Princess* and *Methane Progress*. The first cargo arrived in 1964 and regular shipments, amounting to one-tenth of Britain's gas requirements, have been maintained except for a period during the Israel–Egyptian hostilities, when the Algerian Government cut off supplies.

M.S. ALBRIGHT PIONEER (1968)

Owners: ALBRIGHT AND WILSON LTD.
Builders: SWAN HUNTER AND TYNE SHIPBUILDERS
Deutz diesels, 4,832 b.h.p.
Single controllable pitch propeller
Service speed 14 knots
Length overall 414 ft.
Beam 56 ft.
Deadweight tonnage 5,000

The *Albright Pioneer* is built to carry liquid phosphorus, and as such, is the first ship to carry such tonnages. With a sister ship the *Albright Pioneer* is required to carry 70,000 tons per year between Long Harbour (Newfoundland) and Portishead, or Long Harbour via the St. Lawrence Seaway to Port Maitland on Lake Erie.

The phosphorus is carried at a temperature of 140°F. (60°C.) and is contained in four tanks in holds nos. 2, 3, 5 and 6. Holds 1, 4 and 7 are suitable for carrying other cargo as required.

The M.S. *Albright Pioneer*.
Photo courtesy: Albright & Wilson Ltd.

Each tank is designed to hold elemental white or yellow liquid phosphorus to a capacity of 1,210 tons. The lower portion of the tank is cylindrical with an internal diameter of 36 ft., the top portion is hemispherical with a 6-ft. diameter cylindrical neck. The lower part of the tank is surrounded by a water jacket through which water, at a maximum temperature of 80°C. is pumped to ensure that the cargo is kept in a liquid state. Exposed surfaces of the tank are insulated, and when the tank is loaded, a water seal is maintained in the neck; the space above the water seal is filled with nitrogen.

Each tank is constructed of Grade B mild steel, the necks being lined with stainless steel to minimise corrosion at the interface of the phosphorus and water.

The tanks are loaded or discharged one at a time and the transfer pipes and the shore storage (or vice versa) are always filled with hot water at 60°C. before any pumping starts in order to purge the lines of air and to test for leaks. All cargo piping is of stainless steel surrounded with mild steel hot-water jackets. As the phosphorus is pumped out of the ship's tanks, a shore pump transfers water from the storage tank to the ship's tanks, thus ensuring that the phosphorus never comes into contact with the air. An extremely efficient automatic and manually operated fire-fighting system is fitted in the holds and in the two control rooms from which all cargo operations are directed.

The main engine is controlled from a centralised control area and a propulsion alarm system is installed in mimic diagram form and providing continuous monitoring of 54 points. Additionally the auxiliary panels provide monitoring of 47 points. The propeller is controlled from the bridge, where there is also located a simplified propulsion plant alarm panel. Further alarm systems in strategic points of the officers' accommodation allows the engine room to be unmanned for periods.

M.S. HUMBOLDT (1968)

Owners: OCEAN GAS TRANSPORT LTD. (HOULDER GROUP)
Builders: CHANTIERS NAVALS DE LA CIOTAT
M.A.N. diesel, 5,600 b.h.p.
Single screw
Service speed 15 knots
Length overall 384 ft.
Beam 54 ft.
Deadweight tonnage 5,165

Over 200 chemical and LPG (liquid petroleum gas) carriers

have been built, the majority in the last ten years; a few of these ships having deadweight tonnages of over 20,000. Several prominent cargo liner companies operate, or are about to operate this type of vessel and the Houlder Line has now a fleet of four.

The Humboldt is designed to carry ammonia, propane, propylene, butane and butadienne. Cargo is contained in six tanks built of a special grade steel, which can withstand temperatures of 48°C. without becoming brittle. The hull, in way of the tanks, is built of the same steel, in order to obviate the need for insulation. The tanks in the hold are insulated with sprayed polyurethane foam to a thickness of 60 mm., the tanks on deck are similarly treated with 80 mm. of plastic and a covering of glass fibre.

Four similar refrigeration units are installed, also a vaporiser to reliquify vapour and to pressurise the tanks, which can withstand a working pressure of 6·3 atmosphere or an 80% vacuum.

Tanks are arranged so that gas can be contained under pressure; provision is also made for refrigeration and heating. The refrigeration units are sufficient to enable different types of liquid/gases with different boiling points to be carried (minimum temperatures: ammonia 33°C., propane 42°C., propylene 48°C.). The combination of pressure and refrigeration enables the cargo to be loaded or discharged under all likely conditions and circumstances, e.g. by liquifying a cargo of gas by cooling as it is pumped in under pressure, or by discharging a refrigerated cargo into a pressure vessel ashore. In addition, to facilitate loading into a pressure vessel, pressure can be applied within the ship by warming the liquid. Cargo can be transferred from tank to tank by the use of the ship's compressors to create different pressure or degrees of vacuum.

M.S. *Humboldt.*

The engines are highly automated and the engine room can be left unmanned at nights and at weekends. All cargo operations are, however, manually controlled, although extensive information about the condition of the cargo is registered automatically on the bridge. Similar information is provided about the gas content of the air in the accommodation. Deck machinery has been carefully planned and the National Union of Seamen has agreed to the employment of fewer than normal crew. These men are capable of carrying out duties either in the engine room or on deck. Six engineers, a storekeeper and an electrician together with the navigating officers and general purpose crew, make up the ship's complement of 23.

M.S. NAESS TEXAS (1964)

Owners: NAESS, DENHOLM & CO. LTD.
Builders: FURNESS SHIPBUILDING CO. LTD.
Sulzer diesel, 13,800 b.h.p.
Single screw
Service speed 16 knots
Length over 620 ft.
Beam 84 ft. 9 in.
Deadweight tonnage 26,562

The *Naess Texas* and a sister ship, the *Naess Louisiana*, are designed to carry molten sulphur. The cargo is carried in four separate tanks at a temperature of about 280°F. and the vessels are equipped with extensive installations to maintain this temperature. The tanks are heavily insulated as are the points at which the tanks come into direct contact with the hull.

M.S. *Naess Texas.*
Photo courtesy: Furness Shipbuilding Co. Ltd.

The *Naess Texas* and *Naess Louisiana* carry cargoes for the Sulphur Export Corporation, between Gulf ports and Rotterdam and Immingham with occasional calls to Ireland. Between 30th November 1968 and 28th January 1969 the *Naess Texas* completed two round voyages from Rotterdam, loading at New Orleans and Port Sulphur, and this indicates the pattern of their voyaging throughout the year. Beaumont is another Gulf port at which these ships often load.

HYDROFOIL MANU WAI

The hydrofoil ferry *Manu Wai* runs from Auckland to the island of Waiheke, about 10 miles away in the Hauraki Gulf, the most populous of New Zealand's small islands.

Hydrofoils have been in limited service for many years and the U.S.S.R. have developed very large craft for service on rivers and short sea journeys. A hydrofoil service has operated for several years between Italy and Sicily. Nevertheless at their present stage of development hydrofoils cannot operate in anything approaching a heavy sea, and several experimental services have been withdrawn, floating debris is also a constant menace to these craft.

Similar restrictions apply to hovercraft, and at the present time it would be rash to prophesy which of these two new types of transport will ultimately come out on top. Both craft have their protagonists and detractors and only recently the Southampton, Isle of Wight and South of England Royal Mail Steam Packet Co. Ltd. (the longest title in British shipping) has introduced an experimental hydrofoil service in the Solent to compete with established British Rail hovercraft services.

Another interesting feature of this race is that whilst the two types of ship compete between themselves, they also compete together against the short sea passenger and car ferry services which have become an accepted part of the shipping scene. Aircraft have killed the passenger liner, it may not be overlong before vehicle ferries themselves find their market taken by hovercraft and/or hydrofoils.

Hydrofoil *Manu Wai.*

R.R.S. JOHN MURRAY

Owners: THE NATURAL ENVIRONMENT RESEARCH COUNCIL

Converted by: WILLOUGHBY'S (PLYMOUTH) LTD.

Bristol Siddeley Maybach diesel, 394 b.h.p.

Single controllable-pitch propeller

Maximum speed 11·5 knots
Endurance 18 days
Length overall 133 ft. 6 in.
Beam 25 ft. 9 in.
Gross tonnage 441

R.R.S. *John Murray.*

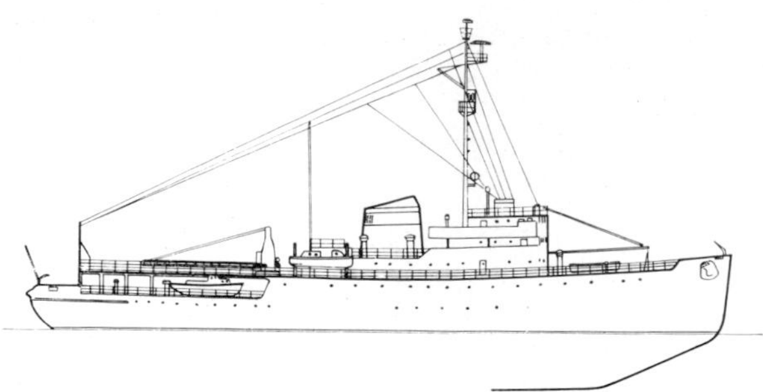

M.S. GENERAL SAN MARTIN (1954)

Owners: The Argentine Government
Builders: A.G. "Weser"
Two M.A.N. diesels, 6,500 b.h.p.
Twin screw
Service speed 16 knots
Length overall 278 ft.
Beam 62 ft.
Draught 21 ft. Gross tonnage 3,640

The *General San Martin*, which presents an interesting comparison with the British *John Biscoe*, is also employed on Antarctic expeditions. She is, however, a full icebreaker, wide in the beam, deep draughted, and with a cut-away bow which lifts the fore end of the vessel onto pack ice and by sheer weight breaks through up to 12 ft. of ice. Apart from supplying and relieving bases, laboratories are provided for the study of oceanography and high-altitude meteorology. A sounding machine can plumb depths up to 18,000 ft. and recover samples of the ocean bed for analysis.

The ship's equipment also includes a helicopter and a seaplane, lighters for inshore duties and a powerful winch for towing other vessels.

During its first voyage, the *General San Martin* reached the most southerly point of the Antarctic coast.

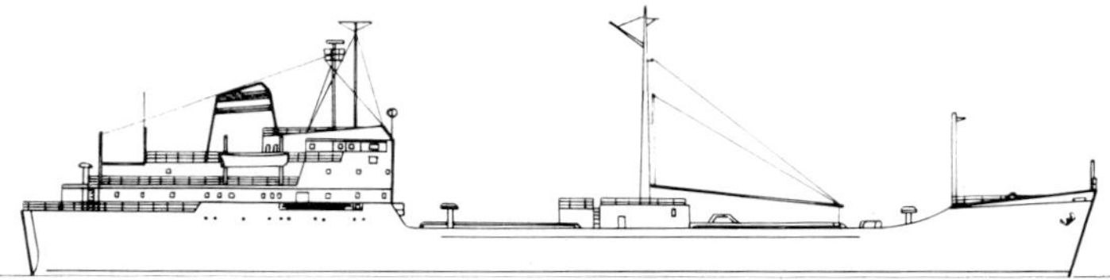

M.S. CEMENTIA (1967)

Owners: Cement Tankers S.A., Panama
Builders: Deutsche Werft A.G.
Twin diesels, 2,000 b.h.p.
Single screw
Service speed 14¾ knots
Length overall 350 ft.
Beam 51 ft.
Deadweight tonnage 5,250

The *Cementia* is a bulk cement carrier. The number of these ships is gradually increasing and they are employed in all parts of the world delivering from cement works to central storage depots or from storage depot to developing areas which have no local cement industry. For example, the *Cementia* works on the East African coast and to the offshore islands. A constant flow of bulk cement cargoes arrive at Kuwait, where enormous building and industrial schemes are under way.

Many bulk cement carriers load and discharge by means of horizontal and vertical screw conveyor systems. The *Cementia* is loaded by pumping aerated cement through a piping system into holds which are maintained at slightly below atmospheric pressure. The air is evacuated from the cement in the holds so that it will settle and not shift during transport. To discharge, the cement, again aerated, moves by gravity to a central tunnel where it is pumped into shore storage.

Complement: officers and crew 19, scientists 8

The Royal Research Ship *John Murray* is owned and operated by the Headquarters of the National Environment Research Council and a Committee of the Council programme and allocate the use of the ship to University Departments and other research organisations. This vessel, together with the Royal Research Ship *Discovery* and a fleet of over 20 other research ships, takes part in a closely co-ordinated programme of oceanography and fishery research; the *John Biscoe* and the *Shackleton*, operated by the British Antarctic Survey, are ships which fall within this group.

The *John Murray* was originally a stern trawler owned by the White Fish Authority. She was purchased in 1965 by the N.E.R.C. and entered service in 1967 after an extensive refit. The ship is equipped with a plotting laboratory, a general laboratory, a wet laboratory, a biological laboratory, a chemical laboratory, a dark room, a gravity room and a scientific workshop. On deck there is a coring winch equipped with 29,844 ft. of galvanised flexible tapered steel wire rope, with provision for a further 1,640 ft. A hydrographic winch carries 3,280 ft. of conductor cable, whilst a hand operated buoy mooring winch has a capacity of 3,500 fathoms of 2 mm. diameter galvanised steel wire. This wire is usually discarded after use and the winch is recharged with preloaded replaceable barrels. There is also a small bathythermograph winch equipped with 1,680 ft. of ⅛-in. diameter flexible steel wire rope.

In addition to the several navigational and plotting aids provided in the plotting laboratory, the ship is also equipped with its own comprehensive set of gear, including radar, direction-finder, Decca Navigator, Loran type "A" Navigator and echo sounder. The *John Murray* also carries gantries for lowering and retrieving heavy gear, a 1-ton crane and various davits and sheaves for working wires.

The accommodation for officers, crew and scientists is fully air conditioned.

Apart from a short period for annual refit, the *John Murray* is employed throughout the year and the following extracts from the ship's 1968 programme indicates the nature and breadth of the work undertaken on board:

9 Jan.–12 Feb.	North African waters	Geochemical and geophysical investigations
12 Mar.–4 Apr.	Central and South Irish Sea	Coring and sonar survey
14 May–1 June	Eastern English Channel	Geological survey
19 Aug.–13 Sept.	West Hebrides Shelf	Biological cruise
20 Nov.–21 Dec.	South West approaches to English Channel	Gravity and magnetic survey

The M.S. *Lady Brigid*. This illustration shows the clear working deck and the cement tank of an oil rig supply vessel. The bridge has all-round visibility and the engine exhausts are at the after end of the vessel. Also visible is the stern roller. The *Lady Brigid* can carry 650 tons of drilling equipment, chemicals, fuel oil, and water.

Photo courtesy: P. & O.

The other vessels previously mentioned vary in size from the R.S.S. *Discovery*, 2,665 gross tons, to the R.S. *Cypris* of less than 10 tons and a length of 29 ft. The R.S. *Ernest Holt* is a purpose-built vessel of 319 tons gross for biological research. The following information which has also been provided by the N.E.R.C., gives some further indication of the work undertaken in the fields of oceanography and fishery research.

Ernest Holt (Ministry of Agriculture, Fisheries and Food) 1968

12 Jan.–1 Feb.	Western Channel and Celtic Sea	Investigations of horse mackerel, sand-eels and sprats
23 Apr.–21 May	Barents Sea	Algal studies, sediment chemistry, hydrography

Scotia (D.A.F.S. Marine Laboratory, Aberdeen) 1968

5 Sept.–25 Sept.	North Sea	Herring larval survey
4 Oct.–24 Oct.	Northern North Sea	Hydrographic studies of Baltic outflow
6 Dec.–12 Dec.	Northern North Sea	Fish capture experiments with detachable codends

Tellina (Ministry of Agriculture, Fisheries and Food) 1968
Inshore fishing vessel

8 Jan.–19 Jan.	Sizewall Bank	Sole investigations
25 Sept.–16 Oct.	South coast	Scallop survey

Sula (Marine Biological Association)
Motor fishing vessel
1968—An extensive programme of bacteriological investigations

Discovery (National Institute of Oceanography) 1968

4 June–24 June	Bay of Biscay	Geophysical investigations
28 June–6 Aug.	North East Atlantic North Sea	Wave measurements
14 Aug.–7 Oct.	North East Atlantic	Geological long range inclined Asdic survey

A model of the M.S. *Alcoa Seaprobe.*

M.S. ALCOA SEAPROBE

Three 800 h.p. diesel electric generators
Propulsion forward: two 400 h.p. omnidirectional propellers
Propulsion aft: two 800 h.p. omnidirectional propellers
Length overall 244 ft.
Beam 50 ft.
Displacement 2,000 tons

The *Alcoa Seaprobe* is under construction for Alcoa International. This vessel will have the ability to hold its position in rough seas to search, core, drill and sample mineral deposits on the sea floor, locate and retrieve heavy objects more than a mile below the surface, and to perform other research functions.

The *Alcoa Seaprobe* will have a cruising range of 10,000 miles and will be able to stay at sea for up to 45 days. Equipment includes radio telephones, radar, sonar of various frequencies, undersea cameras and television as well as a variety of special-purpose retrieving gear.

The missions of this ship will include undersea geological exploration in connection with Alcoa's exploration for new sources of minerals. The Ocean Research Science Engineering Company Inc. also plans to operate the ship under charter for such projects as undersea drilling for oil, gas and minerals, the salvage of valuable objects from the sea bed and deep marine archaeology to record historical treasures.

The *Alcoa Seaprobe* is the largest vessel yet to be built entirely of aluminium. Alcoa were also responsible for the first aluminium vessel ever to be built—the *Alumette.* This tiny vessel was 13 ft. long, 10 ft. beam and 5 ft. deep. She was placed in the water at Newport News (Va.) in January 1936. Its purpose was to provide a means of studying the effects of sea water on a variety of aluminium alloys, painting systems and dissimilar metal connections. In 1962, after 27 years of exposure, the *Alumette* was found to be in excellent condition.

Aluminium alloys are now regularly used in the construction of big ships, particularly passenger ships. The *Queen Elizabeth 2* is the largest British ship to have an all-welded aluminium superstructure, part of it being an integral part of the stress bearing hull. The *United States* has a superstructure containing more than 2,000 tons of aluminium alloy, whilst that of the *France* incorporated 1,600 tons.

The Russian Fishery Research vessel *Persey III.* Several similar adapted stern fishing factory vessels are in service. They have extensive laboratory facilities and can operate in any part of the world.

A Dutch-built bucket dredger. Vessels of this type are engaged in maintaining the depths cf channels and berths. They are often of the "dumb" type and are moved from place to place by tugs. Limited movement is obtained by adjusting the length of the mooring chains.

CHAPTER 13

Trawlers

MODERN trawling is a refined version of a system which has been used for centuries. Until recently the basic plan of a trawler had not changed since steam gradually took over from sail in the last two decades of the 19th century. For economic reasons the size of trawlers increased and vessels of 150 ft. or more in length were in service by the late '30s. After the war oil-fired boilers superseded coal and, after a slow start, diesel engines became accepted; now only diesel or diesel-electric ships are built.

Throughout this period the system of side fishing was employed and developments in techniques were limited. Working conditions for crews showed only limited improvements and it was not until the introduction of stern fishing that any marked development occurred. Now the crew can work in the shelter of high bulwarks and the superstructure, and the gutting of fish is carried on below deck. Freezer trawlers have machinery for heading the catch and fish rooms in which frozen blocks of fish are stored under refrigerated conditions.

The fishing deck of the *Coriolanus*. The fitting of additional winches has reduced the amount of manual work required in shooting and hauling the nets. Whereas all heading and gutting of fish is carried out on deck on conventional trawlers, all work on factory trawlers is carried out below decks. The fish are shot through hydraulically operated hatches, which can be seen in the foreground, and only a few hands are required to work on deck. The group of trawlers, of which the *Coriolanus* is the fourth, is the first in Britain to have the engines located aft.

Photo courtesy: Hellyer Bros. Ltd., Hull.

FACTORY TRAWLER CORIOLANUS

1. WHEELHOUSE, Radio Room, Chart Room. **2.** CAPTAIN'S DECK, Owners' Spare Cabin, Captain's Day Room and Bedroom, Captain's Bathroom, Stores. **3.** FORECASTLE DECK, Cabins for First and Second Mates, two factory managers, radio operator, bathroom. **4.** UPPER DECK Cabins for Chief Engineer, Second and Third Engineers, crew in two, four and six-berths, officers' and crews' messes, galley and messrooms, drying rooms, laundry, washrooms. **5.** MAIN DECK, two-, three-, and four-berth crews' cabins, recreation room, washrooms.

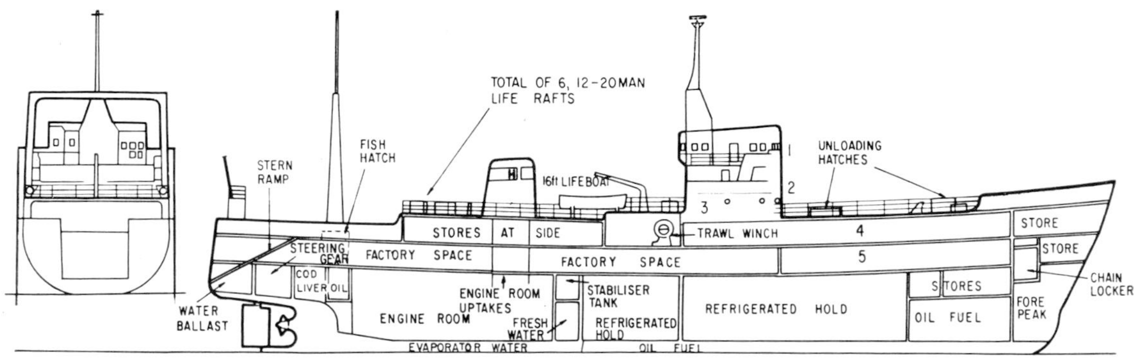

The M.T. *Portia*, a large distant water conventional trawler owned by Hellyer Bros. Ltd. In ships of this type the catch is packed in ice, and because fish stored in this way soon becomes unfit for consumption, the voyages undertaken are strictly limited in duration. The single trawl winch and the unprotected deck on which the hands work can be clearly seen.

Side fishing trawlers still comprise the greatest proportion of the fleet. In December 1967 there were 182 registered distant water trawlers and 395 near and middle water vessels. Of these less than 40 were factory or freezer trawlers. Also included in these totals was a small number of stern fishing trawlers without freezer facilities. In addition there were 739 Seine net craft of various sizes in operation.

Since 1951 there has been a decline of 110 and 148 in the numbers of distant water and near and middle water trawlers respectively. It must also be borne in mind that many of the registered ships were laid up for a part or the whole of the year.

Photo courtesy: Hellyer Bros. Ltd., Hull.

Factory trawlers carry the process one stage further and skin and fillet the catch before it is frozen.

In co-operation with the trawler owners the White Fish Authority has carried out experiments and improved the effectiveness of gear and the methods of locating fish. Tests have also been conducted on the transfer of fish at sea and experimental voyages to the West and South coasts of Africa have been undertaken. Trawler owners on their own initiative have also invested large sums of money in development work. Nevertheless the industry has faced many difficulties since the war and the older and less efficient units have been laid up, many of them not returning to service. The overfishing of traditional grounds and the extension of territorial waters by nearly all of those countries whose economies are supported by their fishing industries have forced distant and middle water trawlers further afield, and the cost of building ships for this purpose has increased considerably. The British industry has also been affected by a fluctuating demand for fish, the poor quality and haphazard method of landing fish, and competition from imports by heavily subsidised foreign fleets. Over and above all this fishing is still an undertaking which, despite every development, is much dependent upon weather and upon the elusive nature of the quarry which the trawlers seek—the last food commodity which is not farmed.

The *Altair* of Eyemouth, a typical Scottish wooden seine net fishing vessel.

Photo courtesy: White Fish Authority.

Trawlers are divided into four classes:

(a) *Distant Water Trawlers*

These vessels are above 140 ft. in length and include freezer trawlers and factory ships. Crews vary from about 20 in conventional trawlers to about 40 in factory ships. The conventional ships are able to stay at sea for up to 21 days whereas the factory ships have fuel and stores for voyages of about 60 days. These trawlers fish grounds off Greenland, Labrador, the Barents Sea, Bear Island, the White Sea, Iceland and the Newfoundlands Banks.

Distances to some of the fishing grounds are:

The problem of laying alongside of trawlers in a seaway has been the subject of research by the White Fish Authority. Dracone inflatable fenders were designed and tested with scale models in the tank at the National Physical Laboratory at Feltham. Full scale tests were carried out at sea with two 140-ft. trawlers. The fenders were each 100 ft. long with a diameter of 5 ft. Fish in boxes was transferred at the rate of 20 tons per hour. This method is now ready for commercial trials.
Photo courtesy: White Fish Authority.

	Miles
Barents Sea	1,750
Bear Island	1,490
Greenland (Davis Strait)	2,450
Newfoundland Banks	2,500
Iceland (West)	1,037
White Sea	1,697

(b) *Middle Water Trawlers*

Both stern fishing and side fishing vessels between 110 ft. and below 140 ft. are included in this class. They are equipped in the same way as distant water trawlers, but in general they have considerably less endurance. The largest ships of the class occasionally undertake distant voyages, but fishing is usually confined to the grounds around the Faroes, South East Iceland and Rockall.

(c) *Near Water Trawlers*

These vessels vary between 80 and 109 ft. They are small versions of middle water trawlers and confine their fishing to the North Sea, English Channel and Irish Sea grounds.

(d) *Inshore Vessels*

These vessels, including shell fishing craft, are under 80 ft. in length. Their activities are confined to coastal waters and range from open beach boats which rarely spend more than a night at sea to decked vessels which can remain at sea for several days.

Of the fish landed in the United Kingdom (850,000 tons in 1967/8) the first place is taken by cod, which accounts for about 50%. Haddock takes second place with approximately 10% of the total. Cod and haddock are the principal types of fish caught by distant water trawlers. Middle and near water trawlers land cod and haddock in smaller proportions and also whiting, hake, turbot, plaice and other flat fish.

Landings of fish frozen at sea, whether from the trawlers of large or small companies, are sold on

Three small inshore fishing vessels at Shoreham, Sussex. Although these craft are using harbour facilities they are designed to be hauled up on beaches. This was a common practice when Brighton was a fishing port of some consequence and very much larger decked sailing boats were regularly dealt with in this way. The design follows traditional lines and similar types of vessel can be seen all along the Sussex and South Kent coast. Other regions are also known for craft which have been developed for particular coasts and particular types of fishing and it is interesting to study how various basic designs have emerged.

Inshore fishing is at the moment the most prosperous branch of the industry. Voyages are of short duration, often not exceeding one night, and as the catch is usually disposed of locally the fish are sold in prime condition.
Photo courtesy: White Fish Authority.

The M.T. *British Guiana* was one of the first diesel deep sea fishing trawlers. The war halted developments and it was many years afterwards that the diesel was accepted as the standard type of propulsion.

Photo courtesy: Ross Trawlers Ltd.

contract, sometimes to the merchanting division of the same company, but often to outsiders. All fresh fish landings are auctioned and the merchanting division of trawler companies buy that fish which is the most suitable for their needs without reference to the ownership of the vessels from which the fish is landed.

Government grant is paid both in respect of the building of new ships and the improvement of existing ships. Operating subsidies amounting to an approximate total of £1,600,00 were made in 1967/8.

The factory trawler *Coriolanus* is owned by Hellyer Bros. Ltd. of Hull, and is the fourth of a series. This vessel is operated by a crew of 37 and almost all of the operations are carried out by machinery. Heading, gutting, filleting, boning, skinning and cleaning are all carried out automatically. Fish fingers are frozen into 27 lb. blocks and are stored in wax cartons at a temperature of −20°F. Cod fillets are frozen in 13½ lb. blocks, having been previously sorted for size and quality, and also stored at −20°F. in the cold store, which has a capacity of 375 tons.

Unusable fish, including species other than cod or codling, are turned into fish meal for which there is a storage capacity of 95 tons.

The *Coriolanus* is 224 ft. in length overall, and has a beam of 39 ft.

Following the enquiry into the loss of the three trawlers *St. Romanus*, *Kingston Peridot* and *Ross Cleveland* in 1968, the Board of Trade chartered the sister ship *Orsino* and stationed her off the North coast of Iceland to act as a communications ship and to give weather advice; an experimental medical service was also organized from the ship. The *Orsino* remained on station during the period December 1968–April 1969 and all trawlers in the area were required to report their approximate position twice a day. Failure to make contact would have led to the institution of search and rescue procedures. Regular weather reports were broadcast although it remained the responsibility of individual trawler skippers to decide whether to accept advice to stop fishing and seek shelter.

The *Orsino* carried out similar duties during the winter of 1969/70.

M.S. ROSS VANGUARD (1966)

Owners: ROSS TRAWLERS LTD., GRIMSBY
Builders: COCHRANE & SONS LTD., SELBY
Ruston and Hornsby diesel, 2,160 b.h.p.
Single controllable pitch propeller
Service speed 14 knots
Length overall 234 ft.
Beam 39·9 ft.
Gross tonnage 1,488

A distant water freezer trawler equipped to gut and freeze fish.

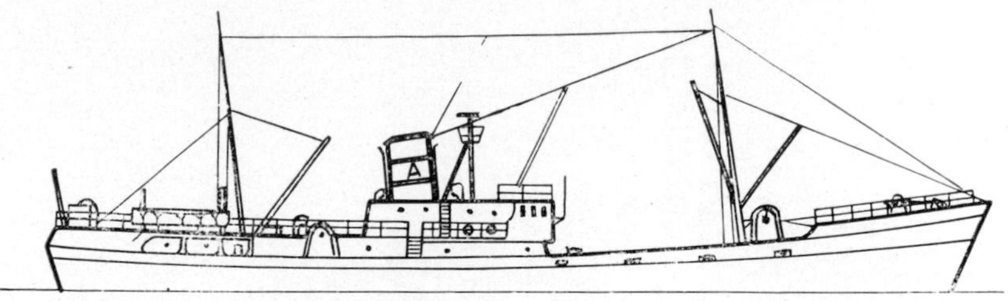

S.T. VANNESSA (1952)
Owners: The Atlas Steam Fishing Co. Ltd.
Builders: Cook, Welton and Gemmell Ltd.
Reciprocating steam engine, 1,100 i.h.p.
Length overall 197·5 ft.
Beam 32 ft.
Single screw
Service speed 13¾ knots

A typical distant steam trawler built in some numbers during the late '40s and early '50s. By this time diesel-powered trawlers were also in operation, and it is the steam trawlers which are in the main proving to be uneconomic.

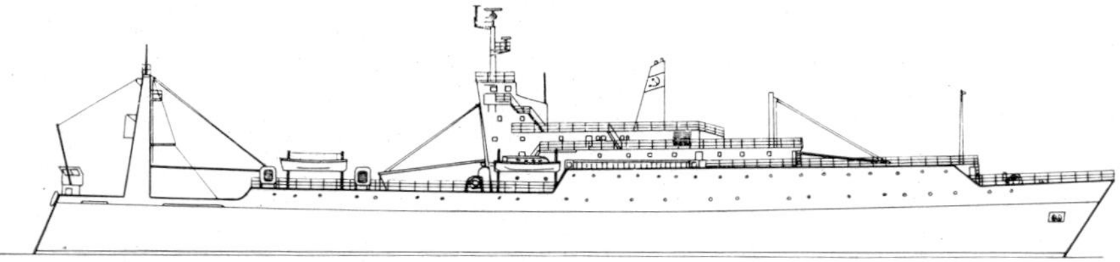

M.T. MARIA POLIVANOVA (1967)
Owners: U.S.S.R.
Builders: Ateliers et Chantiers de Nantes (Bretagne-Loire)
Diesel electric, three Pielstick diesels, 7,560 b.h.p.
Single screw
Service speed 14 knots
Length B.P. 377 ft. 4 in.
Beam 62 ft. 4 in.
Gross tonnage 8,425

One of three similar stern trawling factory ships, the *Maria Polivanova* can operate in Arctic and semi-tropical conditions. She can also undertake a variety of types of fishing, ranging from cod to sardines. Although highly automated the vessel follows modern practices and it is the sheer size which is remarkable. The *Maria Polivanova* can produce 100,000 cans of fish in a working day and these can be unloaded and despatched direct to the consumer. A voyage can last up to 160 days. Through greed and an inability to refrain from hunting whilst new stocks built up, the sperm whale has been nearly eliminated. The continuous entry into service of such ships as the *Maria Polivanova* must therefore give rise to fears that in the not remote future scarcity of fish may lead to international fishing agreements not only in respect of net sizes but also in regard to the amount of fish taken in any one year.

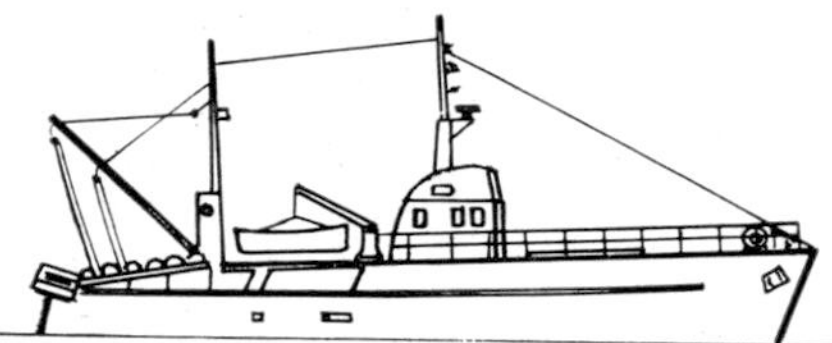

M.T. ROSS DARING (1963)
Owners: Ross Trawlers Ltd.
Builders: Cochrane & Sons Ltd.
Paxman diesel, 450 b.h.p.
Single screw
Service speed 10¼ knots
Length overall 99 ft.
Beam 23 ft.

A prototype inshore trawler which has proved to be remarkably successful. The engine is remotely controlled from the wheelhouse and no engineer is carried. The adoption of stern fishing methods and the mechanisation of the tasks which were previously carried out manually, again with remote control from the wheelhouse, has made it possible to limit the crew to five. This is just under half the complement of a conventional trawler of similar size and ships like the *Ross Daring* can operate when other ships are laid up because of the low market price of fish.

The majority of operational trawlers were built between 1955 and 1962. These vessels have many years of life left in them, and if they are to become really profitable it will be necessary to improve the quality of the catch which they bring back. One method under investigation is the transfer of fish on the grounds from trawlers fishing in fleets either to refrigerated cargo ships or freezer trawlers. Such a system not only maintains quality, but allows the side fishing trawlers to extend their voyages.

This illustration shows the practical application of the dracone fenders which are shown under test on page 194.

The Texaco tanker *Texaco Hamburg* approaching Milford Haven at the end of her maiden voyage in November, 1969. She discharged a full cargo of 206,100 tons (1,500,000 barrels) of crude oil from Ras Tanura. The *Texaco Hamburg* was the first of four similar ships to enter service: a further four, each with a deadweight tonnage of 255,000, are under construction. In order to handle these big ships, the Texaco Terminal at Milford Haven has been modified by the strengthening of two berths and the blasting and dredging to a new depth so that they may remain afloat, fully laden, at low water springs. Three additional storage tanks, each with a capacity of 600,000 barrels, have been built together with new automatic loading arms and a 36-inch pipeline. Discharge of cargo is carried out at a rate of 100,000 barrels an hour.

In 1960, Milford Haven handled 2,800,000 tons of oil; in 1964, 17,700,700 tons. In 1968, 28,300,000 tons passed through the port, and in 1969 a total of 29,073,941 tons had been reached by September. 3,366 ships used the port in 1968.

Photo courtesy: Texaco.

The Corporation of Lloyd's

In 1688 a coffee house in Tower Street in London was owned by Edward Lloyd and called "Lloyd's Coffee House".

Being situated near the River Thames the coffee house customers consisted mainly of ships' masters, merchants, bankers and others with a maritime interest.

At that time the practice was for insurance on ships and their cargoes to be accepted by individual merchants as a sideline, each of whom would take a share of any particular risk—perhaps on a vessel's voyage to the New World. These insurers were called "Underwriters" because they wrote their signatures and shares "one under the other" beneath policies of insurance.

Lloyd's Coffee House proved a favourite place for underwriters to gather, and for seekers of insurance cover also, for there, more than at any other place, could be found sufficient underwriters to accept their risks.

The practice of businessmen meeting at the coffee house to transact insurance prospered, and was encouraged by Edward Lloyd supplying pens, ink and paper, shipping information obtained from the waterfront and, for a short time, a news sheet called *Lloyd's News*.

Lloyd died in 1713, but the character of the coffee house remained. As years went by the business aspect grew more and more important and Lloyd's became something in the nature of a private club with the customers controlling the premises and restricting entry to those interested in insurance and shiping.

In 1771 a committee of customers was elected to find new premises and, in 1774, a move was made to the Royal Exchange; this was the beginning of the modern Lloyd's.

Lloyd's became a Corporation by Act of Parliament in 1871 with its affairs governed by a Committee elected from among its Members.

In many respects the Corporation of Lloyd's can be compared with the original Mr. Lloyd. It owns the premises where underwriting is carried on by individuals and provides services to assist without itself accepting insurance.

But here the likeness ends. For the Corporation administers the market through a Committee and, by financial rules and other regulations, it ensures that only those of the highest integrity and sound financial standing can transact business at Lloyd's. Thus it has become accepted that anyone insuring with Lloyd's underwriters can do so with complete confidence.

Apart from the premises themselves, the Committee of Lloyd's provides the market with a system of Lloyd's Agents, world-wide shipping intelligence, claims and administrative offices, a central accounting system and departments for checking, signing and sealing policies and settling claims on behalf of underwriters.

Underwriting Members

It is important in understanding what Lloyd's is and how it functions to realise that insurance is placed *at* Lloyd's (with individual underwriters) and not *with* Lloyd's (the Corporation).

Only Underwriting Members of Lloyd's may accept insurance at Lloyd's. Each has been nominated by one Member and supported by five others, elected by ballot, and has agreed to the conditions of Membership laid down by the Committee of Lloyd's.

Years ago the practice of individuals each accepting a part of a risk personally was a simple process because values were small and the underwriters required to cover a particular risk were therefore few in number.

Nowadays, when the value of a vessel, an aeroplane, or a factory can be millions of pounds it would obviously not be practicable to find sufficient individuals each to accept a portion of such risks; the number of persons required and the time it would take to find them make this impossible.

The change in values has therefor brought change at Lloyd's, and the result has been the syndicate system that developed during the late 19th century.

Syndicates

There are over 6,000 Underwriting Members of Lloyd's. Instead of all of them transacting their own business personally they are formed into groups called syndicates, varying in size from a few to several hundred Members in each syndicate. Insurance of all types is accepted on behalf of these syndicates by underwriting agents who represent the groups at Lloyd's. An underwriting agent, therefore, is able to take a sizeable proportion of a large risk because he is not accepting on behalf of himself alone, but on behalf of many other individuals of his syndicate.

Members of syndicates who transact their business through agents are known as "names", but they are still responsible for the business accepted on their behalf by the underwriting agents, even to the extent of their private estate.

There are some 300 syndicates of underwriters accepting insurance at Lloyd's.

Brokers

Insurance can only be placed with Lloyd's underwriters through some 220 firms of approved Lloyd's brokers.

The broker represents the assured, not underwriters, and it is his duty to obtain for clients the most favourable terms available, and later, if a claim arises, to present it to underwriters and to arrange a single settlement. But the Lloyd's broker is not restricted to the Lloyd's market and can, if need be, approach the insurance companies with whom the Lloyd's underwriters are in competition.

If members of the public were allowed to transact their own business at Lloyd's they would be unable to find the right underwriter for their particular risks, or the most favourable premium, for no division of markets at Lloyd's exists other than that marine, motor and aviation business is conducted on the ground floor and general non-marine business on the gallery floor surrounding the Underwriting Room.

Placing a Risk

When a Lloyd's broker receives a request for insurance he makes out a "slip"—a folded sheet of paper on which are written the details of the risk to be covered.

With the slip the broker goes to the Underwriting Room at Lloyd's and sees several underwriters who accept the type of risk he has to place and from whom he obtains quotations of premium.

The broker having selected the most satisfactory proposition from the aspect of his client, agreement is acknowledged by the underwriter concerned writing on the slip the amount of risk he is prepared to accept (on behalf of his syndicate) together with his initials; the acceptance is called "writing a line".

With these initials, known as a "lead", the broker approaches other underwriters, persuading them to accept proportions of the risk in the same way and at the same rate until he has sufficient to cover the full amount of the value. Thus the risk is spread over a large number of individuals and if a claim arises each underwriter is only responsible for his portion.

By this method exceptional losses can be borne that would be too heavy for any one individual or syndicate.

Underwriters' initials on a slip are in the first instance the only evidence of agreement until a policy is prepared by the broker; but underwriters will always honour these initials even though a claim may arise before time has allowed the preparation of the policy which is made up from the details of the slip in the broker's office.

When completed the policy is sent to a department of the Corporation of Lloyd's called "Lloyd's Policy Signing Office" where it is checked with the slip and signed on behalf of each member of the syndicates who have accepted a share of the risk.

Finally the policy is affixed with the seal of the Lloyd's Policy Signing Office, without which no policy issued by Lloyd's underwriters is valid, before being returned to the broker who forwards it to the assured.

Casualty Board

The Casualty Board stands inside the Main Entrance to the Underwriting Room. Each day casualty sheets are posted giving details of marine and aviation casualties and reports of non-marine losses such as fires, floods, robberies, etc.

Casualty Book

The Casualty Book rests upon a lectern in the centre of the Underwriting Room and contains the names of vessels which have become or are likely to become total losses. The book enables Lloyd's underwriters to be kept informed of vessels which have sustained serious damage and in which they may have an insured interest.

Lloyd's Agents

The Committee of Lloyd's maintains a system of some 1,500 Lloyd's Agents and Sub Agents throughout the world. They are the representatives of the Corporation of Lloyd's, not of underwriters, and are in no way insurance agents.

Lloyd's Agents are responsible for sending shipping movements and other information to Lloyd's relating to their ports, towns and areas, but in addition their services are often sought in connection with damage to vessels and cargoes and it is the practice for insurance policies issued by Lloyd's underwriters and the marine insurance companies to state that, in the event of loss or damage, settlement of claims will be facilitated if Lloyd's Agents are called in to hold survey.

Lloyd's Agents may also be authorised to settle claims on behalf of Lloyd's underwriters, and this is of particular benefit to assureds overseas as it enables their claims to be dealt with locally.

Intelligence and Publications

Lloyd's provides the world with the most comprehensive shipping intelligence service available.

The enormous volume of shipping information received at Lloyd's from Lloyd's Agents, radio stations, shipowners and other sources, is collated and distributed to newspapers, radio and television services, and throughout the marine and commercial communities in general.

The information is edited and published by editorial departments in a number of shipping publications printed in Lloyd's own printing department on the premises and sent all over the world. *Lloyd's List* is London's oldest daily newspaper and contains news of general interest as well as shipping information which includes arrivals and sailings in most ports of the world. *Lloyd's Shipping Index* is also published daily and list some 16,000 ocean-going vessels in alphabetical order and gives the latest known report of each: these are only two of a wide range of Lloyd's shipping publications.

All classes of insurance, with the exception of long term life business, are transacted by Lloyd's underwriters, and the annual premium income of the Lloyd's market is now over £400,000,000, nearly three quarters of which is derived from abroad.

2 Lloyd's Register of Shipping

LLOYD'S Register of Shipping dates from 1760, when a group of marine underwriters, who gathered regularly in Edward Lloyd's coffee house, formed themselves into a committee for the purpose of issuing a register giving details of ships likely to be offered to them for insurance. The first existing register, dated 1764–5–6, used the assessments A, E, I, O and U to indicate the state of the hull; the letters G, M, B (good, middling, bad) were used to classify masts, rigging, etc. Surveying and assessment was carried out by a small group of men with a knowledge of shipping, such as retired sea captains.

In 1834, after some rivalry with another register issued by shipowners, the Society was constituted in its present form with the title of Lloyd's Register of British and Foreign Shipping. In that year underwriters and shipowners combined to form a General Committee, which also included merchants, and it was established that the classification of a ship would in future be decided not by the individual surveyors, as hitherto, but by the Committee itself, informed by the surveyors' reports.

Since 1775 the highest class had been indicated by the now famous symbol "A1" and the desire of shipowners to have their ships placed in the top grade led to requests from shipbuilders for guidance as to the standard required. The result was the issue by the Society of rules for the construction and maintenance of ships. With the enormous developments which have taken place in shipbuilding and engineering, the rules have been expanded to cover first iron, then steel ships, boilers, steam and diesel engines, electrical and refrigerating machinery, air cushion vehicles, hydrofoil craft, drilling rigs, ships' cargo handling gear, containers and other equipment, as well as specific types of ship.

The useful function which the Society was performing in Great Britain soon prompted requests for its services from other countries. In 1852 a surveyor was appointed at Quebec and, following that, other appointments were made at ports all over the world. The spread of the Society's activities in turn led to the establishment of national committees in most of the leading shipbuilding countries. In 1949 Lloyd's Register of Shipping was united with another classification society which had existed in Britain for the previous 60 years, the British Corporation Register of Shipping.

More recent years have seen expansion in a direction not contemplated in 1760. The Society's knowledge of engineering problems common to both marine and land-based installations, together with its world-wide distribution of specialists, has given rise to requests for surveys of land-based equipment. A special Non-Marine Department organises this branch of the Society's work.

Today classification societies exist in a number of maritime countries. The features which combine to distinguish Lloyd's Register of Shipping are its freedom from governmental influence (there are no government representatives on the General Committee), its absence of shareholders, and the fact that classification with the Society is entirely voluntary.

In 1967 more than 200 years after the formation of the underwriters' committee, over one third of the entire shipping of the world was classed with Lloyd's Register of Shipping. A similar proportion of tonnage under construction was to the Society's class.

Constitution and Management

Direction of the Society's affairs is in the hands of the General Committee, composed now of underwriters, shipowners, shipbuilders, marine engineers, steelmakers and representatives of various shipping and shipbuilding organisations, all of whom serve voluntarily. Although, as mentioned, the Society is independent of any official control, its authority is such that classification by Lloyd's Register of Shipping is accepted by all maritime governments as evidence that statutory requirements in respect of structural strength have been met.

Committees

National Committees, of similar composition to the General Committee, now exist in Australia, Canada, Denmark, Finland, France, Germany, Greece, Holland, India, Italy, Japan, New Zealand, Norway, Portugal, Spain, Sweden and the U.S.A.; the special interests of Scotland and Liverpool are also represented by Committees.

The Chairmen of all the national committees are *ex-officio* members of the General Committee and in addition each national committee is entitled to elect a representative to the Technical Committee. This latter body, established in 1890, is responsible for recomending to the General Committee alterations in the existing rules or the adoption of new ones.

Finances

As the Society has never had stockholders, shareholders, proprietors, owners, etc., of any kind, it follows that no profits or dividends have ever been distributed. The funds and accounts are under the sole authority and control of the General Committee. Its income is derived from the fees charged for the services of its surveyors and from subscriptions to the Register Book, etc., and is devoted, under the Committee's directions, exclusively to the operation of the Society for the benefit of its clients throughout the world.

Staff

The Society employs over 1,500 surveyors stationed at Head Office, ports and a number of inland industrial centres throughout the world. Trained in naval architecture, marine engineering and associated professions, they include specialists in various fields having application to shipbuilding, for example, electricity, refrigeration and metallurgy. With few exceptions surveyors are the exclusive employees of the Society.

Offices

The Society's Head Office has since 1901 been situated at 71 Fenchurch Street, London, E.C.3, and there are now over 200 "outport" offices in countries throughout the world.

The Printing House

Since 1891 Lloyd's Register of Shipping has owned its own printing house. This was originally situated in Southwark, London, but in 1953 was transferred to new premises at Crawley, Sussex.

Research Laboratory

Also at Crawley is the research laboratory for the investigation of technical problems arising in connection with its work. This is well equipped with mechanical testing machines of modern design, including 50-ton and 120-ton Universal testing machines, impact, hardness and fatigue testing machines, also facilities for various notch ductility tests, including the Pellini drop weight test. It has also a number of creep testing machines. A recent addition has been a large Goodman electro-magnetic oscillating table vibrator for environmental and similar testing. Other facilities include a workshop, an electronics laboratory, a metallurgical laboratory, a photo-elastic laboratory and a photographic department.

Structural Test House

The Society also maintains a test house at Glengarnock, Ayrshire, for the experimental investigation of ship structural components.

Classification

Lloyd's Register of Shipping derives its description as a classification society from its initial practice of grading ships into classes, but for many years now it has had only one standard—symbolised by "100A1"—to which all classed ocean-going ships are required to conform.

Nearly all such ships are built "to class" which means that, from the earliest days of their construction, they are under the Society's survey. Plans of hull and machinery are submitted by the builders for approval by the Society. If amendment is necessary, the builders are told in detail what is required. The steel is tested by surveyors at the maker's works, which must be on the Society's approved list. Forgings and castings are also inspected and tested, and the supervision continues throughout the construction of hull and machinery up to the final trials. On completion of the ship, surveyors' reports are checked by the staff at Head Office and then submitted to the Committee, who assign the class and authorise the issue of the classification certificates. Details of the construction and of the class assigned then appear against the ship's name in the Register Book, a cross (✠) indicating special survey during construction.

Periodical Surveys

It is a requirement of the rules that inspections should be carried out by the Society's surveyors at regular intervals during the life of a ship. It is a further requirement that repairs, whether arising from wear and tear or from damage, should be subject to survey.

A report on every survey is sent to head office where it is examined by a special staff of surveyors before submission to the Committee who, if satisfied, confirm continuation of class and make appropriate entry in the register book. A survey may be commenced at one port and continued at another, and the work involved in these periodical surveys on about 11,000 ships forms a major part of the Society's operations.

The Register Book

The original purpose of the Register, from which the Society takes its name, was to make known details of ships, including an assessment by surveyors of their condition. Today it both shows the results of the Society's survey work, and records the mercantile tonnage of the world, whether classed with Lloyd's Register of Shipping or not. The present Register, issued annually in two volumes and kept up to date by means of a monthly cumulative supplement, contains a complete list of the merchant seagoing ships of the world over 100 tons gross (about 45,000 in number) as well as the more important particulars of dimensions, type, etc. Also published are a list of shipowners and their fleets, and an appendix giving shipbuilders and the ships they have built, engine builders, dry and wet docks, etc.

Rules

Rules covering all aspects of shipbuilding and marine engineering which come under the Society's survey are now published in four languages—English, French, German and Spanish. These are issued for guidance in building and establish the standards required for classification.

Constant re-examination of the rules is required to ensure that they are kept up to date. In carrying out this task the Society's Chief Surveyors have at their disposal the records of service performance of thousands of ships compiled from the reports of surveyors all over the world, together with the results of investigations by the technical research staff. Any new rules or alterations to existing ones are submitted to the Technical Committee, which consists of elected representatives of the different sections of the industry, worldwide shipowners, underwriters, engineers, shipbuilders, steelmakers and others—and is thus in keeping with the international character of the Society as a whole. When specially important alterations or additions are indicated the Technical Committee appoints a panel of experts to study the particular matter.

Technical Records

The Society maintains extensive technical records on failures, defects and damages. These are stored on a punch-card system which contains hundreds of thousands of cards covering hull and machinery troubles. In addition the Society possesses a comprehensive library

Research

Research is carried out both on land and at sea. This is the responsibility of the Research and Technical Advisory Services Department. Mobile teams of surveyors travel all over the world to investigate the problem of ships in trouble and in difficult cases the teams can draw upon the resources of the Crawley laboratory.

Computer Services

The fact that many of the Society's activities are fundamentally data-processing operations, together with the need to deal with the growing complexity of technical problems, led to the installation of computer services. In 1967 the original computer was replaced by an IBM 360/30 general purposes computer with storage facilities and immediate access to 30,000,000 items.

Load Lines, Safety and Tonnage

The drafts to which ships may be loaded are governed by the regulations of the International Load Line Convention, 1966. The earlier Convention (1930) was signed by most maritime governments, many of whom authorised the Society to survey their ships for the assignment of load lines and issue of International Load Line Certificates.

The construction of ships, including the subdivision of passenger ships into watertight compartments, and their propelling machinery, electrical installations, safety equipment (fire protection, life-saving appliances, etc.), radiotelegraphy installations and arrangements for the carriage of grain in bulk are governed by the regulations of the International Convention for the Safety of Life at Sea, 1960. This also has been signed by most maritime governments, a number of whom have authorised the Society to survey their ships and issue the appropriate certificates, namely:

- Passenger Ship Safety Certificate
- Cargo Ship Safety Construction Certificate
- Cargo Ship Safety Equipment Certificate
- Cargo Ship Safety Radiotelephony Certificate
- Cargo Ship Safety Radiotelegraphy Certificate.

Plans of bulk grain loading arrangements and the associated stability conditions are approved by the Society as complying with the Regulations of Chapter VI—Carriage of Grain—of the Convention.

The Society is also authorised by a number of countries to

measure their ships for the computation of gross and net tonnages under British, American, Oslo Convention, Suez Canal or Panama Canal Tonnage Rules and issue appropriate Tonnage Certificates.

Marine Publications Issued by the Committee of Lloyd's Register of Shipping

- *Lloyd's Register Book*
- *Rules for the Construction and Classification of Ships, etc.*
- *Register of American Yachts*
- *Register of Yachts*
- *Geometric Properties of Rolled Sections and Built Girders*
- *Anchors: Approved Designs*

3 The Baltic Mercantile and Shipping Exchange

THE Baltic Mercantile and Shipping Exchange, known colloquially as the Baltic Exchange, originated from the use of 17th century London coffee houses as business premises by ships' captains and merchants. Foremost among these establishments were the Jerusalem Coffee House and the Virginia and Maryland Coffee House, known from 1744 onward as the Virginia and Baltic. This house was so named because the varied merchandise dealt with there came mostly from the plantations of the American colonies or from the countries of the Baltic seaboard. In addition to the provision of refreshments it was also quite usual for there to be a saleroom on the premises where cargoes were auctioned "by the candle".

By 1810 the increase in the volume of business made it necessary for the Baltic Exchange to take larger premises. At about this time tallow had attained outstanding importance, particularly in the trade which Britain had with the Baltic countries and with Russia. Primarily to control this trade, which was frequently highly speculative, a Committee of Baltic members drew up and published, in 1823, rules and regulations for the "Baltic Club". These rules limited membership to 300, established a committee to control the Baltic's affairs and decreed that a dining room and a saleroom be provided.

From this point onwards the membership and importance of the Baltic Exchange grew steadily. Although the "Ton Tallow" continued as the basis of freight until 1890, the importance of the tallow trade diminished as other means of lighting were developed, and in its place the grain trade came to predominance. This process was much accelerated by the Repeal of the Corn Laws in 1846, marking the recognition by Parliament of the fact that the answer to Britain's grain shortage was not protection but importation of foreign grain at economic prices. When the grain trade was added to the Baltic Exchange's activities the time could scarcely have been foreseen when Britain would be compelled to import the vast majority of its grain from overseas, and when it would become the principal commodity with which the shipping world would concern itself.

In 1857 the Baltic Exchange took the opportunity of buying South Sea House from the liquidators of the Royal British Bank. The new premises provided better facilities for the Baltic Exchange's activities, but in the following decades two developments revolutionised world shipping, increasing the membership of the Baltic Exchange in the process. These were the development of the tramp steamer and the opening of the Suez Canal. The Baltic Exchange was the centre of the growing market in steamer freight and its expansion was uninterrupted throughout the century.

In 1891 the London Shipping Exchange was founded to meet the needs of liner shipping, and became an institution whose activities overlapped if they did not seriously rival those of the Baltic Exchange. Both institutions were in need of more space and better facilities, and a joint committee representing both exchanges was established to plan a merger and to purchase a suitable building site. Jeffrey Square in St. Mary Axe was eventually purchased, and after three years, by 22nd April 1903, the Baltic Exchange as it is today had been built and was ready for the then Lord Mayor to declare open.

Chartering operations represent the most numerous transactions on the Baltic Exchange. They mainly concern, but are not entirely confined to tramp ships and bulk carriers. The international nature of the shipping industry applies particularly to tramp shipping in the sense that, broadly speaking, the ships of all nations are available for charter by merchants of their own or any other nation. Thus, a great number of deep-sea tramp ships are constantly seeking employment, and merchants and shippers all over the world are in constant need of ships to carry their cargoes. The process of finding the right ship for the right cargo and vice versa is the function performed by the shipping section of the Baltic Exchange, and it is this activity with rates fluctuating from day to day according to supply and demand, that constitutes the London freight market, which is the main freight market of the entire world.

The people who compose the market are chartering agents, representing charterers, and owners' brokers, who represent the shipowners. There are many broking firms who have both charterers and shipowners among their clients and thus work on both sides of the fence. In addition, many merchants and shipowners who are members of the Baltic Exchange have their own chartering staff on the Exchange who take the place of, but perform the same function as, chartering agents or brokers.

Chartering

The "Floor" of the market is composed of the various groups of chartering agents associated with the various geographical subsections of the freight market, much in the same way as jobbers, on the Stock Exchange are known to deal in various groups of securities. Thus the broker knows for instance that chartering agents A, B and C are the group who regularly charter ships for cargoes of sugar from Cuba, and likewise he knows the various agents who charter for cargoes of grain from the Plate, North America, Australia, etc. Similarly the chartering agent keeps track of the ships which are named to him from day to day, especially those which are or will be proceeding with outward cargoes in the direction of the area in which he is concerned. Consequently these agents and brokers are not suddenly confronted with a confused picture of hundreds of ships and freights. They are in daily contact with one another and are constantly noting changes that occur each day—that a freight has been covered here, a new requirement has emerged there, that this ship has been provided for, and that ship will now be a month later. This is known as "working the market".

An actual deal, or "fixture" as it is called, can best be explained by describing a hypothetical operation.

By way of illustration let it be assumed that a ship is going to Hamburg with a cargo of grain, which should be discharged in about three weeks' time, when she will be available for further employment. Unless the market is obviously rising it is undesirable to leave things until the last minute, as negotiations often extend over many days, so the shipowner's brokers go into action. They scour the market and collect details of all the freights for which the ship seems to be suitable in regard to size and date of readiness. Voyage estimates are made to ascertain the probable profit from each of these freights, and the choice is narrowed down to four, namely fertilisers from Bremen to China, pig iron from Antwerp to Argentina, coal from Hampton Roads to Rio, or sugar from Cuba to Japan. The owner's brokers offer for the fertilisers to China, but charterers won't pay the rate they want, so they then offer for the coal cargo to Rio, but they are to late—the charterers have taken another ship. They therefore commence negotiations for the sugar cargo from Cuba to Japan. Offers and counter-offers are exchanged until both sides are only 10 cents a ton apart on the rate, and the owners are on the point of conceding this margin to effect a fixture when their brokers report that there is a new enquiry on the market for a ship for a six months' time charter and that their ship seems to be just what is wanted. So negotiations are abandoned on the sugar freight and discussions are opened with the time charterers' brokers this eventually leading to the fixture of the ship for six months' time charter at a relatively satisfactory rate per ton deadweight per month. Thus negotiations for a charter, whether for a single cargo for a specific voyage, or for a time charter, involve a process of bargaining. Obviously the broker acting for the owner must try to secure the highest rate possible, while the broker representing the charterer must strive to do exactly the opposite. Consequently the negotiations usually require exercise of the wiles of diplomacy, in which not only the skill and experience of the respective parties, but also their personalities come into play.

Time chartering is a prominent feature of the freight market, and the various liner companies, both British and foreign, frequently resort to time chartering of ships to supplement their own fleets.

Sale and Purchase of Ships

There are under a dozen firms on the Baltic Exchange whose principal activity is the sale and purchase of ships, but in addition about a score of chartering brokers maintain a department for this particular branch of shipbroking.

Even in these days of intense international competition probably a good 50% of the world sale and purchase business passes through firms represented on the Baltic Exchange.

Their function is to act as agents

for shipowners in buying and selling tonnage and to advise them of the sale market. This they are able to do by maintaining a constant correspondence with shipowners and other brokers all over the world so that within literally a few minutes a London broker can tell, for example, which ships are being offered for sale in New York or which particular Far Eastern shipowner is in the market to buy a ship. The result of this constant interchange of information centring in London —and particularly through the Baltic Exchange—is that nobody finds it strange that a sale between, say, Greece and Turkey should be negotiated on the London market.

Negotiations generally involve offer and counter offer, conditions frequently being of utmost importance. Once a negotiation is successful the broker then proceeds to draw up a Memorandum of Agreement; this document varies in each case, unlike the printed forms of charter parties.

In due course an exchange of documents takes place (very frequently in London—wherever the ship may be). The buyer receives a Bill of Sale or whatever document of title is appropriate to her flag and the seller a banker's draft or is otherwise satisfied on the purchase price. Physical transfer of the ship is arranged to follow immediately after.

The seller of the ship usually pays a brokerage to the broker who introduces the buyer to him but this has frequently to be shared with at least one other broker.

In almost every case a considerable amount of time and experience has to be used in advising on price or conditions during the negotiations and in the wording of the Memorandum of Agreement. There are many pitfalls: accidents and delays which cannot be anticipated may have to be faced before or during delivery and the sums of money involved are frequently extremely large. A ship is not an empty shell and some of her contents, such as bunkers and unbroached stores in the ship on transfer, are usually paid for extra. It is not surprising that, with such matters, disputes can easily arise in the settlement of which the broker's experience can be useful. Various government import/export licences, currency permits and other regulations may be involved which the broker should know about or deal with for his principal.

The procedure is much the same when a ship is sold for scrap. The broker advises the owner of the best market—prices vary internationally with supply and demand—so that price in relation to delivery conditions can be evaluated. The broker will also advise various shipbreakers with whom he is friendly of the best prospects available for scrap, particularly when he knows they have an early requirement.

Most sale and purchase brokers also maintain correspondence with various shipbuilders throughout the world so that they are able to advise their shipowner clients at any time where it is most advantageous to build a ship both from the point of view of delivery as well as price.

A less exciting but highly useful function carried out by sale and purchase brokers is that of valuers. Market valuations of ships are constantly being required for company purposes, insurance, general average and salvage. Valuations are frequently required in court proceedings and thus exposed to challenge, so considerable skill and care are required in their preparation.

The Baltic Exchange is also closely concerned with commodity markets, the principal ones being grain, oil and oilseeds.

The most recent addition to the markets of the Baltic Exchange is the Air Market. The process of air chartering is the same as for shipping and the advantages are similar as well. More and more foreign air brokers and charterers are recognising the leading role of the Baltic Exchange and are directing their enquiries to this centre.

The shipping companies who fostered the development of the Air Market from the outset have used, and still use, the market extensively for the exchange of ships' crews. The despatch of spare parts to immobilised ships is also undertaken by charter aircraft, thus reducing delay from weeks to days or even hours.

4

The Chamber of Shipping of the United Kingdom

THE Chamber of Shipping was founded in 1878 by a small number of shipowners who felt that there was a definite need for such an organisation "inasmuch as subjects affecting the shipping industry would be carefully and periodically discussed by representatives from all the out-ports and that ship-owning opinion would be more reliably known by the Government and the public."

A new constitution was written in 1917, and the Royal Charter which was granted in 1918 set out the objects and purposes of the Chamber in these words: "To promote and protect the interests of British Shipowners."

Between the wars the Chamber's organisation expanded steadily on the new lines especially following the establishment in 1921 of the International Chamber of Shipping (originally called the International Shipping Conference). The growth of the Chamber led to the division of its work into sections dealing respectively with deep-sea liners, deep-sea tramps, coasting liners, short-sea liners, intermediate tramps, coasting and home trade tramps and whalers. Each section functioned, and continues to do so, independently within the general organisation of the Chamber, each having its own chairman and vice-chairman.

After the second world war the Chamber really became established in its present form due to the increasing interest of government organisation and governments themselves in the commercial operation of shipping. In addition, the need emerged for one body to speak for all shipowners. This was finally achieved in 1964 when the influential Liverpool Steam Ship Owners' Association linked up with the Chamber of Shipping.

Membership is made up of about 400 shipping companies and 45 local shipowners' associations from all the port areas, defence clubs and protection and indemnity clubs. The day-to-day running of the Chamber is conducted by a permanent staff of about 100 under the supervision of a Director, and under the general guidance of the President. The work is financed by an annual call on members based on gross registered tonnage, and the total tonnage owned by member companies represents practically the whole of the British merchant fleet—more than 20 million tons.

Through the sections of the Chamber and the local shipowners' associations there is close and constant contact with sectional as well as national and international matters. There are 25 standing committees of which the most important is the General Purposes Committee. The others deal with such diverse subjects as the carriage of dangerous goods, documentation, insurance, load line, ports, radio, research and taxation. Overall policy is coordinated through the Council of the Chamber with whom rests the final authority for policy decisions.

The Chamber of Shipping has access to the Government at the highest level, usually through the Board of Trade. Successive governments have recognised the unique position of shipping compared with that of other industries; this is due to its international character, the fierce world-wide competition it has to contend with (lacking a protected home market), and the colossal size and expense of the tools of its trade. For these reasons the Chamber of Shipping stands alone and has not sought affiliation or direct connection with other industrial bodies in its main aims of serving shipowners and providing an organisation run by shipowners for shipowners. In its efforts to create and maintain conditions in which its members' ships can best serve international trade, both cargo and passenger, it does not seek to regulate the way in which business can be developed and expanded—that is the responsibility of individual shipping companies.

The Chamber is active in re-research and conducts a number of special projects. It also co-operates in and helps to co-ordinate many other matters through the Shipowner Committee of the British Ship Research Association. Through its members, the Chamber is able to provide the practical experience of ship operation which is indispensable to the scientists and technicians engaged in the various investigations. These fields of research include automation, corrosion and fouling problems, mooring studies, ship design and the analysis of ships' performance data.

Another specialised department is the Radio Advisory Service which is concerned with almost every aspect of radio and aids to navigation in the marine field. The internationally-agreed VHF channels for port and estuarial communication started largely as the brain-child of the R.A.S. The Chamber has also produced a Tanker Safety Code which has been adopted by all U.K. tanker owners and is supported by the officers' and seamen's organisations. It also maintains extensive records probably unequalled by any other organisation dealing with shipping. It supports its own statistical and economics division and produces monthly statistics and information such as indices of tramp voyages and details of laid-up shipping.

Because it is the shipowners' national body, the Chamber also has to concern itself very much with international matters. Shipping is one of the most international of all industries and is sensitive to the actions of foreign governments, for there is no trade route and very few ports in the world where British ships do not go. The Chamber provides the secretariat for the International Chamber of Shipping and also did so exclusively, until recently, for the Committee of European Shipowners and the Committee of European National Shipowners' Associations, on both of which British owners are represented. These two Committees now have international secretariats, though the principal officers, as well as the Chairmen, are British.

The Chamber has also worked for more than 25 years in close co-operation with the International Chamber of Commerce with the purpose of securing the support of the business world as a whole in the constant task of removing trade barriers and promoting the expansion of world trade.

5

The British Shipping Federation

The British Shipping Federation, which was formed by a merger of the 76-year-old Shipping Federation and the Employers' Association of the Port of Liverpool in 1967, deals with industrial relations on behalf of British shipping companies, and represents shipowners on the National Maritime Board, the industry's joint industrial council. The Shipping Federation is also concerned with the recruitment and training of Merchant Navy personnel, the supply of crews to ships and many other routine services such as medical examinations to individual companies.

In addition to its large and busy administrative staff, the Federation employs 19 doctors full-time and nearly 80 part-time, examining new entrants, applicants for contracts, sick and injured seafarers and those claiming compensation for personal injury, etc.

In recent years, the Federation has taken an increasing interest in training, providing professional and educational courses for both officers and ratings and co-operating with various technical colleges in establishing courses for seafarers. It has several standing committees concerned wholly with training which consult regularly with the National Union of Seamen and other similar organisations and it makes specific recommendations on training to the Merchant Navy Training Board.

The Federation also administers the National Sea Training School for deck and catering boys at Gravesend. This school, which cost nearly one million pounds to build and equip, is recognised as the largest and most modern training establishment of its kind in the world. It will accommodate 576 boys and will train something like 2,800 new entrants to Britain's merchant fleet every year.

The Federation employs a permanent staff of about 400 under its Director and, apart from the head office in London, it maintains 30 district offices throughout the United Kingdom. At seven of these, co-ordinated through head office, there are departments specialising in the recruitment of potential officers and ratings. "Selection" officers take an active part in careers conventions (about 400 a year), keep in touch with youth employment officers and schools careers masters and give talks (about 600 a year) on the prospects of a career at sea to schools, youth clubs, sea cadet units and the like.

6 Shipping Conferences

THE history of shipping is full of accounts of companies which failed to meet the competition of other lines. It is also full of accounts of companies which survived, but only just, the vicious rate wars which were part and parcel of passenger and cargo operations after the mid-19th century. So severe did the situation become on the Atlantic and the Far East routes that British shipowners consulted together to protect their joint interests against the inroads of foreign competitors and the crippling effects of rate cutting amongst themselves.

These were remarkable happenings in an era when industrialists and merchants alike applauded unimpeded enterprise and competition, but from these small beginnings developed the modern shipping conferences, the largest of which embrace owners of many nationalities who share similar trading interests.

Conferences are in effect committees set up by shipowners, and their main purpose is to protect their interests and to offer to shippers a regular and adequate service of well-found ships which would be beyond the resources of any single company to provide. Cargo and passenger rates are settled on the basis of costs and future trading prospects. Once settled they are held for a specified period in order to allow manufacturers and shippers to plan ahead. *Ad hoc* increases are, however, applied in certain circumstances such as the closure of the Suez Canal and the persistent congestion in particular ports. A further function of conferences is to inspect the accommodation of new passenger ships and to assess the class and rates for the various cabins and public rooms.

Conferences also allocate the number of sailings which a particular owner may make from any given port and consider representations from shippers for rate modifications, additional sailings to cope with changing circumstances or to develop trade in a new commodity.

From time to time new shipping companies are admitted and election depends upon an undertaking to abide by the rules of the conference and to operate ships of certain standards of operational efficiency and maintenance.

Shippers are attracted to use conference lines by the offer of reduced rates on individual shipments on the condition that they do not use independent lines for a certain period. Another method is to offer a rebate on payments made at the end of the period.

Shipping conferences have continued to be the subject of criticism from many quarters on the grounds that there is insufficient competition between the lines involved. Recently the activities of conference lines have been challenged by certain governments with resultant concessions to the ships of the nations concerned or a general reduction in rates. Other opposition comes from independent lines who attempt to offer more attractive rates, but they make little impression. Recently, however, the refusal of the conference concerned to admit the U.S.S.R. on terms which they considered to be unreasonable, led to an immediate and severe reduction in rates by the U.S.S.R. for the conveyance of wool from Australia. Several shippers, who had to that date used the conference line ships, immediately transferred their business. The conference was forced to reappraise the position and finally decided to amend its own charges and offer better terms to its customers. Nevertheless, it would seem that in the shipping industry, which is the most highly capitalised in the world, there is little alternative to this form of co-operation and control, especially in present times when the complexities and costs involved in operating new types of services are forcing shipping companies for the first time to invest capital jointly. This investment is not only national, but international in nature and, as in industry, the competition will be between fewer but enormously more efficient organisations.

7 The Salvage Association

WHEN a ship set sail in the days before wireless and submarine telegraph, many months might elapse before the owner and underwriters learned anything of her progress. In the majority of ships the master also acted as his owner's business agent, even to the extent of being required to fix a cargo for the voyage home. In these circumstances, and especially when the ship became a casualty or the cargo was damaged, it was an onerous task for underwriters to exercise any control over the situation. Inflated salvage and repair claims were constantly received and the conditions of the times even led to the submission of fraudulent claims.

As a result, discussion took place between interested parties in London and in the spring of 1856 it was decided to set up an association whose main purpose was to be the ascertainment of the "cause of the undue increase of losses arising from damage to ships and cargoes, and of finding, as far as practicable a remedy for such a state of things—injurious alike to every fair trader whether merchant, shipowner or underwriter."

In the same year the proposal received the blessing of the Committee of Lloyd's who, together with upwards of 170 members of Lloyd's, the five marine insurance companies then practising in London, certain insurance interests in India and China and certain shipowners, created the initial fund to set the association in being. Action followed swiftly for the Annual Report of 1858 records the successful prosecution of a master for making away with his vessel.

In 1863 the Association's activities in connection with doubtful losses, of which there were many during this and succeeding years, were fully acknowledged by the adoption of the second rule which read—"The investigation by all lawful means, of frauds practised or attempted or intended to be practised, with respect to vessels or their cargoes, or with respect to insurances effected or purporting to be effected thereon; and the taking or facilitating of all lawful means, or proceedings for the punishment of the offenders."

In 1867 the Association became incorporated by Royal Charter, and its functions, which continue to this day, are broadly set out in the full title of the Association: "The Association for the Protection of Commercial Interests as respects Wrecked or Damaged Property".

Under the secretaryship of Sir Joseph Lowrey, who was appointed in 1897, the status of the Association was greatly enhanced. During his term of office the system of appointing surveyors in various ports with power to act for the Association immediately on receipt of instructions was developed. In later years offices were opened in many ports and salvage officers and surveyors are now regularly sent to major casualties all over the world.

The recent development of larger ships with vastly more powerful engines and sophisticated systems and vessels built for specific purposes has produced a crop of new problems. To deal with these the Association, with its wealth of experience including knowledge of salvage contractors, their location and ways of working, the availability of shiprepairing facilities and costs in various parts of the world produces a useful guide, while the co-operation on the part of the various bodies concerned has developed a state of goodwill and mutual trust which facilitates the prompt handling of the many problems which arise.

The Association is also closely concerned with loss and damage to cargo, and it has developed an organisation of cargo experts. This particular type of work requires a detailed knowledge of the characteristics of the very many commodities now carried in ships and the varied ways in which they may be affected either by stranding or flooding or the many other possible mishaps. These can occur during a journey from factory to customer, often involving carriage by rail, road and lighter.

The services of the Association are always available to underwriters, but no action is taken without specific instructions in each particular case. The usual practice is that as soon as a broker receives notification of a casualty from the assured or from reports at Lloyd's, he informs the underwriter who will decide whether or not to request him to instruct the Association. As soon as the Association is instructed, machinery is set in motion which has the sole purpose of minimising the loss. Subject to the approval of the underwriter, however, arrangements can be made, when vessels of a particular fleet regularly trade to, or repair at certain ports, for instructions to be given to the Association's Agents at one of those ports to arrange for the attendance of surveyors on the Association's behalf. This procedure does much to cut the delay which might otherwise occur.

The Salvage Association is a non-profit making organisation financed solely from fees charged to clients. There are, therefore, no shareholders to satisfy by way of dividends and the full resources of the Association are devoted to those who engage them.

8 The Corporation of Trinity House

THREE of the functions of the Corporation of Trinity House are:

The general lighthouse authority for England and Wales, Channel Islands and Gibraltar and dealing with wrecks around the coast, except for those occurring within local port limits and wrecks of H.M. ships.

The principal pilotage authority in the U.K.

Trinity House maintains nearly 90 lighthouses, over thirty light vessel stations and almost 700 buoys. Most of the lighthouses are electrically operated and individually manned, but current practice is towards automation whereby a group of lights can be operated from a central point. Reduction in manpower is expected as a result, but this will not occur until absolute reliability of control and performance of lights is assured.

The powers of Trinity House in respect of lighthouses derive in the main from the Merchant Shipping Act, 1894, and the service is financed from light dues. These are levied at every port in the U.K. and are based on the net registered tonnage of the vessel entering. Local Customs Officers act as agents and for the year ending 1967 light dues amounted to £6,200,000.

For organisational purposes the coast of England and Wales is divided into six districts: Yarmouth, Harwich, East Cowes, Penzance, Swansea and Holyhead. Each district maintains one or more lighthouse tenders which have the job of relieving crews of lighthouses and light vessels, towing light vessels to harbour for refit and mooring their replacements, servicing buoys and beacons and laying refitted ones every year, and replacing and repairing buoys which have drifted or become damaged.

Keepers of offshore lights maintain a watch for two months, with one month ashore. Masters of lightships remain afloat for one month with one month ashore; members of the crew are aboard for one month with two weeks ashore. Lighthouse tenders carry out a major relief once a month with a minor relief also at monthly intervals. Lighthouses and light vessels are therefore visited every fortnight as a routine measure.

All information relevant to navigational hazards, e.g. extinguished lights and buoys not in position, and proposals to alter the position of buoys or establish new ones is broadcast by the Admiralty and notified to ports and other appropriate bodies in the form of Trinity House and Admiralty Notices to Mariners.

Trinity House is the pilotage authority for London and 40 other districts. The Corporation licenses, but does not employ pilots, although it is financially responsible for the construction and maintenance of the larger pilot tenders and launches. Control of the service is carried out under the provision of the Pilotage Act, 1913, and Bye-Laws made thereunder. The service is self-supporting, income deriving from a levy on pilots' earnings, dues paid by vessels for shipping and landing pilots, and from licence fees. There are at present about 800 Trinity House pilots for the S.W. approaches to the London District.

In order to improve services to shipping in the London District the Corporation recently brought into service the two high-speed pilot launches *Vedette* and *Valiant* and the larger, but slower launch the *Lodesman.* Pilots are now based at Folkestone in place of Dungeness and are taken to ships and landed from them by the two high-speed launches. In heavy weather the *Lodesman* takes over. The system, which has proved to be highly successful, has allowed the withdrawal of the expensive cutters which cruised on station with up to 22 pilots. A permanent pilot station at Folkestone is now being built and similar schemes have been introduced at other Trinity House stations.

Trinity House has accepted a considerable extra amount of work since the arrival of oil and gas drilling rigs in the North Sea between Flamborough Head and Cromer. These rigs need adequate marking with lights, buoys and fog signals if they are not to become a danger to navigation, and in 1965 the International Association of Lighthouse Authorities, in whose affairs Trinity House plays a leading part, drew up a set of recommendations to ensure world-wide uniformity in the marking of these rigs.

Trinity House has accepted the task of recommending what lights and buoys should be used for each rig and then placing them in position and maintaining them. Whenever a drilling rig changes its position, the buoys are also moved by Trinity House.

The equipment is rented from Corporation stocks by the rig operators and a fee is also paid for laying and maintenance. Much of the extra work has fallen upon the tender *Mermaid* which, over and above her routine work, now undertakes round voyages of up to 150 miles from her base at Great Yarmouth to the rigs.

Recently the Corporation has entered into a contract with a private aircraft operating company for the trial relief of certain lighthouses by helicopter.

9 Entry to the Merchant Service

Navigating Officers

A Young man who wishes to make his career as a navigating officer and ultimately to command his own ship, should begin as a cadet officer in a foreign-going shipping company. A cadet officer will receive the training and experience necessary, both practical and theoretical, to enable him to become an efficient and competent officer and to provide him with the knowledge required to pass his professional examinations.

The navigating or deck officer, as he is sometimes called, is usually one of three watchkeeping officers on board ship whose duties, broadly defined, involve the safe navigation of the ship and the care, carriage and stowage of her cargo. He is also responsible for the general upkeep and maintenance of the ship and her gear. As shown in the progress chart, the cadet takes the examinations for the Board of Trade Second Mate's Certificate of Competency immediately upon completion of his cadet training. The Second Mate's Certificate qualifies him to serve as a third navigating officer aboard a foreign-going ship and subsequently he takes the First Mate's and Master's Certificate examinations. The Master's Certificate, which an officer generally obtains by the time he is 26, qualifies him to command a merchant ship. In practice he will not be promoted to master until he has gained experience as a chief officer whilst holding a Master's Certificate.

Cadet Training

A cadet is required to serve for three years on board ship before attempting the Board of Trade Second Mate's examination. This period may, however, be commuted by up to one year of remission for cadets who can satisfy either of the following requirements:

(a) the possession of certain G.C.E. "A" level passes—or equivalent. (See academic entry qualifications);

(b) satisfactory completion of an approved course at a recognised nautical college. It is desirable for all cadets to undergo a period of preparatory training before starting their sea service.

On commencing their sea service cadets (except those taking the O.N.D. in Nautical Science—see below) start a programme of training geared to the examinations of the Merchant Navy Training Board. The subjects studied are mathematics, physics, navigation, ship construction and stability and English, and two examinations are set during the course of the cadetship to evaluate the cadet's progress and familiarise him with examination procedures. The cadet also follows a planned programme of practical seamanship training and is required to keep a record of his seamanship duties and a journal of his progress.

Many cadets are sponsored by their companies for a mid-cadetship release course at a nautical college. These are full-time residential courses, designed to help a cadet in his studies and to give him a chance to continue his education and plan his further studies. An additional period will be spent in a nautical college prior to the Second Mate's examination.

Those who enter the Ordinary National Diploma scheme pursue a phased sandwich course cadetship as follows:

Phase 1, six–nine months' study at a nautical college,

Phase 2, approximately six–twelve months' service at sea as a cadet officer,

Phase 3, a further six months' study at a nautical college, leading to the O.N.D. examination.

The cadetship is concluded by a further period of sea service during which time the cadet understudies an officer of the watch. Holders of the Diploma may gain exemption from certain parts of the Board of Trade's Second Mate's and First Mate's examinations.

H.M.S. CONWAY

Amongst the many training developments that have taken place recently, one of the most noteworthy is the industry's joint venture with the Cheshire Education Authority to take over the running of the H.M.S. Conway Merchant Navy Cadet School in Anglesey, North Wales, as a voluntary aided secondary school. The excellently appointed school —the new buildings were completed in 1964 at a cost of over £400,000—will offer a two-year course leading to the G.C.E. at "A" level for boys with suitable "O" level passes who wish to make a career in the Merchant Navy, and a course leading to "O" level for younger boys from 13/14 years of age. The syllabus will be designed to offer the normal range of "A" level subjects but courses will have a strong nautical emphasis and aim to provide the character and leadership training required for a potential officer in the Merchant Navy.

Boys with suitable G.C.E. "O" level passes who wish to follow a shorter course at the school will be able to take Phase 1 of the O.N.D. in Nautical Science.

No tuition fees are chargeable to parents under the new arrangements. Parents are responsible for the fees for boarding, but are eligible for a local education authority award depending upon income.

Further information about the school may be obtained from the Captain Superintendent, H.M.S. Conway, Plas Newydd, Llanfair P.G., Anglesey, or from the British Shipping Federation, or from the Director of Education, County Hall, Chester.

Prospects

The prospects for a young navigating officer are excellent. Promotion up to the rank of Chief Officer depends upon the young man obtaining his Board of Trade Certificates. Under normal circumstances he can pass his Master's examination by the time he is 26. When he has gained seniority in a particular shipping company he might expect to find himself master of a tanker or dry cargo ship during his thirties. The extra responsibility of a large passenger ship, however, might mean waiting until considerably later for a command.

Cadets who enter with suitable G.C.E. "A" level qualifications or who have a good Ordinary National Diploma in Nautical Science are eligible for entry to a B.Sc. course in maritime studies. This is a broadly based ordinary degree and is offered at a number of nautical colleges in the form of an eight- or nine-term sandwich course spread over five years. The degree is designed not only to be a useful qualification for an officer in the highly automated ship of the future but also for those wishing to make a career in a branch of the industry ashore after serving as a navigating officer or master in the Merchant Navy.

Entry Qualifications for a Cadetship

Age

Candidates must be at least 16 and preferably not more than 20 years of age on application.

Health

Candidates are required to pass a medical examination on joining a shipping company or on registration with the British Shipping Federation. They must have normal vision in both form and colour and must pass the Board of Trade sight test and the industry's sight test.

Academic

There are two main streams of entry for candidates of G.C.E. "O" level standard:

1. A minimum of three G.C.E. "O" level passes—or equivalent*—including a pass in mathematics or an appropriate science subject;
2. Four G.C.E. "O" level passes —or equivalent*—in suitable subjects including mathematics, an appropriate science subject and English language or literature for those who wish to obtain the Ordinary National Diploma in Nautical Science during their cadetship.

There is also an entry for candidates with the G.C.E. at "A" level in one or more subjects. Those with five G.C.E. passes— or equivalent—two of which are at "A" level and include either mathematics or physics, are eligible for nine months' remission of sea service.

Applications

Applications for cadetships or for further information may be made directly to the British Shipping Federation. The Federation can arrange cadetships with a large number of all types of British shipping companies, but, if it is preferred, applicants may apply directly to the company of their choice.

**Note*

Qualifications which are considerd equivalent to G.C.E. "O" level for Merchant Navy entry are:

Certificate of Secondary Education: Grade 1.

Scottish Certificate of Education: "O" Grade.

Northern Ireland Grammar School: Senior Certificate.

Eire Department of Education: Leaving Certificate.

PROGRESS CHART: Navigating Officers

	Approximate Age	
Full time course B.O.T. Extra Master's Certificate optional after passing Master's Certificate		
MASTER Experience as Chief Officer before promotion		
↑		
CHIEF OFFICER Full-time course—B.O.T. Master's Certificate	25–27	
↑		B.Sc. Maritime Studies optional for those with O.N.D. or G.C.E. "A" level qualifications
SECOND OFFICER Full-time course—B.O.T. First Mate's Certificate	22–23	
↑		
THIRD OFFICER Full-time course—B.O.T. Second Mate's Certificate	21–22	
↑		
NAVIGATING CADET (Mid-Cadetship Release Course)	16–18	
↑		

PRE-SEA TRAINING OR DIRECT ENTRY

Terms of Cadetship—three years' sea service subject to remission. A Cadet follows a planned training programme and may attend a Mid-Cadetship Release Course.

Certain periods of sea service are required by the Board of Trade before officers take their examinations. 1st Mate: One year as an officer of the watch whilst holding a 2nd Mate's Certificate. Master: A further 2½ years as an officer of the watch, including 18 months whilst holding a 1st Mate's Certificate. A minimum of 3½ years' sea service is required between gaining 2nd Mate's Certificate and Master's Certificate.

Engineering Officers

Merchant Navy engineer officers were, in the past, entirely recruited from those who had served apprenticeships in shipyards and marine engine building works. Today, the industry regards its own engineer cadets as the main source of future engineer officers.

The modern ship, with its highly automated engine room, remote control of machinery and complicated electrical and electronic monitoring equipment, calls for an engineer officer with a broad engineering background and specialist marine training. The engineer cadetship provides the essential academic and practical training ashore and the sea-going experience necessary to equip a young man to assume the responsibilities of a junior engineer officer and also gains him exemption from certain parts of the Board of Trade examinations.

Cadet Training

The engineer cadet training scheme is at present divided into three phases totalling approximately 4½ years of service and divided as follows:

Phase 1, two years at an approved technical college,

Phase 2, 18 months' to two years' training at sea,

Phase 3, six months to one year of theoretical and practical training ashore.

The cadet takes a course leading to an Ordinary National Diploma in Engineering, the Ordinary National Certificate or Part "A" of the Board of Trade 2nd Class Certificate of Competency during the first two years of his cadetship, depending on his qualifications at entry.

The O.N.D. in Engineering carries exemptions from Part "A" of the Board of Trade examinations for the 1st and 2nd Class Certificates of Competency. The O.N.C. examination is taken in Phase 3 of that course and carries exemption from Part "A" of the Board of Trade examination for the 2nd Class Certificate only.

The Part "A" Course leads to Part "A" of the 2nd Class Certificate. In some colleges it may also lead to the Mechanical Engineering Technician's Certificate.

In Phase 1, when cadets are studying at technical college, they are employed and paid by a shipping company and study alongside cadets from other shipping companies. During Phase 2, the cadet normally spends a period of some 18 months to two years at sea as an engineer cadet on board his own company's vessels. This training will enable him to gain experience in the running and operation of ship's machinery and his training will be the responsibility of the chief engineer officer. Phase 3 is that part of the cadetship where he obtains further theoretical instruction and practical training. This is usually undertaken in one of the specially equipped technical college workshops. In some shipping companies, the cadetship has been rephased so that the cadet can take Phases 1 and 3 (shore training) before Phase 2 (sea service).

Prospects

There are two Board of Trade Certificates of Competency—the 2nd and 1st Class—which a future chief engineer officer needs to obtain. On completion of his cadetship, the young man goes to sea as a junior engineer officer for some 18 months before becoming eligible to take the full 2nd Class Certificate examination. A further similar period of sea service is then needed to permit the officer to sit for the 1st Class examination. This qualification entitles the holder to be employed as chief engineer officer on a merchant ship, and promotion to that rank can be fast for those who are prepared to work and study hard for these examinations. Those who may wish to extend their careers into the shipping or marine engineering industries ashore may take the Board of Trade Extra 1st Class examination or one of the degree courses in marine engineering.

Entry Qualifications for Cadetship

Age

Candidates must be 16 and preferably not more than 18 years of age on entry.

Health

Candidates are required to pass a medical examination on joining a shipping company or on registration with the British Shipping Federation. They must have normal vision, with glasses if necessary, and are required to pass a simple colour vision test.

Academic

O.N.D. Course, either:

1. Four G.C.E. "O" level passes — or equivalent — including mathematics and one of the following: physics with chemistry, mechanics, engineering science, mechanical science (building and engineering);
2. The satisfactory completion of the General Course in Engineering and the General Course Certificate with credits in mathematics and engineering science, and a pass in engineering drawing.

O.N.C. and Part "A" Courses

Candidates should have shown mechanical aptitude and ability in English, mathematics and a science subject. No specific G.C.E. passes are required. The candidate's suitability for the courses will be assessed before he is accepted. This is done either by interview or by interview and examination.

Applications

Applications may be made to any of the shipping companies which train engineer cadets. Alternatively, applications may be made directly to the British Shipping Federation which will be pleased to give advice and, if requested, arrange cadetships with any of these shipping companies. The main entry to the training scheme takes place in September of each year, but some cadets are also accepted for a January entry. Normally, those wishing to enter in September should apply for entry by May of the year in which they wish to commence their training, and those who wish to enter in January should apply by November of the preceding year.

Traditional Entry

The shipping industry also accepts as junior engineer officers young men who have satisfactorily completed a craft apprenticeship in a heavy engineering workshop.

Names and addresses of firms to which application for a shore apprenticeship may be made can be obtained from:

1. The Secretary of the National Association of Marine Engine Builders, 91 Grosvenor Place, London, S.W.1.
2. The Engineering Employers' Federation, Broadway House, Tothill Street, London, S.W.1.

Pursers and Assistant Pursers

Pursers and assistant pursers are normally carried in passenger liners and passenger/cargo ships only. In large liners the purser is usually head of the catering department, the chief steward being responsible to him for stewarding service in cabins,

PROGRESS CHART: Engineer Officers

A full-time course leading to the Extra 1st Class Certificate is voluntary at any time after obtaining the 1st Class Certificate. Suitably qualified candidates may, alternatively, take a marine engineering degree.	Approximate Age
CHIEF ENGINEER OFFICER (Full-time course—1st Class Certificate)	Age according to experience and seniority
↑	
SECOND ENGINEER OFFICER (Full-time course—2nd Class Certificate) (Those who have completed engineer cadetships will normally have gained exemption from part of the 2nd Class Certificate examination)	23–25
↑	
THIRD ENGINEER OFFICER	
↑	
FOURTH ENGINEER OFFICER	
↑	
JUNIOR ENGINEER OFFICER	21–23
↑ ↑	
ENGINEER CADET ($4\frac{1}{2}$ years' service)	16–18
ENGINEER CRAFT APPRENTICE (Suitable engineering workshop training ashore. 4–5 year.)	16–18

dining rooms and other public rooms. The purser is responsible for arranging entertainment for passengers, answering their enquiries, providing a banking service on board, meeting and dealing with Customs and Immigration officials in foreign and home ports, and handling all the accounts and clerical work for the ship. On passenger ships he is usually helped by a number of assistant pursers.

On smaller vessels the purser's duties are mainly clerical. He is responsible for the checking and stowage of special cargo, such as bullion or high dutiable packages. He also attends to cargo manifests and bills of lading, and the calculation and payment of crew wages.

Pursers and assistant pursers are usually recruited from the shore staff of a shipping company, and they must have a good education, some commercial experience, preferably a working knowledge of one or more languages, a pleasant personality, and plenty of patience and tact. As openings are very limited there is keen competition for vacancies, and most companies keep a waiting list of suitable applicants. The British Shipping Federation is seldom asked to fill such a vacancy, and application should be made direct to the shipping companies.

Radio Officers

All British ships of 1,600 tons gross or over must carry a qualified radio officer. The majority of general traders need to carry one radio officer only but many larger passenger ships carry two or more to cope with the large amount of radio traffic encountered on these vessels. The radio officer's duties are to maintain communications between the ship and shore stations in all parts of the world and with other ships for the purpose of sending and receiving messages connected with the ship's business as well as private messages for the passengers, officers and crew. There are also weather, safety and navigational messages and the radio officer is required to keep a special watch for distress traffic from other ships. Although great use is made of radio telephone and VHF equipment, morse code is very widely used especially for long-distance communications, and the officer must be able to send and receive messages at a speed of 20 words per minute.

The radio officer is also responsible for the maintenance of all his radio equipment, the radio direction finder and, in many ships, for maintaining other electronic navigational equipment such as radar.

Training

Training takes the form of 18 months' to two years' full-time education at a marine radio college. This is usually taken immediately after the student has completed his secondary education.

Prospects

Promotion for radio officers during their sea-going service is to passenger vessels in which the highest rates are paid. In the marine radio companies, the majority of shore technical staff are recruited from radio officers with five years' service or more and most managerial positions are held by former radio officers.

Qualifications for Entry

Age

Candidates should be not less than 16 years of age on commencing training.

Health

All candidates are required to pass a medical examination and particular emphasis is placed on hearing. The wearing of glasses is permitted.

Academic

All candidates must be in possession of at least the Postmaster General's Second Class Certificate (wireless telegraphy), and the First Class Certificate if over 12 passengers are carried. Some companies also expect their radio officers to have the B.O.T. Radar Maintenance Certificate. Courses leading to the Postmaster General's Certificates are available at a number of marine radio schools throughout the country. Applicationts for courses should preferably be in possession of the G.C.E. at "O" level—or equivalent—with passes in mathematics, physics and English.

Employment

The majority of radio officers are employed by two marine radio companies, and are appointed to vessels of shipping companies with which these marine radio companies have contracts. A number of shipping companies do, however, employ their own radio officers direct.

Applications

Applications for courses may be made to one of the marine radio colleges and further information can be obtained by writing to the companies below. The British Shipping Federation will also be pleased to provide further information and assistance.

Companies Installing Radio Apparatus who Employ Qualified Radio Officers

International Marine Radio Co. Ltd., Peall Road, Croydon, Surrey.

Marconi International Marine Co. Ltd., Elettra House, Westway, Chelmsford, Essex.

Ratings—Deck and Catering Departments

The great majority of boys intending to join the Merchant Navy as deck or catering ratings receive initial training at the National Sea Training School, Gravesend, Kent, which occupies a magnificent position on the south shore of the Thames Estuary. The courses, which last from eight to twelve weeks, accustom the boy to a sea-going environment and the conditions of his future job.

Age limits for entry are 15½–17¼ years.

Cost

A deposit of £7 is required on admission to the school. Boys who complete the course and proceed to sea are given a kit grant of £6 and this together with their deposit is set against the total cost of uniform supplied at the school, which averages £21. Any balance remaining may be paid during the course or may be deducted from the boy's earnings at sea.

It is suggested that trainees should bring with them to the school enough pocket money to meet incidental expenses (say, 5s. per week).

Training

The internal organisation of the sea training establishment is similar to that of a ship. The Captain Superintendent is in command, and is assisted by Navigating Officers and Instructors. The boys serve in a similar capacity to members of a ship's crew. The training is comprehensive.

Deck Ratings are instructed in basic seamanship covering the normal duties of the deck rating—including steering, signalling, ropework, deep-sea soundings, rigging and handling cargo work-

PROGRESS CHART: Radio Officers

After at least five years' service radio officers may apply for shore service

CARGO VESSELS	*PASSENGER VESSELS*	
	1st RADIO OFFICER P.M.G. 1st Class Certificate ↑	1st Class Certificate can be taken immediately after 2nd Class or after sea service
	2nd RADIO OFFICER ↑	
RADIO OFFICER ↑	**3rd RADIO OFFICER** ↑	

JUNIOR RADIO OFFICER
(Six months) probationary sea service

↑

FULL-TIME COURSE P.M.G. 2nd CLASS CERTIFICATE

ing gear, hatch work, mooring and general ship maintenance.

Catering Ratings are trained in the general duties of ship catering—the preparation, laying and serving of meals, cabin hygiene and duties in public rooms and pantries, a knowledge of menus and wines, etc. They put their classroom knowledge to practical use by undertaking many of the catering and domestic duties of the school under the supervision of the Catering Training Officer.

All trainees are instructed in the use of lifesaving appliances, and must become proficient in lifeboat handling and rowing. Upon completion of his course the trainee returns home and registers with his nearest British Shipping Federation office for the first job of his sea-going career. A systematic and progressive training scheme aboard ship ensures that the pre-sea training is followed up, and continued, to bring the rating up to the necessary standard of competency to enable him to gain promotion in his department.

Evening Classes

Evening classes in mathematics and English are available at the school for those boys who may wish to pursue studies whilst at sea for their own improvement. Upon completion of training every encouragement is provided by the Seafarers' Education Service to enable suitable ratings to undergo directed private study at sea to help them reach the highest positions in their chosen department. There are special arrangements under which the Federation's Selection Officers watch a boy's general progress during his first two years at sea with the aim of guiding him in his career and giving personal advice when requested.

Recreation

Designed to encourage a full range of interests and to develop initiative and self-reliance, recreational activities include canoeing, woodwork and model making, music (including "beat" groups), photography, art and many other hobbies, all under expert supervision. The playing fields occupy 14 acres, with the River Thames "on the doorstep". Outdoor sport is encouraged, particularly sailing, football, cricket, and archery. There is also an active following for the Duke of Edinburgh's Award Scheme.

Prospects

Deck Department

As a rating the deck entrant can rise to the position of bosun or petty officer—first as junior deck rating, then junior ordinary seaman, senior ordinary seaman, efficient deck hand, and able seaman. Any deck rating who has completed four years' qualifying service at sea may sit for the examination leading to the Board

PROGRESS CHARTS: Ratings

Deck ratings who have completed 4 years' qualifying service at sea, may sit for the examination for Second Mate.

BOSUN

↑ Promotion from Able Seaman to Bosun is entirely on merit

ABLE SEAMAN
Board of Trade Qualification
Minimum sea service 3 years

↑

EFFICIENT DECK HAND

↑

EFFICIENT DECK HAND'S CERTIFICATE COURSE
18 years minimum age limit
Qualifying sea service 12 months

↑

18 month's sea service. Senior Ordinary Seaman
9 months' sea service. Junior Ordinary Seaman
3 months' sea service. Eligible for General Service Contract

↑

JUNIOR DECK RATING

↑

PRE-SEA TRAINING

of Trade Certificate of Competency as Second Mate, and many from the National Sea Training School have gained promotion to officer rank and ultimate command. Every encouragement is provided in the way of study leave pay, correspondence courses, and the provision of educational services through the Seafarers' Education Service.

Catering Department

Initial employment at sea may be in any type of vessel—cargo, tanker or passenger. The new entrant can follow his bent either in the galley/kitchen or the saloon by undertaking specially designed vocational courses. He can rise to the rank of a fully qualified chef, or he can become a Chief Steward.

Established Service Scheme

On completion of three months' satisfactory sea service, junior ratings in both departments who have completed a recognised pre-sea training course may apply for enrolment in the Merchant Navy Established Service Scheme for two-year contracts which guarantee continuous employment or money benefits in lieu. Provision is also made for payments during sickness and study leave. A brochure dealing with the scheme is available.

Requirements

First class character; a good school reference and report; smart appearance, and good references from shore employers for the period between leaving school and acceptance for training. Certain physical standards apply, and boys wishing to enter the deck department must have normal form and colour vision, and the wearing of glasses will bar a candidate. Spectacles are permitted in the catering department provided that the candidate reaches the eyesight standard required.

Entry Procedure

All applications, in writing or in person, should be made to the British Shipping Federation.

PROGRESS CHART: Catering

CATERING OFFICER OR CHIEF STEWARD

↑

PASSENGER VESSEL		*TANKER/CARGO VESSEL*	
Saloon	*Kitchen/Galley*	*Saloon*	*Kitchen/Galley*
2nd Steward Storekeeper Pantryman Barman Wine Steward Bedroom Steward Public Room Steward 1st Class Waiter Tourist Waiter Commis Waiter	Chef* 2nd Cook Specialist Cooks: Sauce, Salad Soup, Entree Fish, Grill Vegetable Baker, Roast Pastry Cook Assistant Cook	2nd Steward Assistant Steward Messroom Steward	Chief Cook* 2nd Cook and Baker Assistant Cook
↑	↑	↑	↑

CATERING REFRESHER COURSE

↑

3 months' sea service. Eligible for General Service Contract

↑

JUNIOR CATERING RATING
(Cabin, galley, messroom)

↑

PRE-SEA TRAINING

* *Approved courses are available leading to the Higher Cookery Certificate and the Ships' Cook Certificate of Competency.*

Recommended Further Reading

(1) SHIPPING WORLD & SHIP BUILDER
Benn Bros (Marine) Ltd.,
7/17 Jewry Street, London, E.C.3
Monthly – First Thursday

(1) THE MOTOR SHIP
Engineering, Chemical & Marine Press Ltd.,
33-40 Bowling Green Lane, London, E.C.1
Monthly – First Tuesday

(1) SHIPBUILDING & SHIPPING RECORD
Engineering, Chemical & Marine Press Ltd.,
33-40 Bowling Green Lane, London, E.C.1
Weekly – Friday

(1) SEA BREEZES
The Journal of Commerce & Shipping Telegraph Ltd.,
19 James Street, Liverpool, 2
Monthly – 1st of Month

(1) JOURNAL OF COMMERCE & SHIPPING TELEGRAPH
The Journal of Commerce & Shipping Telegraph Ltd.,
19 James Street, Liverpool, 2
Daily

(1) LLOYD'S LIST
Lloyd's,
Lime Street, London, E.C.3
Daily

(1) P.L.A. MONTHLY
(2) The Port of London Authority,
242 Trinity Square, London, E.C.3
Monthly

SCHIP EN WERF
Uitgevers Wyt,
P. de Hoochweg III, Rotterdam, Holland
Alternate Fridays

(4) NAVIRES, PORTS & CHANTIER
190 Bd. Haussmann, Paris, France
Monthly

(4) HANSA
Postfach 329, 2 Hamburg II, W. Germany
Alternate weeks

(4) HOLLAND SHIPPING & TRADING
Van Konteren's Publishing Co. Ltd.,
40 St. Jobsweg, Rotterdam, Holland
Monthly (Printed in English)

(3) MERCHANT SHIPS, WORLD BUILT
Adlard Coles Ltd.,
3 Upper James Street, Golden Square, London, W.1
Annual

(1) Order through any newsagent
(2) By subscription from P.L.A.
(3) From larger bookshops
(4) Direct subscription